PROBABILITY, STATISTICS AND RANDOM PROCESSES

LOUIS MAISEL

Sperry Rand Research Center

SIMON AND SCHUSTER, NEW YORK

A SIMON AND SCHUSTER TECH OUTLINE
RAJ MEHRA, EDITOR

Published by
Simon and Schuster
Technical and Reference Book Division
1 West 39th Street
New York, N.Y. 10018

Published simultaneously in Canada
Printed in the United States of America

PREFACE

There is scarcely a discipline of any importance that does not benefit from the application of the principles of probability, statistics, and random processes. In recent years, this application has substantially increased, due in part to the wide use of digital computers in studying large-scale systems. This book is intended not only as an aid in the understanding of the underlying principles of probability, statistics, and random processes, but also to illustrate the potential applications and the wide variety of problem-solving techniques pertaining to the subject matter. While the format of a considerable portion of the book is devoted to solved problems, the book can serve as either a primary or a supplementary text for the engineering student in particular, but also for students in the physical and social sciences taking a first course in probability and statistics.

The solved problems in each chapter generally encompass a wide range of difficulty ranging from relatively straightforward application of basic formulas to those requiring considerable insight into fundamental concepts. A working knowledge of elementary calculus is assumed throughout. Derivations of many important formulas are given although strict mathematical rigor has frequently been avoided in favor of a more intuitive approach.

The book is divided into three basic parts, the first dealing with probability theory, the second with statistics, and the third with random processes. The first two chapters are concerned mainly with providing the elementary basis and introducing the mathematical tools needed in the analysis of probabilistic problems. In this regard, extensive use is made of the Dirac delta function in the representation of discrete random variables. In Chap. 3, a wide range of commonly encountered distributions are described while in Chaps. 4 and 5 the more advanced topics of derived distributions, two-dimensional distributions and characteristic functions are treated. Chapters 6, 7, and 8 are concerned primarily with sampling distributions and statistical hypothesis testing. Chapters 9 and 10 are devoted to continuous random processes and emphasize discussions of correlation functions and power density spectra. Chapter 11 deals with random processes in which the independent variable assumes only discrete values (as, for example, in digital computer processing).

Other features incorporated into this book to enhance its usefulness include: the tinting in grey of important theorems, definitions, and results, the inclusion of a wide variety of mathematical tables in the appendices, the additional supplementary problems in each chapter with answers supplied, and the extensive use of diagrams as visual aids.

The author wishes to acknowledge the invaluable suggestions of Raj Mehra in the preparation of the manuscript, and the considerable effort and assistance given by Rhea Nichols of Simon & Schuster, Inc., and Prof. A. Nickolakis of Long Island University.

Louis Maisel

Sudbury, Mass.

TABLE OF CONTENTS

PROBABILITY

1.1 Definitions of Probability

In the study of probability an *experiment* is any process of trial and observation.

An *event* is the occurrence of either a prescribed outcome or any one of a number of possible outcomes of an experiment.

If N is the total number of times the experiment is performed, and N_A is the total number of times one event A occurred, the *relative frequency of occurrence* of A is N_A/N, and the *probability P* of an event A is

$$P(A) = \lim_{N \to \infty} \frac{N_A}{N}, \tag{1.1}$$

where the existence of the limit $N \to \infty$ is assumed.

The relative frequency definition (1.1) is often used to calculate probabilities from empirical data. For example, if an experiment is prescribed in which a coin is tossed repeatedly, the frequency ratio for the number of heads N_H, as shown in Fig. 1.1, is

$$\frac{N_H}{N},$$

and the probability of a head at any one trial is

$$P(H) = \lim_{N \to \infty} \frac{N_H}{N}.$$

In Fig. 1.1, $N_H/N \to \frac{1}{2}$ as $N \to \infty$. Note that this curve has meaning only for integral values of the variable N, and it represents a

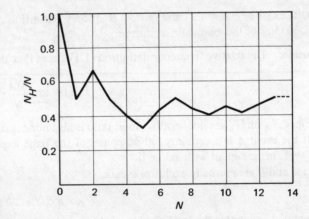

Fig. 1.1 The frequency ratio N_H/N for the number of heads N_H.

particular series of tosses of the coin. Repeating the experiment generally results in a completely different plot, even though $N_H/N \to \frac{1}{2}$ as $N \to \infty$.

If A and B are two events, the *event (A or B)* occurs when A occurs, B occurs, or *both A and B occur.*

The expression *mutually exclusive* signifies that the occurrence of one event as a result of any given experiment excludes the occurrence of any other events. Thus, if A and B are mutually exclusive, the event $(A \text{ or } B)$ occurs only if either A or B occurs, but *not both*.

The *axiomatic definition* of the *probability $P(A)$ of an event A* obeys the following axioms:

I The probability of an event A is *nonnegative*; i.e.,

$$P(A) \geqslant 0. \tag{1.2}$$

II The probability of a *certain event* (an event that must occur) is *unity*.

III If A and B are mutually exclusive events,

$$P(A \text{ or } B) = P(A) + P(B). \tag{1.3}$$

If A is an event, let $\overline{A}$ represent the event that A does not occur. Thus, the event $(A$ or $\overline{A})$ is a certain event. Hence, from axiom II,

$$P(A \text{ or } \overline{A}) = 1.$$

Since A and $\overline{A}$ are mutually exclusive events, from axiom III,

$$P(A) = 1 - P(\overline{A}).$$

From axiom I,

$$0 \leqslant P(A) \leqslant 1.$$

Thus, the probability of an event is some real number between 0 and 1, inclusive.

Note that these results do not indicate the method of assigning probabilities to the outcomes of an experiment; they merely restrict the ways it can be done.

PROBLEM 1.1   List all the possible outcomes of an experiment where two coins are tossed simultaneously.

Solution: The four possible outcomes with H and T denoting heads and tails, respectively, are

$$\begin{array}{lcccc} \text{Coin 1:} & H & H & T & T \\ \text{Coin 2:} & H & T & H & T. \end{array}$$

PROBLEM 1.2   List all the possible outcomes of an experiment where one coin is tossed three successive times.

Solution: The eight possible outcomes with H and T denoting heads and tails, respectively, are

$$HHH, \ HHT, \ HTH, \ HTT, \quad THH, \ THT, \ TTH, \ TTT.$$

PROBLEM 1.3   Show that the relative frequency definition of probability (1.1) is consistent with the three basic axioms of the axiomatic definition.

Solution: The relative frequency definition (1.1) states that the probability of an event A is

$$P(A) = \lim_{N \to \infty} \frac{N_A}{N}.$$

Since N_A and N are nonnegative, their ratio is also nonnegative, and axiom I is satisfied.

If the event A is a certainty, all outcomes of the basic experiment yield event A. Therefore, $N_A = N$ and $P(A) = 1$, in agreement with axiom II.

If A and B are mutually exclusive events,

$$N_{A+B} = N_A + N_B,$$

where N_{A+B} denotes the total number of times events A or B occur. Thus,

$$P(A \text{ or } B) = \lim_{N \to \infty} \frac{N_{A+B}}{N} = \lim_{N \to \infty} \frac{N_A + N_B}{N} = \lim_{N \to \infty} \frac{N_A}{N} + \lim_{N \to \infty} \frac{N_B}{N} = P(A) + P(B),$$

in agreement with axiom III.

Events $A, B, \cdots, R$ are said to be *equally likely* when

$$P(A) = P(B) = \cdots = P(R).$$

PROBLEM 1.4   A die is rolled once. List the possible outcomes, and choose two allowable sets of probabilities in accordance with the three basic axioms.

Solution: The possible outcomes are the numbers on the die; i.e., the numbers 1–6, inclusive.

Take one set of probabilities when a die is fair and the other set when the die is loaded.

For a fair die, each of the six numbers are equally likely. Thus,

$$P(1) = P(2) = P(3) = P(4) = P(5) = P(6).$$

Since these six events are mutually exclusive, from axiom III,

$$P(1 \text{ or } 2 \text{ or } 3 \text{ or } 4 \text{ or } 5 \text{ or } 6) = P(1) + P(2) + P(3) + P(4) + P(5) + P(6) = 6P(1).$$

But, one of the six events is certain to occur; thus,

$$6P(1) = 1.$$

Hence, $P(1) = \frac{1}{6}$. This gives one allowable set of probabilities in accordance with the axioms; i.e.,

$$P(1) = \tfrac{1}{6}, \qquad P(2) = \tfrac{1}{6}, \qquad P(3) = \tfrac{1}{6}, \qquad P(4) = \tfrac{1}{6}, \qquad P(5) = \tfrac{1}{6}, \qquad P(6) = \tfrac{1}{6}.$$

A second set of probabilities can be selected from the case of a loaded die, whereby any probabilities may be assigned to each one of the six events as long as the conditions of the axioms are not violated. One such set of probabilities is

$$P(1) = 1, \qquad P(2) = 0, \qquad P(3) = 0, \qquad P(4) = 0, \qquad P(5) = 0, \qquad P(6) = 0.$$

PROBLEM 1.5 Determine the probability of each outcome of an experiment which has k possible, mutually exclusive, outcomes that are equally likely.

Solution: Since $P(1) = P(2) = \cdots = P(k)$, from axioms II and III,

$$P(1) + P(2) + \cdots + P(k) = 1, \qquad \text{or} \qquad k\,P(k) = 1.$$

Thus,

$$P(k) = 1/k.$$

Hence, $P(1) = P(2) = \cdots = P(k) = 1/k$.

PROBLEM 1.6 An experiment has two mutually exclusive events A and B, where A is five times as probable as B. Determine $P(A)$ and $P(B)$.

Solution: Since $P(A) + P(B) = 1$ and $P(A) = 5P(B)$, on substitution,

$$5P(B) + P(B) = 1.$$

Thus,

$$P(B) = \tfrac{1}{6}, \qquad P(A) = \tfrac{5}{6}.$$

PROBLEM 1.7 Find the probability of rolling a seven with a pair of fair dice; that is, the sum of the numbers on the two dice is seven.

Solution: Since each number on one die is paired with the six numbers on the other, the total number of outcomes is 36. As each outcome is equally likely, the probability of each outcome is $\frac{1}{36}$. Hence, the probability of obtaining a seven is

$$P(7) = P(6 \text{ and } 1) + P(5 \text{ and } 2) + P(4 \text{ and } 3) + P(3 \text{ and } 4) + P(2 \text{ and } 5) + P(1 \text{ and } 6) = 6P(6 \text{ and } 1) = 6 \cdot \tfrac{1}{36} = \tfrac{1}{6}.$$

PROBLEM 1.8 An integer between 1 and 100 is selected at random. Find the probability of selecting a perfect square if (a) all integers are equally likely to be selected, (b) an integer between 1 and 50 is twice as likely to occur.

Solution: (a) Since the number of possible outcomes is 100 and each integer is equally likely to be selected, the probability of randomly selecting a given integer between 1 and 100 is $\frac{1}{100} = 0.01$.

The number of outcomes having the attribute of being a perfect square is the number of values of k for which

$$1 \leqslant k^2 \leqslant 100, \qquad k \text{ an integer}.$$

Since all values of k between 1 and 10, inclusive, satisfy the above inequalities, the probability of selecting a perfect square is

$$P = P(1^2) + P(2^2) + \cdots + P(10^2) = 10P(1^2) = 10(0.01) = 0.1.$$

(b) Since, in this case, the outcomes are not equally likely, evaluate the probability of each perfect square. Thus, from the assumptions,

$$\sum_{i=1}^{50} P(i) + \sum_{i=51}^{100} P(i) = 1, \qquad \sum_{i=1}^{50} P(i) = 2 \sum_{i=51}^{100} P(i),$$

where the conventional summation notation is used; i.e.,

$$\sum_{i=1}^{N} P(i) = P(1) + P(2) + \cdots + P(N).$$

Solving the above simultaneous equations,

$$\sum_{i=1}^{50} P(i) = \frac{2}{3}, \qquad \sum_{i=51}^{100} P(i) = \frac{1}{3}.$$

Since $P(1) = P(2) = \cdots = P(50)$ and $P(51) = P(52) = \cdots = P(100)$,

$$50P(1) = \tfrac{2}{3}, \qquad 50P(51) = \tfrac{1}{3}.$$

Hence,

$$P(i) = \tfrac{1}{75} \quad \text{for } 1 \leqslant i \leqslant 50$$
$$= \tfrac{1}{150} \quad \text{for } 51 \leqslant i \leqslant 100.$$

Since there are seven integers whose squares are less than 50 and three whose squares are between 51 and 100, the probability of a perfect square is

$$P = 7\left(\tfrac{1}{75}\right) + 3\left(\tfrac{1}{150}\right) = \tfrac{17}{150}.$$

1.2 Permutations and Combinations

The *number of permutations* $P_{n,r}$ of n symbols taken r at a time is the number of total distinct arrangements of the r symbols in a specific order, without any duplication of symbols. The symbols $_nP_r$, $P(n,r)$, ^nP_r and $(n)_r$ are sometimes used to represent the number of permutations.

The *number of combinations* $C_{n,r}$ of n symbols taken r at a time is the number of distinct selections in which the order or arrangement is not specified. No duplication of symbols is allowed. The symbols $_nC_r$, $C(n,r)$, ^nC_r, and, more recently, $\binom{n}{r}$ are frequently employed to represent the number of combinations.

PROBLEM 1.9 List all the possible permutations of the three symbols a_1, a_2, and a_3 taken three at a time.

Solution: The distinct arrangements that are possible are

$$a_1a_2a_3, \qquad a_2a_1a_3, \qquad a_3a_1a_2,$$
$$a_1a_3a_2, \qquad a_2a_3a_1, \qquad a_3a_2a_1,$$

so that a total of six permutations is possible.

PROBLEM 1.10 Determine the possible permutations of three symbols a_1, a_2, and a_3 taken two at a time.

Solution: The distinct arrangements that are possible are

$$a_1a_2, \qquad a_2a_1, \qquad a_3a_1, \qquad a_1a_3, \qquad a_2a_3, \qquad a_3a_2,$$

so that a total of six permutations is possible.

PROBLEM 1.11 Determine the possible combinations of three symbols taken three at a time.

Solution: Since the order of the symbols is immaterial in determining the number of combinations, the symbols have only one combination; viz., $a_1\ a_2\ a_3$.

PROBLEM 1.12 Determine the possible combinations of three symbols a_1, a_2, a_3 taken two at a time.

Solution: The distinct selections without regard to order are

$$a_1 a_2, \qquad a_1 a_3, \qquad a_2 a_3,$$

so that there are three combinations.

PROBLEM 1.13 Show that, in general, the number of permutations of n distinct symbols taken r at a time is

$$P_{n,\ r} = \frac{n!}{(n-r)!}, \tag{1.4}$$

where the symbol $n!$ (read as "n factorial") denotes the product of the first n integers; i.e.,

$$n! = n(n-1)(n-2)\cdots(2)(1).$$

Note that when n is large, $n!$ can be approximated by using Stirling's formula; i.e.,

$$n! \approx \sqrt{2\pi}\ e^{-n}\ n^{n+\frac{1}{2}}, \tag{1.5}$$

which is in error by less than 1% for $n > 10$. A short table of values of $n!$ is given in Table 1.1.

TABLE 1.1. Factorials

n	$n!$	$\dfrac{1}{n!}$	n	$n!$	$\dfrac{1}{n!}$
1	1	1.	16	$209{,}228 \times 10^8$	0.477948×10^{-13}
2	2	0.5	17	$355{,}687 \times 10^9$	0.281146×10^{-14}
3	6	0.166667	18	$640{,}237 \times 10^{10}$	0.156192×10^{-15}
4	24	0.416667×10^{-1}	19	$121{,}645 \times 10^{12}$	0.822064×10^{-17}
5	120	0.833333×10^{-2}	20	$243{,}290 \times 10^{13}$	0.411032×10^{-19}
6	720	0.138889×10^{-2}	21	5.1091×10^{19}	0.19573×10^{-19}
7	5,040	0.198413×10^{-3}	22	1.1240×10^{21}	0.88968×10^{-21}
8	40,320	0.248016×10^{-4}	23	2.5852×10^{22}	0.38682×10^{-22}
9	362,880	0.275573×10^{-5}	24	6.2045×10^{23}	0.16117×10^{-23}
10	3,628,800	0.275573×10^{-6}	25	1.5511×10^{25}	0.64470×10^{-25}
11	$399{,}168 \times 10^2$	0.250521×10^{-7}	26	4.0329×10^{26}	0.24796×10^{-26}
12	$479{,}002 \times 10^3$	0.208768×10^{-8}	27	1.0889×10^{28}	0.91836×10^{-28}
13	$622{,}702 \times 10^4$	0.160590×10^{-9}	28	3.0489×10^{29}	0.32799×10^{-29}
14	$871{,}783 \times 10^5$	0.114707×10^{-10}	29	8.8418×10^{30}	0.11310×10^{-30}
15	$130{,}767 \times 10^7$	0.764716×10^{-12}	30	2.6525×10^{32}	0.37644×10^{-32}

Solution: The first symbol is selected in n ways.

The second symbol is selected in only $(n-1)$ ways because symbols are not repeated.

This process is repeated until the last symbol, i.e., the rth symbol, is selected in $(n - r + 1)$ ways. Then,

$$P_{n,\ r} = n(n-1)(n-2)\cdots(n-r+1),$$

which is equivalent to

$$P_{n,\,r} = n(n-1)(n-2)\cdots(n-r+1)\,\frac{(n-r)}{(n-r)}\,\frac{(n-r-1)}{(n-r-1)}\cdots\frac{(2)}{(2)}\frac{(1)}{(1)}.$$

The numerator is just $n!$, while the denominator is $(n-r)!$, so that

$$P_{n,\,r} = \frac{n!}{(n-r)!}.$$

PROBLEM 1.14 Show that, in general, the number of combinations of n distinct symbols taken r at a time is

$$C_{n,\,r} = \frac{n!}{r!\,(n-r)!}. \tag{1.6}$$

Solution: Each combination of r symbols can be permuted in $r!$ ways. This is obtained from (1.4) by calculating the number of permutations of r symbols taken r at a time. Accordingly, there are $r!$ times as many permutations of n symbols taken r at a time than combinations. Thus,

$$P_{n,\,r} = r!\,C_{n,\,r}.$$

Using the results of Prob. 1.13,

$$C_{n,\,r} = \frac{1}{r!}\,P_{n,\,r} = \frac{n!}{r!\,(n-r)!}.$$

PROBLEM 1.15 Determine the number of four-letter "words" that are possible in the English language. Assume that no letter appears more than once in each word, and any combination of four letters forms a possible word.

Solution: The number of four-letter words that are possible is the number of permutations of 26 letters taken four at a time. Thus, from (1.4),

$$P_{n,\,r} = \frac{n!}{(n-r)!} = \frac{26!}{(26-4)!} = \frac{26!}{22!} = 26 \times 25 \times 24 \times 23 \times \frac{22!}{22!} = 358{,}800.$$

The number of combinations, using (1.6), is

$$C_{n,\,r} = \frac{n!}{r!\,(n-r)!} = \frac{1}{4!}\,P_{26,\,4} = 14{,}950.$$

The *binomial expansion of* $(a+b)^n$ is

$$(a+b)^n = a^n + na^{n-1}b + \frac{n(n-1)}{2!}a^{n-2}b^2 + \cdots + \frac{n(n-1)\cdots(n-r+1)}{r!}a^{n-r}b^r + \cdots + b^n.$$

PROBLEM 1.16 Express the coefficients of the binomial expansion in terms of $C_{n,\,r}$.

Solution: The coefficient of the general term of the expansion is

$$\frac{n(n-1)(n-2)\cdots(n-r+1)}{r!},$$

which can be written as

$$\frac{n(n-1)\cdots(n-r+1)}{r!}\cdot\frac{(n-r)(n-r-1)\cdots 1}{(n-r)(n-r-1)\cdots 1}.$$

The numerator is just $n!$, while the denominator is $r!\,(n-r)!$. Hence, on comparison with the results of Prob. 1.14, the general binomial coefficient is

$$\frac{n!}{r!\,(n-r)!} = C_{n,\,r}.$$

Therefore,

$$(a+b)^n = a^n + C_{n,1}\,a^{n-1}\,b + C_{n,2}\,a^{n-2}\,b^2 + \cdots + C_{n,r}\,a^{n-r}\,b^r + \cdots + b^n = a^n + \sum_{r=1}^{n} C_{n,r}\,a^{n-r}\,b^r.$$

PROBLEM 1.17 Find the probability that three cards drawn at random, without replacement, from a fair deck of 52 playing cards are spades.

Solution: The probability is equal to the ratio of the number of ways, or the number of possible combinations, or drawing three spades from 13 to the total number of ways of drawing three cards from 52. Thus,

$$P = \frac{C_{13,3}}{C_{52,3}} = \frac{\dfrac{13!}{3!\,10!}}{\dfrac{52!}{3!\,49!}} = \frac{11}{850}.$$

The above example illustrates the *classical definition of probability*, which is a special case of the axiomatic definition. In this definition, if a given experiment has n mutually exclusive, equally likely outcomes $A_1, A_2, \cdots, A_n$, in which m of the outcomes $A_1, A_2, \cdots, A_m$ have a certain attribute B, the probability of occurrence of B is

$$P(B) = \frac{m}{n}.$$

Thus, since the experiment involves obtaining three spades in a random drawing from 52 cards, $m = C_{13,3}$ and $n = C_{52,3}$.

PROBLEM 1.18 Find the probability that at least two of the three cards drawn from a standard deck of playing cards are spades.

Solution: The number of combinations of three cards that contain either three or two spades is $C_{13,3} + C_{13,2} \cdot C_{39,1}$, where $C_{13,3}$ is the number of combinations of three-spade hands. The number of combinations of possible two-spade hands is the number of two-spade combinations times the number of non-spade cards that can be chosen for the remaining card. Thus,

$$P = \frac{C_{13,3} + C_{13,2} \cdot C_{39,1}}{C_{52,3}} = \frac{\dfrac{13!}{3!\,10!} + \dfrac{13!}{2!\,11!} \cdot \dfrac{39!}{1!\,38!}}{\dfrac{52!}{3!\,49!}} = \frac{\dfrac{13 \cdot 12 \cdot 11}{3 \cdot 2 \cdot 1} + \dfrac{13 \cdot 12}{2 \cdot 1} \cdot 39}{\dfrac{52 \cdot 51 \cdot 50}{3 \cdot 2 \cdot 1}} = \frac{64}{425}.$$

1.3 Additive Law of Probability

If A_1 and A_2 are two mutually exclusive events, from the axiomatic definition (1.3),

$$P(A_1 \text{ or } A_2) = P(A_1) + P(A_2),$$

where

$$P(A_1) = \text{Probability of event } A_1, \qquad P(A_2) = \text{Probability of event } A_2.$$

This basic definition can be extended to include cases where more than two events are considered and also where they are not necessarily mutually exclusive.

PROBLEM 1.19 Determine $P(A_1 \text{ or } A_2 \text{ or } \cdots \text{ or } A_i)$ if $A_1, A_2, \cdots, A_i$ are mutually exclusive events.

Solution: This is found by successive applications of (1.3). For example,

$$P(A_1 \text{ or } A_2 \text{ or } A_3) = P[(A_1 \text{ or } A_2) \text{ or } A_3],$$

where $(A_1 \text{ or } A_2)$ is considered to define a new event. Thus, using (1.3) twice,

$$P(A_1 \text{ or } A_2 \text{ or } A_3) = P(A_1 \text{ or } A_2) + P(A_3) = P(A_1) + P(A_2) + P(A_3).$$

In a similar manner,

$$P(A_1 \text{ or } A_2 \text{ or } \cdots \text{ or } A_i) = \sum_{j=1}^{i} P(A_j). \tag{1.7}$$

Note that (1.7) can be easily extended to include cases where the number of possible outcomes is infinite. From Prob. 1.19, note that axiom III can be modified and, thus, generalized, to axiom III′:
III′ If $A_1, A_2, \cdots, A_n, \cdots$ are mutually exclusive events,

$$P(A_1 \text{ or } A_2 \text{ or } \cdots \text{ or } A_n \text{ or } \cdots) = P(A_1) + P(A_2) + \cdots + P(A_n) + \cdots. \tag{1.7′}$$

(Cf., p. 1-2.)

PROBLEM 1.20 In the experiment of randomly choosing an integer between 1 and 10, each integer is equally likely to be selected. Evaluate $P(A_1 \text{ or } A_2)$ if events A_1 and A_2 correspond to the selection of an even integer and an integer between 1 and 6, respectively.

Solution: Event A_1 occurs if either 2, 4, 6, 8, or 10 is selected. Event A_2 occurs if either 1, 2, 3, 4, 5, or 6 is selected. Note that A_1 and A_2 are not mutually exclusive. If (1.3) is used to calculate the probability, the outcomes 2, 4, and 6 are counted twice since they are common to both A_1 and A_2. Accordingly, (1.3) must be modified so that

$$P(A_1 \text{ or } A_2) = P(A_1) + P(A_2) - P(A_1, A_2), \tag{1.8}$$

where $P(A_1, A_2)$ is the probability of occurrence of both A_1 and A_2. Probabilities of combined events are referred to as *joint probabilities*. Thus,

$$P(A_1) = \tfrac{5}{10}, \qquad P(A_2) = \tfrac{6}{10}, \qquad P(A_1, A_2) = \tfrac{3}{10}.$$

Substituting these values into (1.8),

$$P(A_1 \text{ or } A_2) = \tfrac{8}{10} = \tfrac{4}{5}.$$

Note that in Prob. 1.20 if (1.3) is used, the fact that $P(A) \leqslant 1$, for any event A, is violated. Hence, if $A_1, A_2, \cdots, A_i$ are arbitrary events,

$$P(A_1 \text{ or } A_2 \text{ or } \cdots \text{ or } A_i) = \sum_{j=1}^{i} P(A_j) - \sum_{\substack{j,k \\ j \neq k}} P(A_j, A_k) + \sum_{\substack{j,k,l \\ j \neq k \neq l}} P(A_j, A_k, A_l) + \cdots \pm P(A_1, A_2, \ldots, A_i), \tag{1.9}$$

where $P(A_1, A_2, \cdots, A_i)$ is the probability of $A_1, A_2, \cdots,$ and A_i occurring simultaneously. The second and all subsequent sums are over all combinations of the numbers $1, 2, \cdots, i$ taken two, three, $\cdots$, at a time. The positive or negative sign for the last term depends on whether i is odd or even, respectively.

PROBLEM 1.21 Show that the case of mutually exclusive events (1.7) is a special case of (1.9).

Solution: If $A_1, A_2, \cdots, A_i$ are mutually exclusive events, the probability of any two or more of them occurring simultaneously is zero. Thus, since

$$P(A_j, A_k) = 0 \qquad \text{for } j \neq k,$$

$$P(A_j, A_k, A_l) = 0 \qquad \text{for } j \neq k \neq 1,$$

. .

. .

. .

$$P(A_1, A_2, \cdots, A_i) = 0,$$

all terms beyond the first on the right-hand side of (1.9) are zero. Hence, (1.9) is identical to (1.7).

PROBLEM 1.22 A real number between 0 and N is selected at random and each number (rational as well as irrational) is equally likely to be selected. Let event A_1 correspond to the selection of a number between n_1 and n_2, and event A_2, to the selection of a number between n_3 and n_4. Determine $P(A_1 \text{ or } A_2)$ if

(a) $n_2 > n_1$, $\quad n_3 < n_4$, $\quad$ and $\quad n_2 < n_3$,

(b) $n_2 > n_1$, $\quad n_4 > n_3$, $\quad$ and $\quad n_3 < n_2 < n_4$,

(c) $n_2 > n_1$, $\quad n_4 > n_3$, $\quad$ and $\quad n_2 > n_4$.

Note that the probability of a number being selected in a subinterval J between 0 and N is given by the ratio of the length of J to the length of the interval from 0 to N.

Solution: (a) The graphical representation is given in Fig. 1.2(a). Since A_1 and A_2 are mutually exclusive events, from (1.3),

$$P(A_1 \text{ or } A_2) = P(A_1) + P(A_2) = \frac{n_2 - n_1}{N} + \frac{n_4 - n_3}{N} = \frac{(n_2 + n_4) - (n_1 + n_3)}{N}.$$

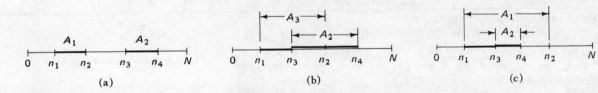

(a)   (b)   (c)

Fig. 1.2 Solution to Prob. 1.22.

(b) The graphical representation is given in Fig. 1.2(b). Events A_1 and A_2 are not mutually exclusive since they can occur simultaneously. The probability $P(A_1, A_2)$ of selecting a number that occurs in both A_1 and A_2 is the probability of selecting a number n with $n_3 \leq n \leq n_2$. Hence,

$$P(A_1, A_2) = \frac{n_2 - n_3}{N}.$$

Thus, from (1.8),

$$P(A_1 \text{ or } A_2) = P(A_1) + P(A_2) - P(A_1, A_2) = \frac{n_2 - n_1}{N} + \frac{n_4 - n_3}{N} - \frac{n_2 - n_3}{N} = \frac{n_4 - n_1}{N}.$$

(c) The graphical representation is given in Fig. 1.2(c). From (1.8),

$$P(A_1 \text{ or } A_2) = P(A_1) + P(A_2) - P(A_1, A_2) = \frac{n_2 - n_1}{N} + \frac{n_4 - n_3}{N} - \frac{n_4 - n_3}{N} = \frac{n_2 - n_1}{N}.$$

PROBLEM 1.23 Give a graphical representation and interpretation of (1.8).

Solution: The graphical representation and interpretation of (1.8) is given in Fig. 1.3.

The outcomes that produce event A_1 are represented by points in the plane within circle A_1 and those producing A_2, by points within circle A_2. If the number of possible outcomes is finite, only a finite number of points in each circle is considered. Certain outcomes are common to both circles (those in the shaded region). The quantity $P(A_1)$ represents the probability of an outcome in circle A_1, while the quantity $P(A_2)$ represents the probability of an outcome in circle A_2. The quantity $P(A_1, A_2)$ represents the probability of an outcome in the common region.

The quantity $P(A_1 \text{ or } A_2)$ is found by adding the probabilities of outcomes occurring in each of the three regions a, b, and c (two unshaded and one shaded), because these regions do not overlap and are, therefore, mutually exclusive. Thus,

$$P(A_1 \text{ or } A_2) = [P(A_1) - P(A_1, A_2)] + P(A_1, A_2) + [P(A_2) - P(A_1, A_2)]$$
$$= P(A_1) + P(A_2) - P(A_1, A_2).$$

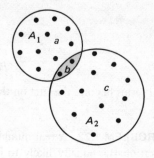

Fig. 1.3 Solution to Prob. 1.23.

PROBLEM 1.24 Evaluate $P(A_1 \text{ or } A_2 \text{ or } A_3)$ by a graphical model as in Prob. 1.23. Compare the result to that of (1.9).

Solution: Referring to Fig. 1.4, the outcomes corresponding to the events A_1, A_2, and A_3 are represented by points inside circles A_1, A_2, and A_3, respectively. The regions common to two circles are shown shaded while the region common to A_1, A_2, and A_3 is shown crosshatched. The quantity $P(A_1 \text{ or } A_2 \text{ or } A_3)$ is equal to $P(A_1)$ $+ P(A_2) + P(A_3)$ minus the contributions to this sum from the overlapping areas, which are counted more than once. As seen from Fig. 1.4, outcomes in areas A, B, or C are counted twice, while the outcomes in D are counted three times.

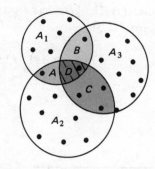

Fig. 1.4 Solution to Prob. 1.24.

The probability of an outcome in A is $P(A_1, A_2) - P(A_1, A_2, A_3)$. Similarly, the probabilities of an outcome in B and C are $P(A_1, A_3)$ $- P(A_1, A_2, A_3)$ and $P(A_2, A_3) - P(A_1, A_2, A_3)$, respectively. The probability of an outcome in D is $P(A_1, A_2, A_3)$. Thus,

$$P(A_1 \text{ or } A_2 \text{ or } A_3) = P(A_1) + P(A_2) + P(A_3)$$
$$- [P(A_1, A_2) - P(A_1, A_2, A_3)]$$
$$- [P(A_1, A_3) - P(A_1, A_2, A_3)]$$
$$- [P(A_2, A_3) - P(A_1, A_2, A_3)]$$
$$- 2P(A_1, A_2, A_3)$$
$$= P(A_1) + P(A_2) + P(A_3) - P(A_1, A_2)$$
$$- P(A_1, A_3) - P(A_2, A_3) + P(A_1, A_2, A_3).$$

Solving for (1.9), with $i = 3$,

$$P(A_1 \text{ or } A_2 \text{ or } A_3) = \sum_{j=1}^{3} P(A_j) - \sum_{\substack{j,k \\ j \neq k}} P(A_j, A_k) + P(A_1, A_2, A_3).$$

The second sum is taken over all combinations of the numbers 1, 2, 3, taken two at a time. The three combinations are (1, 2), (1, 3), (2, 3). Thus,

$$P(A_1 \text{ or } A_2 \text{ or } A_3) = P(A_1) + P(A_2) + P(A_3) - P(A_1, A_2) - P(A_1, A_3) - P(A_2, A_3) + P(A_1, A_2, A_3),$$

which agrees with the result obtained from Fig. 1.4.

1.4 Conditional Probability and Multiplicative Law of Probability

The *conditional event of A given B*, denoted by (A/B), is the event A under the stipulation that event B has already occurred. The *conditional probability of A given B*, denoted by $P(A/B)$, is the probability of the event (A/B). The probability of event A alone and that of the event (A/B) are, in general, different since the latter represents the probability of A after certain information has been gained, namely, that B has already occurred. Also, observe that the two conditional events (A/B) and (B/A) are not equivalent; hence, in general,

$$P(A/B) \neq P(B/A).$$

If A_1 and A_2 are two events, then the *probability $P(A_1, A_2)$ of the simultaneous occurrence of A_1 and A_2* is

$$P(A_1, A_2) = P(A_1) \cdot P(A_2/A_1)$$
$$= P(A_2) \cdot P(A_1/A_2).$$

(1.10)

Let $A_1, A_2, \cdots, A_i$ be events that occur simultaneously. Since $P(A_1)$ and $P(A_2/A_1)$ represent the probabilities of the occurrence of the events A_1, and A_2 given A_1, respectively, let $P(A_3/A_1, A_2)$ denote the probability of the occurrence of event A_3, given that A_1 and A_2 have already occurred, $\cdots$; let $P(A_i/A_1, A_2, \cdots, A_{i-1})$ denote the probability of occurrence of event A_i, given that $A_1, A_2, \cdots, A_{i-1}$ have already occurred. *The probability of the simultaneous occurrence of the i events, $A_1, A_2, \cdots, A_i$,* is

$$P(A_1, A_2, \cdots, A_i) = P(A_1) \cdot P(A_2/A_1) \cdot P(A_3/A_1, A_2) \cdot \cdots \cdot P(A_i/A_1, A_2, \cdots, A_{i-1}).$$

(1.11)

Thus, (1.11) is known as the *Multiplicative Law*, and it is useful in calculating probabilities of *compound events*, i.e., events that consist of two or more single events.

PROBLEM 1.25 A fair die is rolled twice. Determine the probability of a six showing up in both rolls.

Solution: Let A_1 be the event of getting a six on the first roll, and A_2, the event of getting a six on the second. Since the probability of getting a six on the second roll is not affected by the result of the first,

$$P(A_1) = \tfrac{1}{6}, \qquad P(A_2/A_1) = P(A_2) = \tfrac{1}{6}.$$

Hence from (1.10),

$$P(A_1, A_2) = P(A_1) \cdot P(A_2/A_1) = \tfrac{1}{6} \cdot \tfrac{1}{6} = \tfrac{1}{36}.$$

PROBLEM 1.26 An urn contains one black and one white ball. They are drawn one at a time, without replacement. Determine the probability that the first ball drawn will be white, and the second, black.

Solution: Let event A_1 represent the selection of a white ball on the first drawing, and A_2, the selection of a black ball on the second. Hence, the probability $P(A_1)$ is $\tfrac{1}{2}$ and the conditional probability $P(A_2/A_1)$ is 1. From (1.10), $P(A_1, A_2) = P(A_1) \cdot P(A_2/A_1) = \tfrac{1}{2}.$

PROBLEM 1.27 An urn contains six black and four white balls. Two balls are drawn one at a time, without replacement. Determine the probability of choosing a white ball on the first drawing and a black ball on the second.

Solution: Let A_1 be the event of choosing a white ball on the first drawing, and A_2, the event of choosing a black ball on the second. Since after the first drawing, six black and three white balls remain,

$$P(A_1) = \tfrac{4}{10} = \tfrac{2}{5}, \qquad P(A_2/A_1) = \tfrac{6}{9} = \tfrac{2}{3},$$

where $P(A_2/A_1)$ is the probability of drawing a black ball on the second draw, given that a white ball has been drawn on the first draw. Hence, from (1.10),

$$P(A_1, A_2) = \tfrac{2}{5} \cdot \tfrac{2}{3} = \tfrac{4}{15}.$$

PROBLEM 1.28 Determine the probability that all four cards drawn at random, without replacement, from a fair deck of 52 playing cards will be aces.

Solution: Let the Events $A_1, A_2, A_3,$ and A_4 represent the first, second, third, and fourth drawings, respectively. Then,

$$P(A_1) = \frac{4}{52} = \frac{1}{13}, \quad P(A_2/A_1) = \frac{3}{51} = \frac{1}{17}, \quad P(A_3/A_1, A_2) = \frac{2}{50} = \frac{1}{25}, \quad P(A_4/A_1, A_2, A_3) = \frac{1}{49}.$$

From (1.11), with $i = 4$,

$$P(A_1, A_2, A_3, A_4) = P(A_1) P(A_2/A_1) P(A_3/A_1, A_2) P(A_4/A_1, A_2, A_3) = \frac{1}{13} \cdot \frac{1}{17} \cdot \frac{1}{25} \cdot \frac{1}{49} = \frac{1}{270,725}.$$

Note that the result is identical to that for the case in which all four cards are drawn simultaneously; thus, from previous considerations,

$$P = \frac{1}{C_{52,4}} = \frac{4!}{52 \cdot 51 \cdot 50 \cdot 49} = \frac{1}{270,725}.$$

PROBLEM 1.29 Determine the probability that four of the five cards drawn at random, without replacement, from a standard deck of playing cards, are aces.

Solution: Let A_1, A_2, A_3, A_4, and A_5 represent the outcomes of each of the five drawings. Assume that the first four drawings A_1, A_2, A_3, and A_4 yield aces, while the fifth gives a non-ace. Then,

$$P(A_1) = \frac{4}{52} = \frac{1}{13},$$

$$P(A_2/A_1) = \frac{3}{51} = \frac{1}{17},$$

$$P(A_3/A_2, A_1) = \frac{2}{50} = \frac{1}{25},$$

$$P(A_4/A_1, A_2, A_3) = \frac{1}{49},$$

$$P(A_5/A_1, A_2, A_3, A_4) = 1.$$

Note that $P(A_5/A_1, A_2, A_3, A_4) = 1$ since the probability of getting a non-ace on the fifth drawing is a "certain event." Thus, from (1.11), with $i = 5$, the probability of drawing aces on the first four draws is

$$P'(A_1, A_2, A_3, A_4, A_5) = \frac{1}{13} \cdot \frac{1}{17} \cdot \frac{1}{25} \cdot \frac{1}{49} \cdot 1 = \frac{1}{270,725}.$$

Since it is not necessary to get the four aces in the first four drawings, the total number of ways they can be drawn is the number of permutations of four aces out of five cards; i.e., $P_{5,4} = 5$.

Hence, the probability of getting four aces in a drawing of five cards is obtained by multiplying P' by 5 since the probabilities of each of the arrangements are the same. Thus,

$$P(A_1, A_2, A_3, A_4, A_5) = 5 \, P'(A_1, A_2, A_3, A_4, A_5) = 5 \cdot \frac{1}{270,725} = \frac{1}{54,145}.$$

PROBLEM 1.30 Evaluate $P(A_1, A_2)$ for Prob. 1.22(a-c). Also, show that both forms of (1.10) give the same result.

Solution: (a) Referring to Fig. 1.2(a),

$$P(A_1) = \frac{n_2 - n_1}{N}, \quad P(A_2/A_1) = 0, \quad P(A_2) = \frac{n_4 - n_3}{N}, \quad P(A_1/A_2) = 0.$$

Note that $P(A_2/A_1) = 0$ because there are no values of $n\,(n_1 \leqslant n \leqslant n_2)$ that produce the event A_2, while $P(A_1/A_2) = 0$ because there are no values of $n\,(n_3 \leqslant n \leqslant n_4)$ that produce the event A_1.

Thus, from (1.10),

$$P(A_1, A_2) = P(A_1) \cdot P(A_2/A_1) = \frac{n_2 - n_1}{N} \cdot 0 = 0, \quad \text{or} \quad P(A_1, A_2) = P(A_2) \cdot P(A_1/A_2) = \frac{n_4 - n_3}{N} \cdot 0 = 0.$$

Thus, both forms of (1.10) give the same result.

(b) Referring to Fig. 1.2(b) and noting that $P(A_2/A_1)$ is just the fraction of the values of $n(n_1 \leqslant n \leqslant n_2)$ that also result in the event A_2, while $P(A_1/A_2)$ is the fraction of the values of $n(n_3 \leqslant n \leqslant n_4)$ which result in A_1,

$$P(A_1) = \frac{n_2 - n_1}{N}, \quad P(A_2/A_1) = \frac{n_2 - n_3}{n_2 - n_1}, \quad P(A_2) = \frac{n_4 - n_3}{N}, \quad P(A_1/A_2) = \frac{n_2 - n_3}{n_4 - n_3}.$$

Thus, from (1.10),

$$P(A_1, A_2) = P(A_1) \cdot P(A_2/A_1) = \frac{n_2 - n_1}{N} \cdot \frac{n_2 - n_3}{n_2 - n_1} = \frac{n_2 - n_3}{N},$$

and also

$$P(A_1, A_2) = P(A_2) \cdot P(A_1/A_2) = \frac{n_4 - n_3}{N} \cdot \frac{n_2 - n_3}{n_4 - n_3} = \frac{n_2 - n_3}{N}.$$

Once again, both forms of (1.10) yield the same result.

(c) Referring to Fig. 1.2(c),

$$P(A_1) = \frac{n_2 - n_1}{N}, \qquad P(A_2/A_1) = \frac{n_4 - n_3}{n_2 - n_1}, \qquad P(A_2) = \frac{n_4 - n_3}{N}, \qquad P(A_1/A_2) = 1.$$

Thus, from (1.10),

$$P(A_1, A_2) = P(A_1) \cdot P(A_2/A_1) = \frac{n_2 - n_1}{N} \cdot \frac{n_4 - n_3}{n_2 - n_1} = \frac{n_4 - n_3}{N},$$

and also

$$P(A_1, A_2) = P(A_2) \cdot P(A_1/A_2) = \frac{n_4 - n_3}{N} \cdot 1 = \frac{n_4 - n_3}{N}.$$

Thus, both forms of (1.10) yield the same result.

PROBLEM 1.31 Determine the probability of getting an ace on the next card drawn if five spades are removed at random from a deck of 52 playing cards.

Solution: Let A_1 be the event that the five spades have been withdrawn; let A_2, A_3, A_4, and A_5 be the event of drawing the ace of spades, hearts, diamonds, and clubs, respectively.

The probability of drawing an ace is the sum of the probabilities of drawing the ace of spades, hearts, diamonds, and clubs. Thus,

$$P(B/A_1) = P(A_2/A_1) + P(A_3/A_1) + P(A_4/A_1) + P(A_5/A_1),$$

where B is the event of drawing an ace. The latter three quantities are

$$P(A_3/A_1) = P(A_4/A_1) = P(A_5/A_1) = \tfrac{1}{47}.$$

To calculate the quantity $P(A_2/A_1)$, note that $P(A_2/A_1)$ is equal to the probability that the ace of spades is included in the eight remaining spades, and that if it is, it is drawn. Thus,

$$P(A_2/A_1) = \tfrac{8}{13} \cdot \tfrac{1}{47};$$

hence,

$$P(B/A_1) = \tfrac{8}{13} \cdot \tfrac{1}{47} + \tfrac{3}{47} = \tfrac{1}{13},$$

which is the same as $P(B)$, the probability of drawing an ace in a single drawing.

Note that, in general, when $B_1, B_2, \cdots, B_n$ are mutually exclusive events,

$$P(B_1 \text{ or } B_2 \text{ or } \cdots \text{ or } B_n/A) = P(B_1/A) + P(B_2/A) + \cdots + P(B_n/A). \tag{1.12}$$

Theorem of Total Probability: If the events $A_1, A_2, \cdots, A_n$ are mutually exclusive alternatives with $\sum_{i=1}^{n} P(A_i) = 1$, the probability of event B as the outcome is

$$P(B) = P(B/A_1) \cdot P(A_1) + \cdots + P(B/A_n) \cdot P(A_n) = \sum_{i=1}^{n} P(B/A_i) \cdot P(A_i). \tag{1.13}$$

PROBLEM 1.32 The probabilities for the six outcomes of rolling each of the three loaded dice are given in Table 1.2. Determine the probability of rolling a six if one die is selected at random.

TABLE 1.2. Data for Prob. 1.32

Probability of ⟍ Die	1	2	3	4	5	6
1	$\frac{1}{12}$	$\frac{1}{6}$	$\frac{1}{12}$	$\frac{1}{3}$	$\frac{1}{6}$	$\frac{1}{6}$
2	$\frac{1}{6}$	$\frac{1}{6}$	$\frac{1}{6}$	$\frac{1}{12}$	$\frac{1}{12}$	$\frac{1}{3}$
3	$\frac{1}{3}$	$\frac{1}{6}$	$\frac{1}{6}$	$\frac{1}{6}$	$\frac{1}{12}$	$\frac{1}{12}$

Solution: Use the theorem of total probability, with B representing the event of rolling a six, and A_1, A_2, and A_3, the events of choosing dice 1, 2, and 3, respectively. Since the selection of each die is equally likely,

$$P(A_1) = P(A_2) = P(A_3) = \tfrac{1}{3}.$$

From the given table,

$$P(B/A_1) = \tfrac{1}{6}, \qquad P(B/A_2) = \tfrac{1}{3}, \qquad P(B/A_3) = \tfrac{1}{12}.$$

Hence, from (1.13), the probability of rolling a six is

$$P(B) = P(B/A_1)P(A_1) + P(B/A_2)P(A_2) + P(B/A_3)P(A_3) = \tfrac{1}{3}\left(\tfrac{1}{6} + \tfrac{1}{3} + \tfrac{1}{12}\right) = \tfrac{7}{36}.$$

Bayes' Rule: If A_1, A_2, $\cdots$, A_n are n mutually exclusive events of which at least one of the A_i, $i = 1$, $2, \cdots, n$, must occur, the conditional probability of the occurrence of A_i, when the event B has occurred, is

$$P(A_i/B) = \frac{P(B/A_i) \cdot P(A_i)}{P(B/A_1) \cdot P(A_1) + \cdots + P(B/A_n) \cdot P(A_n)}. \qquad (1.14)$$

PROBLEM 1.33 Derive Bayes' rule (1.14).

Solution: Using (1.10), the joint probability of A_i and B is

$$P(A_i, B) = P(A_i/B) \cdot P(B) = P(B/A_i) \cdot P(A_i);$$

hence,

$$P(A_i/B) = \frac{P(B/A_i) \cdot P(A_i)}{P(B)}.$$

Using the theorem of total probability, the value of $P(B)$ is obtained from (1.13). Thus,

$$P(A_i/B) = \frac{P(B/A_i) \cdot P(A_i)}{P(B/A_1) \cdot P(A_1) + \cdots + P(B/A_n) \cdot P(A_n)}.$$

Bayes' Rule enables computation of the *a posteriori* probabilities $P(A_i/B)$ in terms of the *a priori* probabilities $P(A_1), \cdots, P(A_n)$, and the *conditional probabilities* $P(B/A_1), \cdots, P(B/A_n)$.

PROBLEM 1.34 Determine the probability that die 2 was chosen in Prob. 1.32, if a six is rolled with the selected die.

Solution: Let A_2 and B represent the events of selecting die 2 and of rolling a six, respectively. Then, from the data given in Prob. 1.32,

$$P(A_2) = \tfrac{1}{3}, \qquad P(B) = \tfrac{7}{36}, \qquad P(B/A_2) = \tfrac{1}{3}.$$

Using Bayes' rule,

$$P(A_2/B) = \frac{P(B/A_2) \cdot P(A_2)}{P(B)} = \frac{\frac{1}{3} \cdot \frac{1}{3}}{\frac{7}{36}} = \frac{4}{7}.$$

PROBLEM 1.35 An urn contains ten black and five white balls. A second urn contains three black and three white balls. If a ball selected at random from one of the urns is white, determine the probability that it was drawn from the first urn.

Solution: Let A_1, A_2, and B represent the events that the first urn, the second urn, and a white ball are selected, respectively. Since each urn is equally likely to be selected, the *a priori* probabilities are

$$P(A_1) = P(A_2) = \tfrac{1}{2}.$$

The conditional probabilities of selecting a white ball from the two urns are, from the statement of the problem,

$$P(B/A_1) = \tfrac{5}{15} = \tfrac{1}{3}, \qquad P(B/A_2) = \tfrac{3}{6} = \tfrac{1}{2}.$$

Thus, from Bayes' rule, the *a posteriori* probability $P(A_1/B)$ of the white ball being selected from the first urn is

$$P(A_1/B) = \frac{P(B/A_1) \cdot P(A_1)}{P(B/A_1) \cdot P(A_1) + P(B/A_2) \cdot P(A_2)} = \frac{\frac{1}{3} \cdot \frac{1}{2}}{\frac{1}{3} \cdot \frac{1}{2} + \frac{1}{2} \cdot \frac{1}{2}} = \tfrac{2}{5}.$$

1.5 Statistical Independence

Two events are *statistically independent* when knowledge of the occurrence of one event gives no additional information concerning the likelihood of the occurrence of a second event. A similar statement applies for the case of more than two events.

PROBLEM 1.36 Express the joint probability $P(A_1, A_2)$ of two statistically independent events A_1 and A_2, in terms of $P(A_1)$ and $P(A_2)$.

Solution: From (1.10),

$$P(A_1, A_2) = P(A_1) \cdot P(A_2/A_1).$$

If the events A_1 and A_2 are statistically independent,

$$P(A_2/A_1) = P(A_2).$$

Thus,

$$P(A_1, A_2) = P(A_1) \cdot P(A_2). \tag{1.15}$$

PROBLEM 1.37 Express the joint probability (A_1, A_2, A_3) of three statistically independent events A_1, A_2, and A_3 in terms of $P(A_1), P(A_2)$, and $P(A_3)$.

Solution: From (1.11),

$$P(A_1, A_2, A_3) = P(A_1) \cdot P(A_2/A_1) \cdot P(A_3/A_1, A_2).$$

When the events are statistically independent,

$$P(A_2/A_1) = P(A_2), \qquad P(A_3/A_1, A_2) = P(A_3);$$

thus,

$$P(A_1, A_2, A_3) = P(A_1) \cdot P(A_2) \cdot P(A_3).$$

Note that the above condition is not sufficient to ensure that A_1, A_2, and A_3 are statistically independent events (cf., Prob. 1.37). Events A_1, A_2, and A_3 are independent if

$$P(A_1, A_2, A_3) = P(A_1) \cdot P(A_2) \cdot P(A_3), \qquad P(A_1, A_2) = P(A_1) \cdot P(A_2),$$

$$P(A_1, A_3) = P(A_1) \cdot P(A_3), \qquad P(A_2, A_3) = P(A_2) \cdot P(A_3).$$

In general, n events, $A_1, A_2, \cdots, A_n$, are statistically independent if

$$P(A_i, A_j) = P(A_i) \cdot P(A_j),$$

$$P(A_i, A_j, A_k) = P(A_i) \cdot P(A_j) \cdot P(A_k),$$

$$\cdot \qquad \cdot$$
$$\cdot \qquad \cdot$$
$$\cdot \qquad \cdot$$

$$P(A_1, A_2, \cdots, A_n) = P(A_1) \cdot P(A_2) \cdot \cdots \cdot P(A_n),$$

for all combinations of $i, j, k, \cdots$, where $1 \leqslant i < j < k < \cdots \leqslant n$.

PROBLEM 1.38   The probabilities and the joint probabilities of the events of A_1, A_2, and A_3 are

$$P(A_1) = \tfrac{1}{2}, \qquad P(A_2) = \tfrac{1}{4}, \qquad P(A_3) = \tfrac{1}{4}, \qquad P(A_1, A_2) = \tfrac{1}{8},$$

$$P(A_1, A_3) = \tfrac{1}{8}, \qquad P(A_2, A_3) = \tfrac{1}{8}, \qquad P(A_1, A_2, A_3) = \tfrac{1}{32}.$$

Determine whether these events are independent.

Solution: Although $P(A_1, A_2, A_3) = P(A_1) \cdot P(A_2) \cdot P(A_3)$, the events A_1, A_2, and A_3 are *not* statistically independent because

$$P(A_2, A_3) \neq P(A_2) \cdot P(A_3).$$

1.6   Supplementary Problems

PROBLEM 1.39   Three dice are rolled once. How many outcomes are possible?
Answer: 216.

PROBLEM 1.40   A certain experiment has three possible mutually exclusive outcomes *A, B,* and *C.* Can the probability of occurrence of each of the three events be equal to 0.33?
Answer: No, because axiom II is violated.

PROBLEM 1.41   A baseball league has 10 teams. Determine the number of possible standings of the teams at the end of the season.
Answer: 10! = 3,628,800.

PROBLEM 1.42   Determine the number of possible hands which exist in five-card poker.
Answer: 2,598,960.

PROBLEM 1.43   Calculate the probability of drawing a royal flush (that is, ten, jack, queen, king, ace of a suit) from a deck of 52 cards in five-card poker.
Answer: $\frac{1}{649,740}$.

PROBLEM 1.44   A fair die is thrown ten times. What is the probability that at least one odd number will result?
Answer: $1 - (\tfrac{1}{2})^{10} \approx 0.999$.

PROBLEM 1.45 An honest die is rolled six times. What is the probability that each roll produces a different outcome?
Answer: $\frac{5}{324}$.

PROBLEM 1.46 Three independent random samples of the ten digits $0, 1, 2, \cdots, 9$ are taken. Determine the probability that the same digit occurs more than once in the three samples.
Answer: 0.28.

PROBLEM 1.47 If N balls are randomly distributed in N boxes, determine the probability that each box will contain exactly one ball.
Answer: $N!/N^N$.

PROBLEM 1.48 If N balls are randomly distributed in M boxes, determine the probability p that no box will contain more than one ball.
Answer: $p = \dfrac{M(M-1)\cdots(M-N+1)}{M^N}$ for $M \geqslant N$

$\qquad\quad = 0$ for $M < N$.

PROBLEM 1.49 Let N balls be randomly distributed in M boxes. What is the probability that a given box contains K balls?
Answer: $C_{N,K}(M-1)^{N-K}/M^N$.

PROBLEM 1.50 In a city of 10,000 voters, 50% are Republicans and 50% are Democrats. If two voters are selected at random, what is the probability that they are both Democrats?
Answer: $\frac{4999}{19,998}$.

PROBLEM 1.51 Determine the number of possible bridge hands (that is, 13-card hands drawn from a deck of 52 cards) consisting of m spades, n hearts, i diamonds, and k clubs.
Answer: $C_{13,m} \cdot C_{13,n} \cdot C_{13,i} \cdot C_{13,k}$.

PROBLEM 1.52 Evaluate the probability that a bridge hand contains m spades, n hearts, i diamonds, and k clubs.
Answer: $\dfrac{C_{13,m} \cdot C_{13,n} \cdot C_{13,i} \cdot C_{13,k}}{C_{52,13}}$.

PROBLEM 1.53 A closet contains 10 pairs of shoes. If two shoes are selected at random, what is the probability that they will form a pair?
Answer: $\frac{1}{19}$.

PROBLEM 1.54 The probability of rain on a day of the year selected at random is 0.25 in a certain city. The local weather forecast is correct 60% of the time when the forecast is for rain, and 80% of the time for other forecasts. Determine the probability that the forecast on a day selected at random is correct.
Answer: 0.75.

PROBLEM 1.55 For the conditions of Prob. 1.54, determine the probability that a day when the weather forecast is correct is a rainy day.
Answer: 0.2.

PROBLEM 1.56 A toy is assembled from three parts. If the probability that each part is defective is 0.1, calculate the probability that the toy is defective.
Answer: 0.271.

PROBLEM 1.57 A certain manufacturer produces TV sets at two factories. Ten percent of the TV sets produced by factory A are delivered defective while five percent produced by factory B are defective. If factory A produces 100,000 sets per year, and factory B, 50,000 sets per year, what is the probability of purchasing a defective set?

Answer: $8\frac{1}{3}\%$.

PROBLEM 1.58 Under the conditions of Prob. 1.57, if a TV set is purchased and is defective, what is the probability that it was made in factory A?

Answer: 0.8.

PROBABILITY DISTRIBUTIONS

2.1 Random Variables

A *sample point* is a point that is associated with each outcome of an experiment.

A *sample space S* is the totality of points $s_i(i = 1, 2, \cdots, n)$ that correspond to all possible outcomes of an experiment. Sample spaces are classified according to the number of sample points they contain.

A *finite sample space* is a space that contains a *finite* number of sample points, that is, they can be counted. For example, the sample space whose points can be associated with the natural numbers 3, 5, and 7 is finite.

A *countably*, or *denumerable, infinite sample space* is a space that contains an infinite number of sample points, which can be placed in one-to-one correspondence with the set of natural numbers.

A *discrete sample space* is a space that contains a finite or countably infinite number of sample points. For example, the sample space whose points can be put into a one-to-one correspondence with natural numbers is discrete.

A *continuous sample space* is a space that contains sample points that form a continuum. For example, the sample space whose points are all on a line, a line segment, or in a plane is continuous.

A *random variable* is a function $x(s)$ whose value is defined at each sample point $s_1, s_2, s_3, \cdots$ in a sample space.

PROBLEM 2.1 An experiment consists of a single drawing from a standard deck of playing cards. (a) Find the number of sample points in the sample space. (b) Classify the sample. (c) Define a random variable in this sample space.

TABLE 2.1. Tabulation for Prob. 2.1: $x(s) = s$.

Sample point s_i	Outcome	Random Variable $x_i(s)$
1	Ace of clubs	1
2	Two of clubs	2
.	.	.
.	.	.
.	.	.
52	King of spades	52

Solution: (a) Since there are 52 playing cards in a standard deck, they can be put into a one-to-one correspondence with the natural numbers 1–52. Hence, the sample space consists of 52 sample points.

(b) Since the 52 points in this space can be counted, the space is finite and, hence, discrete.

(c) The 52 possible outcomes can be associated with the natural numbers 1–52; $x(s) = s$ can be defined where s is a natural number. Table 2.1 gives the tabulation for $x(s)$.

Note that many other sample points and random variables can be defined; e.g., $s_1 = 1, s_2 = 3, s_3 = 5, \cdots,$ or $x(s) = s^2$.

PROBLEM 2.2 A card is drawn at random from a standard deck of playing cards. Represent the four events that correspond to the four suits by a random variable x.

TABLE 2.2. Tabulation for Prob. 2.2

Event	Random Variable x	Probability $P(x)$
Clubs	1	$\frac{1}{4}$
Diamonds	2	$\frac{1}{4}$
Hearts	3	$\frac{1}{4}$
Spades	4	$\frac{1}{4}$

Solution: If clubs, diamonds, hearts, and spades are represented by the natural numbers 1–4, then x is the random variable that assumes the values 1–4 with probabilities

$$P(1) = \tfrac{1}{4}, \qquad P(2) = \tfrac{1}{4}, \qquad P(3) = \tfrac{1}{4}, \qquad P(4) = \tfrac{1}{4}.$$

Thus, $P(x) = \tfrac{1}{4}$. These values are tabulated in Table 2.2. Other representations are possible.

2.2 Probability Density Functions

Let x represent a continuous random variable in a sample space S.

The *probability density function*, or simply, a *probability density*, $p(x)$ is a function that satisfies the following:

(1) $p(x) \geqslant 0$, for all $x \in S$.

(2) $\displaystyle\int_S p(x)dx = 1.$

(3) For any $x_1 < x_2$ in S, the probability of x lying in the range $x_1 \leqslant x \leqslant x_2$ is

$$\int_{x_1}^{x_2} p(x)dx = P(x_1 \leqslant x \leqslant x_2). \tag{2.1}$$

Note that $P(x_1 \leqslant x \leqslant x_2)$ represents the area under the graph $y = p(x)$ in the xy-plane between two arbitrary points x_1 and x_2.

If $p(x)$ is a *continuous* function of x at $x = a$, from (2.1),

$$P(a) = \int_a^a p(x)dx = 0.$$

Thus, although the event $x = a$ is not impossible in general, the probability that x assumes the particular value a is zero if $p(x)$ is continuous at $x = a$.

PROBLEM 2.3 For a continuous random variable x, the probability density function $p(x) = 0$ for $b < x < a$, as shown in Fig. 2.1. Evaluate $\int_{x_1}^{x_2} p(x)dx$ when (a) $x_1 < a, x_2 < a$, (b) $x_1 > b, x_2 > b$, and (c) $x_1 < a, x_2 > b$.

Solution: (a) Since $p(x) = 0$ for all $x < a$,

$$\int_{x_1}^{x_2} p(x)dx = 0.$$

(b) Since $p(x) = 0$ for all $x > b$,

$$\int_{x_1}^{x_2} p(x)dx = 0.$$

(c) In this case,

$$\int_{x_1}^{x_2} p(x)dx = \int_{a}^{b} p(x)dx,$$

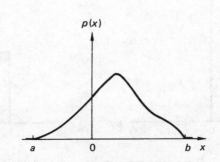

Fig. 2.1 Probability density function $p(x)$ for Prob. 2.3.

which is equal to the total area under $p(x)$. From (2.1), for $a \leqslant x \leqslant b$,

$$\int_{a}^{b} p(x)dx = P(a \leqslant x \leqslant b) = 1.$$

In general, since the probability of a certain event is 1,

$$\int_{-\infty}^{\infty} p(x)dx = 1 \tag{2.2}$$

for any arbitrary probability density function.

PROBLEM 2.4 Determine why $p(x)$ must be nonnegative to be a realizable probability density function.

Solution: From (2.1), the area between arbitrary limits must be nonnegative because it represents a probability. This requires that the integrand be nonnegative and hence, $p(x) \geqslant 0$ for all x.

2.3 Dirac Delta Function

The *Dirac delta function* $\delta(x)$ is a *symbolic* function that is defined by the relation

$$\delta(x) = 0 \quad \text{for } x \neq 0$$
$$= \infty \quad \text{for } x = 0, \tag{2.3}$$

and for any arbitrarily small positive number ϵ, that is, $\epsilon > 0$,

$$\int_{-\infty}^{\infty} \delta(x)dx = \int_{-\epsilon}^{\epsilon} \delta(x)dx = 1. \tag{2.4}$$

Figure 2.2 shows the δ-function, where the ordinate represents (for graphical purposes only) the area.

The Dirac delta function is also called the *unit impulse function* because it can be thought of as a limiting form of a rectangular pulse of height $1/A$ and width A. In Fig. 2.3, the width A of the pulse is allowed to shrink to zero. The area under the pulse $[A(1/A) = 1]$ remains constant as $A \longrightarrow 0$, resulting in a function $\delta(x)$ that is zero everywhere except at $x = 0$ and has unit area. This is expressed by (2.3) and (2.4) and shown graphically in Fig. 2.3.

The function $\delta(x - x_j)$ represents a delta function shifted to the right by an amount x_j, as shown in Fig. 2.4.

Because the δ-function is symbolic, it can also be defined solely by its integral properties. If $\phi(x)$ is a continuous function that vanishes outside some finite interval, by definition,

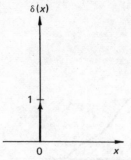

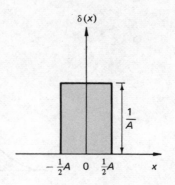

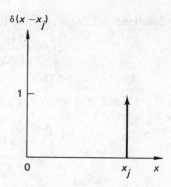

Fig. 2.2 Dirac delta function $\delta(x)$.

Fig. 2.3 Finite amplitude pulse of unit area.

Fig. 2.4 The function $\delta(x - x_j)$.

$$\int_{-\infty}^{\infty} \delta(x)\phi(x)dx = \phi(0), \tag{2.5}$$

and $\phi(x)$ is called a *testing function*.

The *sifting properties* of the δ-function, for an arbitrary x, are

$$\int_{-\infty}^{\infty} \phi(x)\delta(x - x_0)dx = \int_{-\infty}^{\infty} \phi(x + x_0)\delta(x)dx = \phi(x_0), \tag{2.6}$$

$$\int_{-\infty}^{\infty} \phi(x)\delta(ax)dx = \frac{1}{|a|} \int_{-\infty}^{\infty} \phi\left(\frac{x}{a}\right)\delta(x)dx = \frac{1}{|a|}\phi(0). \tag{2.7}$$

PROBLEM 2.5 Verify (2.6) and (2.7).

Solution: Substituting $x - x_0 = \tau$, where $dx = d\tau$,

$$\int_{-\infty}^{\infty} \phi(x)\delta(x - x_0)dx = \int_{-\infty}^{\infty} \phi(\tau + x_0)\delta(\tau)d\tau = \int_{-\infty}^{\infty} \delta(x)\phi(x + x_0)dx;$$

from (2.5),

$$\int_{-\infty}^{\infty} \delta(x)\phi(x + x_0)dx = \phi(x + x_0)\Big|_{x=0} = \phi(x_0). \tag{2.6}$$

Similarly, with $ax = \tau$, $x = \dfrac{\tau}{a}$, $dx = \dfrac{1}{a}d\tau$, and if $a > 0$,

$$\int_{-\infty}^{\infty} \delta(ax)\phi(x)dx = \frac{1}{a} \int_{-\infty}^{\infty} \delta(x)\phi\left(\frac{\tau}{a}\right)d\tau = \frac{1}{a} \int_{-\infty}^{\infty} \delta(x)\phi\left(\frac{x}{a}\right)dx = \frac{1}{a}\phi\left(\frac{x}{a}\right)\Big|_{x=0} = \frac{1}{|a|}\phi(0);$$

if $a < 0$,

$$\int_{-\infty}^{\infty} \delta(ax)\phi(x)dx = \frac{1}{a} \int_{\infty}^{-\infty} \delta(\tau)\phi\left(\frac{\tau}{a}\right)d\tau = \frac{1}{-a} \int_{-\infty}^{\infty} \delta(x)\phi\left(\frac{x}{a}\right)dx = \frac{1}{|a|}\phi(0). \tag{2.7}$$

PROBLEM 2.6 If a function $g(x)$ is continuous at $x = x_0$, show that, for $a < b$,

$$\int_{a}^{b} \delta(x - x_0)g(x)dx = g(x_0) \quad \text{for } a < x_0 < b$$

$$= 0 \quad \text{for } x_0 < a \text{ or } x_0 > b.$$

Solution: The function $g(x)$ is a testing function in this situation; i.e.,

$$\phi(x) = g(x) \quad \text{for } a < x < b$$
$$= 0 \quad \text{for } x < a \text{ or } x > b.$$

Hence, from (2.6),

$$\int_a^b \delta(x - x_0)g(x)dx = \int_{-\infty}^{\infty} \delta(x - x_0)\phi(x)dx = \phi(x_0).$$

Thus,

$$\int_a^b \delta(x - x_0)g(x)dx = g(x_0) \quad \text{for } a < x_0 < b$$
$$= 0 \quad \text{for } x_0 < a \text{ or } x_0 > b.$$

PROBLEM 2.7 If $a < b$, show that

$$\int_a^b \delta(x - x_0)dx = 1 \quad \text{for } a < x_0 < b$$
$$= 0 \quad \text{for } x_0 < a \text{ or } x_0 > b.$$

Solution: Define the testing function $\phi(x)$ as

$$\phi(x) = 1 \quad \text{for } a < x < b$$
$$= 0 \quad \text{for } x < a \text{ or } x > b.$$

Then,

$$\int_a^b \delta(x - x_0)dx = \int_{-\infty}^{\infty} \delta(x - x_0)\phi(x)dx = \phi(x_0).$$

PROBLEM 2.8 If a function $f(x)$ is continuous at $x = 0$, show that $f(x)\delta(x) = f(0)\delta(x)$, and, hence, (a) $x\delta(x) = 0$, (b) $\delta(ax) = \frac{1}{|a|}\delta(x)$, and (c) $\delta(-x) = \delta(x)$.

Solution: Since $f(x)$ is continuous, from (2.5),

$$\int_{-\infty}^{\infty} [f(x)\delta(x)]\,\phi(x)dx = \int_{-\infty}^{\infty} \delta(x)[f(x)\phi(x)]\,dx = f(0)\phi(0) = f(0)\int_{-\infty}^{\infty} \delta(x)\phi(x)dx$$

$$= \int_{-\infty}^{\infty} [f(0)\delta(x)]\,\phi(x)dx.$$

Hence, $f(x)\delta(x) = f(0)\delta(x)$ because $\phi(x)$ is an arbitrary testing function.
(a) If $f(x) = x$, $x\delta(x) = 0$ at $x = 0$.
(b) From the sifting properties of the δ-function (2.7),

$$\int_{-\infty}^{\infty} \delta(ax)\phi(x)dx = \frac{1}{|a|}\phi(0) = \frac{1}{|a|}\int_{-\infty}^{\infty} \delta(x)\phi(x)dx = \int_{-\infty}^{\infty} \left[\frac{1}{|a|}\delta(x)\right]\phi(x)dx.$$

Hence, $\delta(ax) = \frac{1}{|a|}\delta(x)$ because $\phi(x)$ is an arbitrary testing function.

(c) Setting $a = -1$ in part (b), $\delta(-x) = \delta(x)$.

The *derivative* $\delta'(x)$ of the δ-function is, by definition,

$$\int_{-\infty}^{\infty} \delta'(x)\phi(x)dx = -\int_{-\infty}^{\infty} \delta(x)\phi'(x)dx = -\phi'(0), \tag{2.8}$$

where

$$\delta'(x) = \frac{d\delta(x)}{dx}, \qquad \phi'(0) = \frac{d\phi}{dx}\bigg|_{x=0}.$$

Note that the first derivative $\delta'(x) = d\delta(x)/dt$ is a generalized function that assigns the value $-\phi'(0)$ to a testing function $\phi(x)$.

The *nth derivative* of the δ-function is

$$\delta^{(n)}(x) = \frac{d^n \delta(x)}{dx^n}$$

and is obtained by applying (2.8) n times; i.e.,

$$\int_{-\infty}^{\infty} \delta^{(n)}(x)\phi(x)dx = (-1)^n \phi^{(n)}(0),$$

where

$$\phi^{(n)}(0) = \frac{d^n \phi(x)}{dx^n}\bigg|_{x=0}.$$

PROBLEM 2.9 If $f(x)$ is an arbitrary generalized function with a continuous first derivative $f'(x)$, show that

$$\int_{-\infty}^{\infty} f'(x)\phi(x)dx = -\int_{-\infty}^{\infty} f(x)\phi'(x)dx \tag{2.9}$$

is consistent with the standard definition of the derivative $f'(x)$ of $f(x)$.

Solution: Integrating $\displaystyle\int_{-\infty}^{\infty} f'(x)\phi(x)dx$ by parts,

$$\int_{-\infty}^{\infty} f'(x)\phi(x)dx = f(x)\phi(x)\bigg|_{-\infty}^{\infty} - \int_{-\infty}^{\infty} f(x)\phi'(x)dx.$$

Since the testing function $\phi(x)$ vanishes outside a finite interval, that is, it is zero at $x = \pm\infty$,

$$\int_{-\infty}^{\infty} f'(x)\phi(x)dx = -\int_{-\infty}^{\infty} f(x)\phi'(x)dx.$$

Note that the derivative $f'(x)$ of an arbitrary generalized function $f(x)$ is defined by (2.9).

The *product rule* for the derivative of two functions states that if $f(x)$ is a continuous and differentiable function, the function $f(x)\delta(x)$ is also differentiable, and

$$[f(x)\delta(x)]' = f(x)\delta'(x) + f'(x)\delta(x). \tag{2.10}$$

PROBLEM 2.10 Verify the product rule (2.10) for the derivative of two functions.

Solution: Using (2.9),

$$\int_{-\infty}^{\infty} [f(x)\delta(x)]' \phi(x)dx = -\int_{-\infty}^{\infty} [f(x)\delta(x)]\, \phi'(x)dx$$

$$= -\int_{-\infty}^{\infty} \delta(x)\,[f(x)\phi'(x)]\, dx$$

$$= -\int_{-\infty}^{\infty} \delta(x)\left\{[f(x)\phi(x)]' - f'(x)\phi(x)\right\}dx$$

$$= -\int_{-\infty}^{\infty} \delta(x)\,[f(x)\phi(x)]'dx + \int_{-\infty}^{\infty} \delta(x)\,[f'(x)\phi(x)]\, dx$$

$$= \int_{-\infty}^{\infty} \delta'(x)\,[f(x)\phi(x)]\, dx + \int_{-\infty}^{\infty} [\delta(x)f'(x)]\,\phi(x)dx$$

$$= \int_{-\infty}^{\infty} [\delta'(x)f(x) + \delta(x)f'(x)]\,\phi(x)dx.$$

Since $\phi(x)$ is an arbitrary testing function,

$$[f(x)\delta(x)]' = \delta'(x)f(x) + \delta(x)f'(x).$$

The *Heaviside unit function*, or *unit step function* $u(x)$, is a *symbolic* function that is undefined at $x = 0$ and

$$u(x) = 1 \quad \text{for } x > 0$$
$$= 0 \quad \text{for } x < 0. \tag{2.11}$$

Figure 2.5 shows the function $u(x)$.

Because the Heaviside unit function is symbolic, it can be defined solely by its integral properties. If $\phi(x)$ is a testing function, by definition,

$$\int_{-\infty}^{\infty} u(x)\phi(x)dx = \int_{0}^{\infty} \phi(x)dx. \tag{2.12}$$

The function $u(x - x_j)$ represents a *delayed unit step function* that is shifted to the right by an amount x_j, as shown in Fig. 2.6. Because $\delta(x - x_j)$ has unit area,

$$u(x - x_j) = \int_{-\infty}^{\infty} \delta(x - x_j)dx = 1 \quad \text{for } x > x_j$$
$$= 0 \quad \text{for } x < x_j, \tag{2.13}$$

and is discontinuous at $x = x_j$, where it "jumps", as shown in Fig. 2.6.

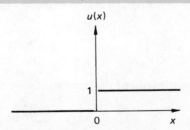

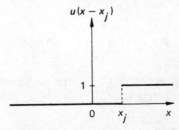

Fig. 2.5 Heaviside unit function or unit step function $u(x)$.

Fig. 2.6 Delayed unit step function $u(x - x_j)$.

PROBLEM 2.11   Show that the δ-function is the derivative of the Heaviside unit function $u(x)$.

Solution: From (2.9),

$$\int_{-\infty}^{\infty} u'(x)\phi(x)dx = -\int_{-\infty}^{\infty} u(x)\phi'(x)dx.$$

But from definition (2.12),

$$\int_{-\infty}^{\infty} u(x)\phi'(x)dx = -\int_{0}^{\infty} \phi'(x)dx = -[\phi(\infty) - \phi(0)] = \phi(0)$$

since $\phi(\infty) = 0$. Hence, using the definition of the δ-function (2.5),

$$\int_{-\infty}^{\infty} u'(x)\phi(x)dx = \phi(0) = \int_{-\infty}^{\infty} \delta(x)\phi(x)dx.$$

Consequently,

$$u'(x) = \frac{du(x)}{dx} = \delta(x).$$

2.4   Probability Density Function of a Discrete Random Variable

Assume that the *discrete* random variable x assumes the values $x_1, x_2, \cdots, x_j, \cdots, x_n$, with probabilities $P(x_1), P(x_2), \cdots, P(x_n)$, respectively. The form of the *probability density function* $p(x)$ is

$$p(x) = \sum_{j=1}^{n} P(x_j)\delta(x - x_j), \tag{2.14}$$

where $\delta(x)$ is the Dirac delta function. The probability density function is shown in Fig. 2.7, where the heights or areas are weighted in accordance with $P(x_j)$.

PROBLEM 2.12   Show that (2.14) is consistent with (2.1).

Solution: The probability at $x = x_i$ is

$$P(x_i) = \lim_{\epsilon \to 0} \int_{x_i - \epsilon}^{x_i + \epsilon} p(x)dx$$

$$= \lim_{\epsilon \to 0} \int_{x_i - \epsilon}^{x_i + \epsilon} \sum_{j=0}^{n} P(x_j)\delta(x - x_j)dx.$$

Since $P(x_i)\delta(x - x_i)$ is the only nonzero term in the interval $x_i - \epsilon < x < x_i + \epsilon$,

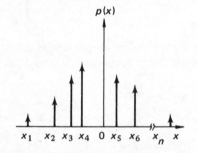

Fig. 2.7 Probability density function $p(x)$ of a discrete random variable.

$$P(x_i) = \lim_{\epsilon \to 0} \int_{x_i - \epsilon}^{x_i + \epsilon} P(x_i)\delta(x - x_i)dx = P(x_i) \lim_{\epsilon \to 0} \int_{x_i - \epsilon}^{x_i + \epsilon} \delta(x - x_i)dx = P(x_i).$$

In the representation (2.14), the coefficients $P(x_j)$, i.e., the strengths of the impulses, are merely the probabilities of the events $x_1, x_2, \cdots, x_n$.

PROBLEM 2.13   A card is drawn at random from a standard deck of playing cards. (a) Represent the four events that correspond to the four suits by a random variable x. (Cf. Prob. 2.2.) (b) Graph $p(x)$.

Solution: (a) If clubs, diamonds, hearts, and spades are represented by the natural numbers 1–4, then x is a random variable that assumes the values 1–4 with the probabilities

$$P(1) = \tfrac{1}{4}, \qquad P(2) = \tfrac{1}{4}, \qquad P(3) = \tfrac{1}{4}, \qquad P(4) = \tfrac{1}{4}.$$

Thus, $P(x) = \tfrac{1}{4}$. This situation is tabulated in Table 2.2. Other representations are possible.

(b) Using (2.14),

$$p(x) = P(1)\delta(x - 1) + P(2)\delta(x - 2) + P(3)\delta(x - 3) + P(4)\delta(x - 4)$$

$$= \tfrac{1}{4}\delta(x - 1) + \tfrac{1}{4}\delta(x - 2) + \tfrac{1}{4}\delta(x - 3) + \tfrac{1}{4}\delta(x - 4),$$

which is shown in Fig. 2.8.

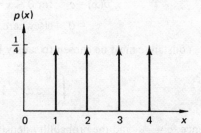

Fig. 2.8 Solution to Prob. 2.13.

PROBLEM 2.14 Graph $p(x)$ for the random variable x that represents the sum obtained in rolling a pair of fair dice.

Solution: Since the possible events are the natural numbers 2–12 inclusive, the probability density function $p(x)$ is

$$p(x) = \sum_{j=2}^{12} P(j)\delta(x - j).$$

There are 36 possible outcomes of rolling a pair of dice, as shown in Table 2.3. The probabilities are

$$P(2) = P(12) = \tfrac{1}{36}, \qquad P(3) = P(11) = \tfrac{2}{36}, \qquad P(4) = P(10) = \tfrac{3}{36},$$

$$P(5) = P(9) = \tfrac{4}{36}, \qquad P(6) = P(8) = \tfrac{5}{36}, \qquad P(7) = \tfrac{6}{36}.$$

These values are graphed in Fig. 2.9.

TABLE 2.3. Tabulation for Prob. 2.14.

Event	Outcomes	No. of Outcomes
2	1+1	1
3	1+2, 2+1	2
4	2+2, 3+1, 1+3	3
5	1+4, 4+1, 2+3, 3+2	4
6	1+5, 5+1, 4+2, 2+4, 3+3	5
7	1+6, 6+1, 2+5, 5+2, 3+4, 4+3	6
8	6+2, 2+6, 5+3, 3+5, 4+4	5
9	6+3, 3+6, 5+4, 4+5	4
10	6+4, 4+6, 5+5	3
11	6+5, 5+6	2
12	6+6	1
Total		36

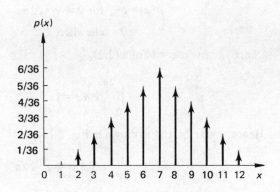

Fig. 2.9 Solution to Prob. 2.14.

PROBLEM 2.15 A real number x in the interval from 0–10, inclusive, is chosen at random with all numbers in the interval equally likely. Find the probability density function $p(x)$.

Solution: In this case x is a continuous variable. For all numbers to be equally likely, $p(x)$ must be constant in the interval so that

$$p(x) = c \quad \text{for } 0 \leqslant x \leqslant 10$$
$$= 0 \quad \text{elsewhere.}$$

The constant c must be chosen to satisfy (2.2), so that

$$\int_0^{10} c \, dx = 1.$$

Hence, $c = \frac{1}{10}$, and the probability density function is

$$p(x) = \frac{1}{10} \quad \text{for } 0 \leqslant x \leqslant 10$$
$$= 0 \quad \text{elsewhere.}$$

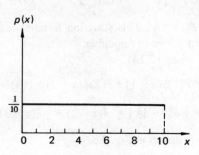

Fig. 2.10 Solution to Prob. 2.15.

The function $p(x)$ is graphed in Fig. 2.10.

Although the probability of choosing a given value of x, for example, $x = 2$, is zero, the event is clearly possible. This is true because there is an infinite number of equally likely outcomes of which $x = 2$ is only one. This does not contradict, however, the fundamental axioms in which impossible events have zero probability, since the converse is not necessarily true.

A probability distribution function $p(x)$ is *uniformly distributed* over an interval from a to b $(a < b)$ if $p(x)$ is constant over the entire interval.

PROBLEM 2.16 The displacement of a mechanical oscillation is given by $x(t) = A \sin \omega t$, where A is a constant and ωt is the number of radians swept out in time t. Find the probability density function for the phase $\varphi = \omega t_0$ of the oscillation if $x(t)$ is observed at some arbitrary time t_0.

Solution: Because the observation time t_0 is completely arbitrary, all values of the phase ωt_0 are equally likely. Since the observer cannot distinguish between the values that differ by integral multiples of 2π, the phase appears uniformly distributed between 0 and 2π. Alternatively, any interval of length 2π can be used, for example, $-\pi$ to π. Thus,

$$p(\varphi) = c \quad \text{for } 0 \leqslant \varphi \leqslant 2\pi$$
$$= 0 \quad \text{elsewhere.}$$

Since $\int_0^{2\pi} p(\varphi) \, d\varphi = 1$ from (2.2),

$$\int_0^{2\pi} c \, d\varphi = 1.$$

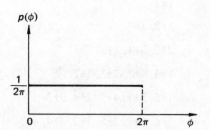

Fig. 2.11 Solution to Prob. 2.16.

Hence, $c = 1/2\pi$, and as shown in Fig. 2.11,

$$p(\varphi) = \frac{1}{2\pi} \quad \text{for } 0 \leqslant \varphi \leqslant 2\pi$$
$$= 0 \quad \text{elsewhere.}$$

PROBLEM 2.17 Evaluate $P(x \geqslant x_0)$ for $x_0 > 0$, when the probability density function is

$$p(x) = \frac{1}{x_0} e^{-x/x_0} \quad \text{for } x \geqslant 0$$
$$= 0 \quad \text{for } x < 0.$$

Solution: From (2.1), the probability for $x \geqslant x_0$ is

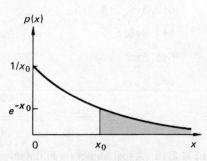

Fig. 2.12 Solution to Prob. 2.17.

$$P(x \geqslant x_0) = \int_{x_0}^{\infty} p(x)\,dx.$$

In Fig. 2.12, $P(x \geqslant x_0)$ is the shaded area. Substituting into the above equation,

$$P(x \geqslant x_0) = \int_{x_0}^{\infty} \frac{1}{x_0} e^{-x/x_0}\,dx = -e^{-x/x_0} \Big|_{x_0}^{\infty} = e^{-1}.$$

PROBLEM 2.18 The weight of a volume of liquid is measured. Because of certain inaccuracies in the measuring device, an error is made. The probability density function $p(w)$ of the measurements is shown in Fig. 2.13(a). Find the probability that for any particular measurement, the error will exceed $\pm\frac{1}{2}\%$ of the true value if the correct weight is 10 lb.

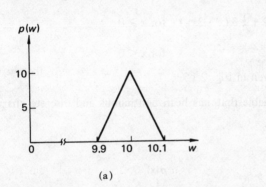
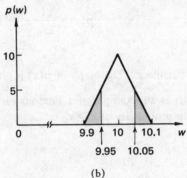

(a)   (b)

Fig. 2.13 (a) Probability density function $p(w)$ for Prob. 2.18. (b) Solution to Prob. 2.18.

Solution: The probability of an error in excess of $\pm\frac{1}{2}\%$ is equivalent to an error of $\pm0.005 \cdot (10 \text{ lb})$ or ±0.05 lb. From (2.1), this is the total area under $p(w)$ for $w < 10.00 - 0.05$ and $w > 10.00 + 0.05$; that is, $w < 9.95$ and $w > 10.05$. This is the shaded area in Fig. 2.13(b). Hence, for the two triangular areas, the probability is

$$P(w < 9.95 \text{ or } w > 10.05) = \tfrac{1}{2}(5)(9.95 - 9.90) + \tfrac{1}{2}(5)(10.10 - 10.05) = 0.25.$$

Thus, the probability that an error in any measurement will exceed $\pm\frac{1}{2}\%$ of the true value is 0.25; in other words, it will occur 25% of the time.

PROBLEM 2.19 Suppose that in Prob. 2.18 the measured weights are rounded off to the nearest 0.05 lb; that is, each measurement is rounded off to 9.90, 9.95, 10.00, 10.05, or 10.10 lb, whichever is closest. Find the probability density function $p(w^*)$ for these quantized measurements w^* if $p(w)$ is a uniform distribution, as shown in Fig. 2.14(a).

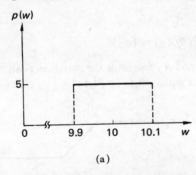
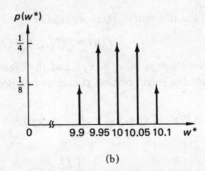

(a)   (b)

Fig. 2.14 (a) Uniform distribution $p(w)$ for Prob. 2.19. (b) Probability density function $p(w^*)$ for Prob. 2.19.

Solution: The values of the probability density function $p(w^*)$ for the quantized values of w are just the areas under $p(w)$ that correspond to the limits on w in each case. Thus,

$$P(9.90) = P(w < 9.925) = 5(9.925 - 9.900) = 0.125,$$

$$P(9.95) = P(9.925 \leqslant w < 9.975) = 5(9.975 - 9.925) = 0.250,$$

$$P(10.00) = P(9.975 \leqslant w < 10.025) = 5(10.025 - 9.975) = 0.250,$$

$$P(10.05) = P(10.025 \leqslant w < 10.075) = 5(10.075 - 10.025) = 0.250,$$

$$P(10.10) = P(10.075 \leqslant w) = 5(10.100 - 10.075) = 0.125.$$

Since the quantized values of w, w^*, assume only discrete values, $p(w)^*$ is comprised of delta functions, where the areas of the delta functions are given by the appropriate values above. Graphically, $p(w^*)$ is shown in Fig. 2.14(b).

PROBLEM 2.20   Calculate $P(x \geqslant x_0)$ for the probability density function

$$p(x) = \frac{1}{2x_0} e^{-x/x_0} + \frac{1}{2} \delta(x - 3x_0) \quad \text{for } x \geqslant 0$$

$$= 0 \qquad\qquad\qquad\qquad\qquad \text{for } x < 0$$

of a random variable x. The graph of $p(x)$ is given in Fig. 2.15.

Solution: This is an example of a random variable that has both continuous and discrete characteristics. Using (2.1), the probability of $x \geqslant x_0$ is

$$P(x \geqslant x_0) = \int_{x_0}^{\infty} p(x)\, dx$$

$$= \int_{x_0}^{\infty} \left[\frac{1}{2x_0} e^{-x/x_0} + \frac{1}{2} \delta(x - 3x_0) \right] dx$$

$$= \frac{1}{2} \int_{x_0}^{\infty} e^{-x/x_0} \frac{dx}{x_0} + \frac{1}{2} \int_{x_0}^{\infty} \delta(x - 3x_0)\, dx$$

$$= -\frac{1}{2} e^{-x/x_0} \Big|_{x_0}^{\infty} + \frac{1}{2}$$

$$= \frac{1}{2}(1 + e^{-1}).$$

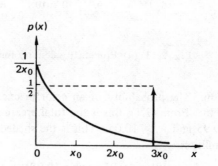

Fig. 2.15   Probability density function $p(x)$ for Prob. 2.20.

PROBLEM 2.21   Two statistically independent random variables x_a and x_b have probability density functions $p_a(x)$ and $p_b(x)$. A third variable x_c is formed by periodically selecting either x_a or x_b by a switch, as shown in Fig. 2.16. Determine $p_c(x)$ if the switch remains an equal length of time at each position.

Solution: From the theorem of total probability (1.13),

$$P(B) = P(B/A_1) \cdot P(A_1) + P(B/A_2) \cdot P(A_2),$$

where $P(B)$ represents $P(x_1 \leqslant x_c \leqslant x_2)$, and the events A_1 and A_2 represent the switch in positions A and B, respectively. Since the length of time at each switch position is equal, $P(A_1) = P(A_2) = \frac{1}{2}$. From (2.1),

$$P(B/A_1) = P(x_1 \leqslant x_a \leqslant x_2) = \int_{x_1}^{x_2} p_a(x)\, dx,$$

$$P(B/A_2) = P(x_1 \leqslant x_b \leqslant x_2) = \int_{x_1}^{x_2} p_b(x)\, dx,$$

$$P(B) = \int_{x_1}^{x_2} p_c(x)\, dx;$$

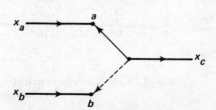

Fig. 2.16   Solution to Prob. 2.21.

hence,

$$\int_{x_1}^{x_2} p_c(x)\,dx = \tfrac{1}{2}\int_{x_1}^{x_2} p_a(x)\,dx + \tfrac{1}{2}\int_{x_1}^{x_2} p_b(x)\,dx,$$

or, on simplification,

$$\int_{x_1}^{x_2}\left[p_c(x) - \tfrac{1}{2}p_a(x) - \tfrac{1}{2}p_b(x)\right]dx = 0.$$

For this to be true, for arbitrary x_1 and x_2, the integrand must vanish so that the probability density function is

$$p_c(x) = \tfrac{1}{2}p_a(x) + \tfrac{1}{2}p_b(x).$$

PROBLEM 2.22 Using the relative frequency definition of probability, outline a procedure for experimentally measuring the continuous probability density function of the random function $n(t)$ shown in Fig. 2.17.

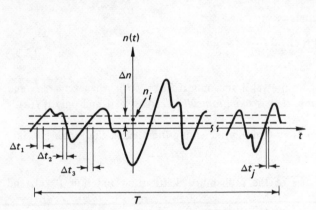

Fig. 2.17 Solution to Prob. 2.22.

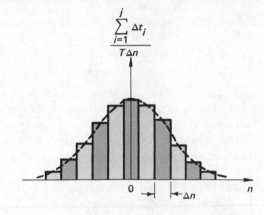

Fig. 2.18 Histogram and true probability density function (dashed line).

Solution: From (2.1),

$$\int_{n_1}^{n_2} p(n)\,dn = P(n_1 \leqslant n \leqslant n_2).$$

If $n_1 \approx n_2$, then $p(n)$ will be approximately constant over the interval, that is, $p(n) \approx p(n_1) \approx p(n_2)$; hence,

$$p(n_1)(n_2 - n_1) \approx P(n_1 \leqslant n \leqslant n_2), \quad \text{or} \quad p(n_1) \approx \frac{P(n_1 \leqslant n \leqslant n_2)}{n_2 - n_1}.$$

According to the relative frequency definition of probability, $P(n_1 \leqslant n \leqslant n_2)$ can be estimated by determining the fraction of time $n_1 \leqslant n \leqslant n_2$ in a length of record. For example, to estimate one point of the probability density function $p(n)$, e.g., $p(n_i)$, from Fig. 2.17,

$$p(n_i) \approx \frac{\displaystyle\sum_{k=1}^{j} \Delta t_k}{T\,\Delta n}. \tag{2.15}$$

The approximation (2.15) of $p(n_i)$ improves as the length T of the sample used increases and the interval width Δn decreases. Essentially (2.15) approximates the true probability density function over the interval $n_i - \tfrac{1}{2}\Delta n \leqslant n \leqslant n_i + \tfrac{1}{2}\Delta n$ by a constant; when this procedure is carried out over the range of variation of n, the result is a plot called a *histogram*, as shown in Fig. 2.18. The true probability density function $p(n)$ is also shown in Fig. 2.18, for comparison.

If the true $p(n)$ is known to be a continuous function of n, a smooth curve can be drawn from the histogram, giving a "smooth" estimate of the probability density function.

2.5   Cumulative Distribution Function

Consider the probability $P^*(x)$ that a random variable x whose probability density function is $p(x)$ assumes a value less than or equal to x_0 and has a probability density function $p(x)$. The corresponding function $P^*(x)$ is called the *cumulative distribution function or probability distribution function*, and is given by

$$P^*(x) = \int_{-\infty}^{x} p(x)\,dx. \tag{2.16}$$

Thus, the value of (2.16) at an arbitrary point $x = x_0$ gives the probability that the random variable assumes a value $x \leqslant x_0$. It therefore can be considered as a special case of (2.1) with $x_1 = -\infty$ and $x_2 = x_0$.

From this definition,

$$P(a \leqslant x \leqslant b) = P^*(b) - P^*(a),$$

and from the fundamental theorem of integral calculus,

$$\frac{dP^*(x)}{dx} = p(x). \tag{2.17}$$

A function $f(x)$ is *monotonically increasing* on an interval if and only if $f(a) \leqslant f(b)$ whenever $a < b$, and a and b belong to the interval. However, the function $f(x)$ is *monotonically decreasing* if and only if $f(a) > f(b)$ whenever $a < b$.

The cumulative distribution function $P^*(x)$ is a monotonically increasing function of the variable x since the probability density function $p(x) \geqslant 0$ for all x.

PROBLEM 2.23   (a) Determine the basic properties of the probability distribution function $P^*(x)$, and (b) sketch its typical behavior versus x.

Solution: (a) Using (2.16),

$$P^*(-\infty) = \int_{-\infty}^{-\infty} p(x)\,dx = 0, \qquad P^*(\infty) = \int_{-\infty}^{\infty} p(x)\,dx = 1.$$

(b) The typical behavior of $P^*(x)$ versus x is shown in Fig. 2.19. Note that $P^*(x)$ is monotonically increasing.

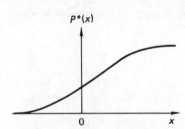

Fig. 2.19 Typical behavior of the
probability distribution function
$P^*(x)$ versus x.

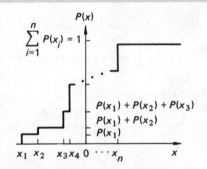

Fig. 2.20 Solution to Prob. 2.24.

PROBLEM 2.24   Determine $P^*(x)$ for the discrete probability density function

$$p(x) = \sum_{i=1}^{N} P(x_i)\,\delta(x - x_i),$$

where $\delta(x)$ is the Dirac delta function.

Solution: Using (2.16), the probability distribution function is

$$P^*(x) = \int_{-\infty}^{x} p(x)\,dx = \int_{-\infty}^{x} \sum_{i=1}^{N} P(x_i)\,\delta(x - x_i)\,dx = \sum_{i=1}^{N} P(x_i) \int_{-\infty}^{x} \delta(x - x_i)\,dx.$$

Since it follows from (2.13) that $\int_{-\infty}^{x} \delta(x - x_i)\,dx$ is the delayed unit step function $u(x - x_i)$,

$$P^*(x) = \sum_{i=1}^{N} P(x_i)\,u(x - x_i).$$

The resulting $P^*(x)$ has a "staircase" behavior, as shown in Fig. 2.20. The discontinuities occur at the location of the impulses. The magnitude of the discontinuities is equal to the areas of the corresponding impulses.

PROBLEM 2.25 Verify (2.17).

Solution: From (2.16), the cumulative distribution function is

$$P^*(x) = \int_{-\infty}^{x} p(x)\,dx.$$

From the fundamental theorem of integral calculus, and on differentiating both sides with respect to x,

$$p(x) = \frac{dP^*(x)}{dx}. \tag{2.17}$$

PROBLEM 2.26 Sketch the cumulative distribution function $P^*(x)$ for the probability density function $p(x)$ shown in Fig. 2.21.

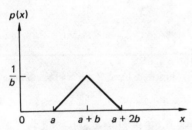

Fig. 2.21 Probability density function $p(x)$ for Prob. 2.26.

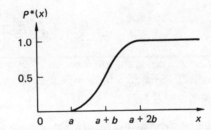

Fig. 2.22 Probability distribution function $P^*(x)$ for Prob. 2.26.

Solution: From (2.16), the cumulative distribution function is

$$P^*(x) = \int_{-\infty}^{x} p(x)\,dx,$$

where

$$p(x) = \frac{1}{b^2}(x - a) \qquad \text{for } a \leqslant x \leqslant a + b$$

$$= \frac{1}{b^2}(a + 2b - x) \qquad \text{for } a + b \leqslant x \leqslant a + 2b$$

$$= 0 \qquad \text{elsewhere.}$$

Because $p(x)$ is piecewise linear, $P^*(x)$ is comprised of parabolic sections in the intervals from a to $a + b$ and from $a + b$ to $a + 2b$, as shown in Fig. 2.22.

PROBLEM 2.27 The probability of an electronic-system failure is $P^*(\tau) = 1 - e^{-\tau/100}$, where $P^*(\tau)$ is the probability of failure before τ hr. Find the probability density function that corresponds to $P^*(\tau)$.

Solution: From (2.17), the probability density function is

$$p(\tau) = \frac{dP^*(\tau)}{d\tau} = \frac{1}{100}\, e^{-\tau/100} \quad \text{for } \tau \geqslant 0$$

$$= 0 \qquad\qquad \text{for } \tau < 0.$$

2.6   Statistical Averages

The *average value* $\overline{x}$ or x_{av} of a random variable x, with a probability density function $p(x)$, is

$$\overline{x} = x_{av} = \int_{-\infty}^{\infty} x p(x)\, dx. \tag{2.18}$$

The average value also is called the *expected value, mean value* or *ensemble average*. Thus, the expected value $E[x]$ of x is

$$E[x] = \int_{-\infty}^{\infty} x p(x)\, dx. \tag{2.19}$$

In general, if $g(x)$ is an arbitrary function of x, the expected value of $g(x)$ is

$$E[g(x)] = \int_{-\infty}^{\infty} g(x)\, p(x)\, dx. \tag{2.20}$$

A special case occurs when $g(x) = x^n$; hence,

$$E[x^n] = \int_{-\infty}^{\infty} x^n\, p(x)\, dx, \quad n = 1, 2, \cdots. \tag{2.21}$$

The quantity $E[x^n]$ is called the *n*th *moment* of $p(x)$ about the origin.

The *n*th moment about an arbitrary point, e.g., $x = x_0$, is denoted by $E[(x - x_0)^n]$. These moments are called *central moments* if $x_0 = \overline{x} = E[x]$.

PROBLEM 2.28 Determine the first two moments of $p(x)$ about the origin.

Solution: The first moment about the origin is obtained from (2.21) by setting $n = 1$; that is, the first moment is

$$E[x] = \int_{-\infty}^{\infty} x p(x)\, dx = \overline{x}.$$

The second moment obtained from (2.21) by setting $n = 2$ is

$$E[x^2] = \int_{-\infty}^{\infty} x^2 p(x)\, dx = \overline{x^2}.$$

The first moment is the expected value of x, whereas the second moment is the expected value of x^2, which is commonly known as the *mean squared value* of x.

PROBLEM 2.29 Determine the moments of x about an arbitrary point $x = x_0$.

Solution: The moments about $x = x_0$ are given by $E[(x - x_0)^n]$. Therefore,

$$E[(x - x_0)^n] = \int_{-\infty}^{\infty} (x - x_0)^n\, p(x)\, dx, \quad n = 1, 2, \cdots.$$

PROBLEM 2.30 Evaluate the first central moment, i.e., $E[(x - \overline{x})^n]$ for $n = 1$.

Solution: From Prob. 2.29,

$$E[x - \overline{x}] = \int_{-\infty}^{\infty} (x - \overline{x}) \, p(x) \, dx = \int_{-\infty}^{\infty} x p(x) \, dx - \overline{x} \int_{-\infty}^{\infty} p(x) \, dx.$$

The first integral is $\overline{x}$ by definition, while $\int_{-\infty}^{\infty} p(x) \, dx = 1$. Hence,

$$E[x - \overline{x}] = \overline{x} - \overline{x} = 0.$$

PROBLEM 2.31 Evaluate the second central moment, that is, $E[(x - \overline{x})^n]$ for $n = 2$.

Solution: From Prob. 2.29, the second central moment is

$$E[(x - \overline{x})^2] = \int_{-\infty}^{\infty} (x - \overline{x})^2 \, p(x) \, dx$$

$$= \int_{-\infty}^{\infty} x^2 p(x) \, dx - 2\overline{x} \int_{-\infty}^{\infty} x p(x) \, dx + \overline{x}^2 \int_{-\infty}^{\infty} p(x) \, dx$$

$$= \overline{x^2} - 2\overline{x}^2 + \overline{x}^2$$

$$= \overline{x^2} - \overline{x}^2$$

since the first integral is $\overline{x^2}$ by definition, $\int_{-\infty}^{\infty} x p(x) \, dx = \overline{x}$, and $\int_{-\infty}^{\infty} p(x) \, dx = 1$.

The quantity $\overline{x^2} - \overline{x}^2$ is known as the *variance* of x and is generally denoted by σ^2. Thus,

$$\sigma^2 = \overline{x^2} - \overline{x}^2; \tag{2.22}$$

that is, the variance is the mean squared value of the deviation from the mean of x.

The *standard deviation* is the square root of the variance, i.e.,

$$\sigma = \sqrt{\overline{x^2} - \overline{x}^2}. \tag{2.23}$$

PROBLEM 2.32 A random variable x assumes the values 0 and 1 with probabilities p and q, respectively. Determine the average $\overline{x}$ and the standard deviation σ.

Solution: The probability density function of x is

$$p(x) = p\delta(x) + q\delta(x - 1),$$

as shown in Fig. 2.23. Thus, the average $\overline{x}$ is

$$\overline{x} = \int_{-\infty}^{\infty} x p(x) \, dx$$

$$= \int_{-\infty}^{\infty} x [p\delta(x) + q\delta(x - 1)] \, dx$$

$$= p \int_{-\infty}^{\infty} x\delta(x) \, dx + q \int_{-\infty}^{\infty} x\delta(x - 1) dx.$$

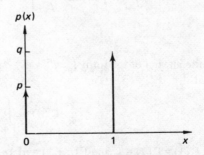

Fig. 2.23 Probability density function $p(x)$ for Prob. 2.32.

The above integrals are of the form $\int_{-\infty}^{\infty} h(x)\delta(x - x_0) dx$, which can be evaluated by using the sifting property (2.6) of the δ-function. Thus, the average is $\overline{x} = p \cdot 0 + q \cdot 1 = q$. Similarly, the second moment is

$$\overline{x^2} = \int_{-\infty}^{\infty} x^2 p(x)\,dx = p \int_{-\infty}^{\infty} x^2 \delta(x)\,dx + q \int_{-\infty}^{\infty} x^2 \delta(x-1)\,dx = p \cdot 0 + q \cdot 1 = q.$$

Using (2.23), the standard deviation is

$$\sigma = \sqrt{\overline{x^2} - \overline{x}^2} = \sqrt{q - q^2} = \sqrt{q(1-q)} = \sqrt{pq}.$$

PROBLEM 2.33 Determine the second moment $\overline{x^2}$ for the probability density function

$$p(x) = \sum_{i=1}^{N} P(x_i)\,\delta(x - x_i).$$

Solution: From Prob. 2.19, the second moment is

$$\overline{x^2} = \int_{-\infty}^{\infty} x^2 p(x)\,dx = \int_{-\infty}^{\infty} x^2 \sum_{i=1}^{N} P(x_i)\,\delta(x - x_i)\,dx = \sum_{i=1}^{N} P(x_i) \int_{-\infty}^{\infty} x^2 \delta(x - x_i)\,dx.$$

Using the sifting property (2.6) of the δ-function,

$$\overline{x^2} = \sum_{i=1}^{N} P(x_i)\,x_i^2.$$

PROBLEM 2.34 Determine the average $\overline{x}$ and the second moment $\overline{x^2}$ of the probability density function shown in Fig. 2.24.

Solution: Since $p(x) = 1/b$ in the interval from a to $a + b$, the required values are

$$\overline{x} = \int_{-\infty}^{\infty} x p(x)\,dx = \frac{1}{b} \int_{a}^{a+b} x\,dx$$

$$= \frac{1}{b} \frac{x^2}{2}\bigg|_{a}^{a+b}$$

$$= \frac{1}{2b}\,[(a+b)^2 - a^2]$$

$$= a + \tfrac{1}{2}\,b,$$

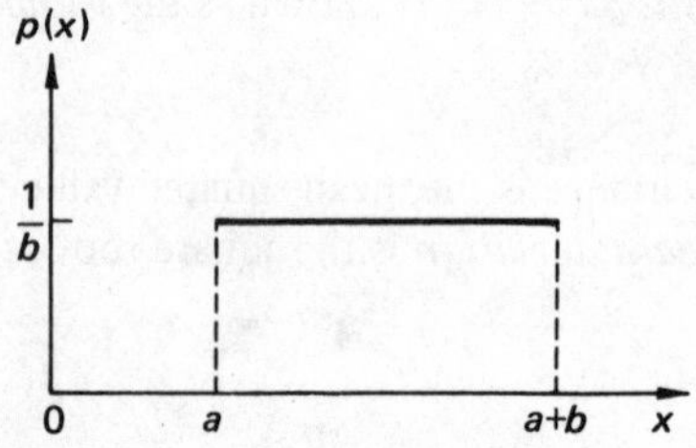

Fig. 2.24 Solution to Prob. 2.34.

$$\overline{x^2} = \int_{-\infty}^{\infty} x^2 p(x)\,dx = \frac{1}{b} \int_{a}^{a+b} x^2\,dx = \frac{1}{3b}\,[(a+b)^3 - a^3] = a^2 + ab + \tfrac{1}{3}\,b^2.$$

A definite integral of the form $\int_{0}^{\infty} x^{n-1} e^{-x}\,dx$ is known as the *gamma function*, $\Gamma(n)$. From calculus, it is known that

$$\Gamma(n) = \int_{0}^{\infty} x^{n-1} e^{-x}\,dx = (n-1)!$$

Note that $\Gamma(1) = \Gamma(2) = 1$, and $\Gamma(n+1) = n\Gamma(n)$.

PROBLEM 2.35 The probability density function for the time τ between failures of a system is

$$p(\tau) = a_1 e^{-a_2 \tau} \quad \text{for } \tau \geqslant 0$$

$$= 0 \qquad\qquad \text{for } \tau < 0,$$

where a_1 and a_2 are constants. Figure 2.25 gives the graph of $p(\tau)$. (a) Express a_1 and a_2 in terms of the mean time between failures τ_0, and (b) determine the standard deviation of the mean time τ between failures.

Solution: (a) Because $\int_{-\infty}^{\infty} p(\tau)\,d\tau = 1$, on substitution,

$$a_1 \int_0^{\infty} e^{-a_2 \tau}\,d\tau = 1.$$

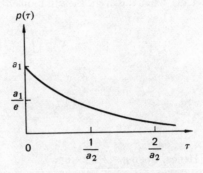

Integrating,

$$\frac{a_1}{-a_2} \cdot e^{-a_2 \tau}\Big|_0^{\infty} = 1,$$

and hence, $a_1 = a_2$. The mean value of τ is

$$\bar{\tau} = \int_{-\infty}^{\infty} \tau p(\tau)\,d\tau = \int_0^{\infty} \tau a_1 e^{-a_2 \tau}\,d\tau = \int_0^{\infty} \tau a_1 e^{-a_1 \tau}\,d\tau.$$

Fig. 2.25 Solution to Prob. 2.35.

Because this integral can be put into the form of a gamma function,

$$\bar{\tau} = \frac{1}{a_1} \int_0^{\infty} (a_1 \tau)\, e^{-a_1 \tau}\, d(a_1 \tau) = \frac{1}{a_1}\,\Gamma(2) = \frac{1}{a_1}.$$

Therefore, the mean time between failures is

$$\bar{\tau} = \frac{1}{a_1} = \frac{1}{a_2} = \tau_0.$$

(b) The standard deviation of τ is

$$\sigma = (\overline{\tau^2} - \bar{\tau}^2)^{1/2}.$$

From Prob. 2.28, the second moment is

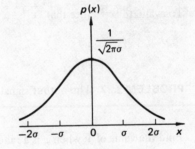

$$\overline{\tau^2} = \int_0^{\infty} \tau^2 p(\tau)\,d\tau = \frac{1}{\tau_0} \int_0^{\infty} \tau^2 e^{-\tau/\tau_0}\,d\tau = 2\tau_0.$$

Thus, the standard deviation is $\sigma = (2\tau_0^2 - \tau_0^2)^{1/2} = \tau_0$. Note that both the mean and standard deviation are equal to τ_0.

Fig. 2.26 Normal or Gaussian distribution.

A function $f(x)$ is said to be *even* if $f(x) = f(-x)$ and *odd* if $f(x) = -f(-x)$. The integral of an odd function between symmetric limits is zero.

The probability density function

$$p(x) = \frac{1}{\sqrt{2\pi\sigma^2}}\, e^{-x^2/2\sigma^2} \tag{2.24}$$

is an even function, and its set of values is called the *normal* or *Gaussian distribution*. (Cf., Fig. 2.26.)

PROBLEM 2.36 Evaluate $\bar{x}$, $\overline{x^2}$, $\overline{x^n}$, $\overline{|x|}$, and $\overline{|x|^2}$ for the probability density function $p(x)$ of the normal distribution.

Solution: Since $p(x)$ is an even function, $xp(x)$ is odd. Hence,

$$\bar{x} = \int_{-\infty}^{\infty} xp(x)\,dx = 0.$$

Similarly, when n is odd, the nth moment is zero; that is $\overline{x^n} = 0$. From a table of definite integrals (cf., Table I in the Appendix),

$$\int_{-\infty}^{\infty} x^{2n} e^{-ax^2} dx = \frac{1 \cdot 3 \cdot 5 \cdots (2n-1)}{2^n a^n} \sqrt{\frac{\pi}{a}}.$$

Thus, when n is even, the nth moment is

$$\overline{x^n} = \int_{-\infty}^{\infty} x^n p(x) dx = \frac{1}{\sqrt{2\pi\sigma^2}} \frac{1 \cdot 3 \cdot 5 \cdots (n-1)}{2^{n/2} \left(\dfrac{1}{2\sigma^2}\right)^{n/2}} \sqrt{2\pi\sigma^2}$$

$$= \frac{1 \cdot 3 \cdot 5 \cdots (n-1)}{2^{n/2}} (2\sigma^2)^{n/2}$$

$$= [1 \cdot 3 \cdot 5 \cdots (n-1)] \sigma^n.$$

Hence, when $n = 2$, $\overline{x^2} = \sigma^2$.

To evaluate $\overline{|x|}$, note that $|x| p(x)$ is an even function. Thus,

$$\overline{|x|} = \int_{-\infty}^{\infty} |x| p(x) dx = 2\int_{0}^{\infty} |x| p(x) dx = 2\int_{0}^{\infty} x p(x) dx = \frac{2}{\sqrt{2\pi\sigma^2}} \int_{0}^{\infty} x e^{-x^2/2\sigma^2} dx.$$

Substituting $u = x^2/2\sigma^2$, and $du = x dx/\sigma^2$,

$$\overline{|x|} = \sqrt{\frac{2\sigma^2}{\pi}} \int_{0}^{\infty} e^{-u} du = \sigma \sqrt{\frac{2}{\pi}}.$$

To evaluate $\overline{|x|^2}$, note that $\overline{|x|^2} = \overline{x^2}$. Therefore,

$$\overline{|x|^2} = \sigma^2.$$

PROBLEM 2.37   The output signal from an electronic system is

$$y = A \cos a \varphi.$$

Find the value of $\overline{y}$ when φ is a random variable whose probability density function is

$$p(\varphi) = \frac{1}{\sqrt{2\pi\sigma^2}} e^{-\varphi^2/2\sigma^2},$$

as shown in Fig. 2.27.

Solution: From Prob. 2.28,

$$\overline{y} = \int_{-\infty}^{\infty} A \cos a\varphi p(\varphi) d\varphi = \frac{A}{\sqrt{2\pi\sigma^2}} \int_{-\infty}^{\infty} \cos a\varphi e^{-\varphi^2/2\sigma^2} d\varphi.$$

From Table I of the Appendix,

$$\int_{-\infty}^{\infty} e^{-\alpha^2 x^2} \cos \beta x dx = \frac{\sqrt{\pi} \, e^{-\beta^2/4\alpha^2}}{|\alpha|}.$$

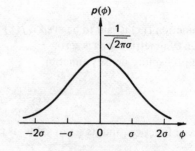

Fig. 2.27   Solution to Prob. 2.37.

Thus, the average is

$$\overline{y} = \frac{A}{\sqrt{2\pi\sigma^2}} \sqrt{\pi} \, e^{-a^2\sigma^2/2} \sqrt{2\sigma^2} = A \, e^{-a^2\sigma^2/2}.$$

PROBLEM 2.38   Evaluate $E[f(x)]$ when $p(x) = \sum_{i=1}^{N} P(x_i) \delta(x - x_i)$.

Solution: From Prob. 2.28, the expected value is

$$E[f(x)] = \int_{-\infty}^{\infty} f(x)\, p(x)\, dx = \int_{-\infty}^{\infty} f(x) \sum_{i=1}^{N} P(x_i)\, \delta(x - x_i)\, dx = \sum_{i=1}^{N} P(x_i) \int_{-\infty}^{\infty} f(x)\, \delta(x - x_i)\, dx.$$

Using the sifting property (2.6) of $\delta(x)$,

$$E[f(x)] = \sum_{i=1}^{N} P(x_i)\, f(x_i).$$

PROBLEM 2.39 Determine the conditions under which $E[x^n] = 0$ for all odd values of n.

Solution: Since $E[x^n] = 0$,

$$\int_{-\infty}^{\infty} x^n\, p(x)\, dx = 0.$$

Referring to Fig. 2.28, since n is odd ($n = 1, 3, 5, \cdots$), x^n is an odd function of x; that is, $(-x)^n = -x^n$. If the product $x^n p(x)$ is an odd function, $E[x^n]$ is zero because an odd function integrated over symmetric limits equals zero. Thus,

$$(-x)^n p(-x) = -(x^n) p(x) \qquad \text{or} \qquad p(-x) = p(x),$$

which is the definition of an even function. Therefore, for example, the mean value of a random variable $\bar{x}$ is zero if $p(x)$ is an even function.

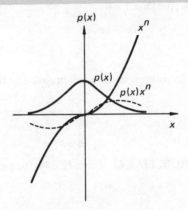

Fig. 2.28 Solution to Prob. 2.39.

2.7 Chebyshev's Inequality

The standard deviation σ of an arbitrary probability density function is a measure of the width or spread of the distribution, that is, it is a measure of the concentration of probability in the neighborhood of the mean. If σ is small, the probability of obtaining a value close to the mean is high; if σ is large, the probability of obtaining a value further from the mean is proportionately higher. Mathematically, this idea is expressed by *Chebyshev's inequality*, which gives an upper bound for the area under an arbitrary density function beyond a certain limit from the mean. Thus, if a probability distribution has a mean $\bar{x}$ and a standard deviation σ, the probability of obtaining a value that deviates from the mean by more than k standard deviations is less than $1/k^2$; i.e.,

$$P(|x - \bar{x}| \geqslant k\sigma) \leqslant \frac{1}{k^2}. \tag{2.25}$$

This bound cannot be reduced without restricting the class of density functions. If the density function is symmetrical with respect to the mean and possesses a single maximum point,

$$P(|x - \bar{x}| \geqslant k\sigma) \leqslant \frac{4}{9k^2}. \tag{2.26}$$

PROBLEM 2.40 Prove Chebyshev's inequality (2.25).

Solution: The variance is

$$\sigma^2 = \int_{-\infty}^{\infty} (x - \bar{x})^2\, p(x)\, dx.$$

Since the integrand of this integral is nonnegative,

$$\sigma^2 \geqslant \int_{|x-\bar{x}| > k\sigma} (x-\bar{x})^2 \, p(x)dx.$$

Over the range of integration,

$$(x-\bar{x})^2 > k^2\sigma^2.$$

Thus,

$$\sigma^2 \geqslant \int_{|x-\bar{x}| > k\sigma} k^2\sigma^2 \, p(x)dx = k^2\sigma^2 \int_{|x-\bar{x}| > k\sigma} p(x)dx.$$

Simplifying,

$$k^2 \int_{|x-\bar{x}| > k\sigma} p(x)dx \leqslant 1.$$

The above integral is the probability that x lies outside the range $\bar{x} - k\sigma < x < \bar{x} + k\sigma$; hence,

$$P(|x-\bar{x}| \geqslant k\sigma) \leqslant \frac{1}{k^2}.$$

PROBLEM 2.41 From (2.24), the probability density function of a normal distribution is

$$p(x) = \frac{1}{\sqrt{2\pi}\sigma} e^{-x^2/2\sigma^2}.$$

Find an upper bound on $P(x \geqslant 3\sigma)$.

Solution: Clearly $p(x)$ is symmetrical about $\bar{x}$ and has only one maximum point. Thus, from (2.26), with $k = 3$,

$$P(|x-\bar{x}| \geqslant 3\sigma) \leqslant \tfrac{4}{81}.$$

Because $p(x)$ is even, $\bar{x} = 0$; hence,

$$P(|x| \geqslant 3\sigma) \leqslant \tfrac{4}{81},$$

or, equivalently,

$$P(-3\sigma \geqslant x \geqslant 3\sigma) \leqslant \tfrac{4}{81}.$$

The fact that $p(x)$ is even also yields

$$P(x \leqslant -3\sigma) = P(x \geqslant 3\sigma).$$

Hence,

$$P(-3\sigma \geqslant x \geqslant 3\sigma) = P(x \leqslant -3\sigma) + P(x \geqslant 3\sigma) = 2P(x \geqslant 3\sigma).$$

Thus, the required upper bound is

$$P(x \geqslant 3\sigma) \leqslant \tfrac{2}{81}.$$

PROBLEM 2.42 Calculate $P(|x - \bar{x}| \geqslant k\sigma)$
for the probability density function

$$p(x) = \frac{1}{2k^2} \delta(x - \bar{x} + k\sigma)$$

$$+ \frac{1}{2k^2} \delta(x - \bar{x} - k\sigma) + \left(1 - \frac{1}{k^2}\right)\delta(x - \bar{x}).$$

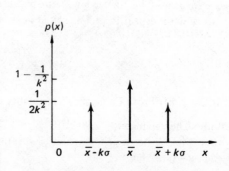

Fig. 2.29 Solution to Prob. 2.42.

Solution: From Fig. 2.29,

$$P(|x - \overline{x}| \geqslant k\sigma) = P(|x - \overline{x}| = k\sigma) = \frac{1}{2k^2} + \frac{1}{2k^2} = \frac{1}{k^2}.$$

Thus, for this probability density function, the equality sign in (2.25) holds, demonstrating that the bound of Chebyshev's inequality cannot be reduced without restrictions on $p(x)$.

PROBLEM 2.43 The temperature of a solution in a chemical process is regulated. The presence of random disturbances causes a fluctuation of the temperature with time. Limited measurements are made from which it is found that the average temperature is $150°F$ with a standard deviation of $1°F$. Determine the fraction of time during which the temperature can exceed $160°F$.

Solution: Using Chebyshev's inequality (2.25), with $k = 10°/1° = 10$,

$$P(|T - 150°| \geqslant 10°) \leqslant \frac{1}{100},$$

where T is the temperature. Thus, the fraction of the time that T is greater than $160°$ or less than $140°$ is less than or equal to 1%. Accordingly,

$$P(T > 160°) \leqslant 0.01.$$

Note that no assumption needs to be made regarding the exact nature of the probability density function. If it can be assumed that the density function of the fluctuations is symmetrical and has only one maximum, then from (2.26),

$$P(T > 160°) \leqslant 0.01 \times \frac{4}{9} \leqslant 0.0044.$$

PROBLEM 2.44 An interfering signal in a radar receiver has the characteristic shown in Fig. 2.30. The average power of the interfering signal is 10^{-8} W, while the standard deviation is 0.5×10^{-9} W. Estimate the minimum length of time the system will operate if the allowable power of the crystal mixer in the receiver before burnout is 10^{-3} W. Assume that the power in each interval is independent of the values in all other intervals.

Solution: Using Chebyshev's inequality (2.25),

$$P(|W - 10^{-8}| \geqslant 10^{-3}) \leqslant \frac{1}{\left[\dfrac{10^{-3}}{(0.5)(10^{-9})} \right]^2} = \frac{1}{4}(10^{-12}).$$

In other words, 10^{-3} W will be exceeded, approximately, less than once every 4×10^{12} intervals. The minimum expected operating time is

$$T \geqslant 4 \times 10^{12} \times 10^{-6} \text{ sec} = 4 \times 10^6 \text{ sec} = 1111 \text{ hr}.$$

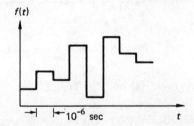

Fig. 2.30 Characteristic of an interfering signal in a radar receiver.

2.8 Supplementary Problems

PROBLEM 2.45 An honest coin is tossed and the occurrence of a head is represented by the value 1, while the occurrence of a tail, by the value 0. What is the corresponding probability density function?
Answer: $p(x) = \frac{1}{2}\delta(x) + \frac{1}{2}\delta(x - 1)$.

PROBLEM 2.46 A coin is weighted in such a manner that when tossed, a head is three times more likely to occur than a tail. If heads and tails are represented by 1 and 0, respectively, determine the corresponding probability density function.
Answer: $p(x) = \frac{1}{4}\delta(x) + \frac{3}{4}\delta(x - 1)$.

PROBLEM 2.47 Determine the probability distribution function for the probability density functions of Probs. 2.1–2.
Answer:

$$P_1^*(x) = \tfrac{1}{2}u(x) + \tfrac{1}{2}u(x-1), \qquad P_2^*(x) = \tfrac{1}{4}u(x) + \tfrac{3}{4}u(x-1),$$

where $u(x)$ is the unit step function

$$u(x) = 1 \quad \text{for } x > 0$$
$$\;\;\;\;\;\; = 0 \quad \text{for } x < 0.$$

PROBLEM 2.48 The probability distribution function of a random variable is given by

$$P^*(x) = 0.1(1 - e^{-x}) + 0.9u(x-3) \quad \text{for } x \geqslant 0$$
$$\;\;\;\;\;\;\; = 0 \qquad\qquad\qquad\qquad\quad \text{for } x < 0.$$

Determine the corresponding probability density function.
Answer: $p(x) = 0.1e^{-x} + 0.9\delta(x-3) \quad \text{for } x \geqslant 0$
$$\;\;\;\;\;\;\;\;\;\;\; = 0 \qquad\qquad\qquad\qquad \text{for } x < 0.$$

PROBLEM 2.49 Are the following functions probability density functions?

(a) $p(x) = \tfrac{1}{3}\delta(x-3) + \tfrac{2}{3}u(x-1) - \tfrac{2}{3}u(x-\tfrac{3}{2})$;

(b) $p(x) = 10[u(x) - u(x-1)] - 9\delta(x-2)$;

(c) $p(x) = \tfrac{1}{4}e^{-x} + \tfrac{3}{2}[u(x-20) - u(x-20.5)]$.

Answer: (a) No. (b) No. (c) Yes.

PROBLEM 2.50 Are the following functions probability distribution functions?

(a) $P^*(x) = 0.976(1 - e^{-x/6}) \quad \text{for } x \geqslant 0$
$$\;\;\;\;\;\;\;\;\;\; = 0 \qquad\qquad\qquad\;\; \text{for } x < 0;$$

(b) $P^*(x) = 1 - \tfrac{1}{3}e^{-4x} - \tfrac{1}{3}e^{-7x} - \tfrac{1}{3}e^{-9x} \quad \text{for } x \geqslant 0$
$$\;\;\;\;\;\;\;\;\;\; = 0 \qquad\qquad\qquad\qquad\qquad\qquad\; \text{for } x < 0;$$

(c) $P^*(x) = 1 - e^{-3x} + u(x-1) - u(x-2) \quad \text{for } x > 0$
$$\;\;\;\;\;\;\;\;\;\; = 0 \qquad\qquad\qquad\qquad\qquad\qquad \text{for } x < 0.$$

Answer: (a) No. (b) Yes. (c) No.

PROBLEM 2.51 The *median* of a random variable x is defined as the value x_m of x that is exceeded 50% of the time; that is, if P^* is the probability distribution function of x, then $P^*(x_m) = \tfrac{1}{2}$. Determine the median value of a random variable x whose probability density function is given by

$$p(x) = \frac{1}{x_0}\,e^{-x/x_0} \quad \text{for } x \geqslant 0$$
$$\;\;\;\;\;\; = 0 \qquad\quad\;\; \text{for } x < 0.$$

Answer: $x_m = x_0 \log_{10} 2$.

PROBLEM 2.52 The *mode* of a random variable x is defined to be the most probable value of x. Determine the mode of the random variable x whose probability density function is given by

$$p(x) = \frac{1}{\sqrt{2\pi}\,\sigma}\,\exp\left(-\,\frac{x^2 - 2x_0 x + x_0^2}{2\sigma^2}\right).$$

Answer: x_0.

PROBLEM 2.53 Find the value of x_0 which minimizes $E(x - x_0)^2$, where x is a random variable.
Answer: $x_0 = \bar{x}$.

PROBLEM 2.54 Find the expected value of y if

$$y = e^{-x} \quad \text{for } x \geqslant 0 \qquad \text{and} \qquad p(x) = e^{-x} \quad \text{for } x \geqslant 0$$
$$= 0 \quad \text{for } x < 0 \qquad \qquad \qquad = 0 \quad \text{for } x < 0.$$

Answer: $E(y) = \frac{1}{2}$.

PROBLEM 2.55 Find the nth moment of y for the conditions of Prob. 2.10.

Answer: $E[y^n] = \dfrac{1}{n+1}$.

PROBLEM 2.56 Find the first and second central moments of the probability density function

$$p(x) = \frac{1}{\sqrt{2\pi}\,\sigma}\ e^{-(x-x_0)^2/2\sigma^2} .$$

Answer: The first central moment $= 0$, and the second central moment $= \sigma^2$.

PROBLEM 2.57 A random variable x has a probability density function $p(x) = \frac{1}{2}e^{-|x|}$. Calculate the mean-squared value of x.
Answer: $\overline{x^2} = 1$.

PROBLEM 2.58 Repeat Prob. 2.21 for the case where the switch remains in position x_a three times as long as in position x_b.
Answer: $p_c(x) = \frac{3}{4}p_a(x) + \frac{1}{4}p_b(x)$.

PROBLEM 2.59 The *asymmetry* or *skewness* of the probability density function of a random variable x is sometimes measured in terms of the *coefficient* of *skewness* γ_1, where $\gamma_1 = \overline{(x - \bar{x})^3}/\sigma^3$ where σ is the standard deviation. Calculate the coefficient of skewness for the following probability density functions:

(a) $p(x) = \dfrac{1}{x_0}\ e^{-x/x_0} \quad \text{for } x \geqslant 0$
$\qquad\quad = 0 \qquad\qquad \text{for } x < 0;$

and

(b) $p(x) = \dfrac{1}{x_0}\ e^{x/x_0} \quad \text{for } x \leqslant 0$
$\qquad\quad = 0 \qquad\qquad \text{for } x > 0.$

Answer: (a) $\gamma_1 = 2$; (b) $\gamma_1 = -2$.

PROBLEM 2.60 Calculate the coefficient of skewness (cf., Prob. 2.59) for the gamma distribution

$$p(x) = \frac{1}{\Gamma(p)}\ x^{\rho-1}e^{-x} \quad \text{for } x \geqslant 0$$
$$= 0 \qquad\qquad\quad \text{for } x < 0.$$

Answer: $\gamma_1 = 2/\sqrt{\rho}$.

PROBLEM 2.61 The degree of flattening of a probability density function $p(x)$ near its mean is sometimes measured by the *coefficient of excess* (or *kurtosis*)

$$\gamma_2 = \frac{\overline{(x - \bar{x})^4}}{\sigma^4} - 3,$$

where σ is the standard deviation. Positive values of γ_2 usually indicate that the probability density function is more sharply peaked, that is, taller and narrower, than the normal density, while negative values usually indicate a less sharply peaked function. Calculate γ_2 for the normal probability density function

$$p(x) = \frac{1}{\sigma\sqrt{2\pi}}\ e^{-(x-\bar{x})^2/2\sigma^2} .$$

Answer: $\gamma_2 = 0$.

PROBLEM 2.62 Calculate the coefficients of skewness and excess (defined in Probs. 2.59 and 2.61) for the probability density function

$$p(x) = 1/C_1 \quad \text{for } C_2 - C_1/2 \leqslant x \leqslant C_2 + C_1/2$$
$$= 0 \qquad \text{elsewhere.}$$

Answer: $\gamma_1 = 0$ and $\gamma_2 = -1.2$.

PROBLEM 2.63 Prove that if a random variable x is bounded, that is, two finite values a and b exist such that $P(a < x < b) = 1$, then all the moments are finite.

PROBLEM 2.64 Show that the moments of the Cauchy distribution do not exist. The probability function of the distribution is $p(x) = \dfrac{1}{\pi(1 + x^2)}$.

3 CHAPTER

SPECIAL DISTRIBUTIONS

3.1 Binomial Distribution

A *Bernoulli trial* is an experiment that has only two possible outcomes, called *success s* and *failure f*. The *probabilities* of success and failure are

$$P(s) = p, \qquad P(f) = q,$$

where

$$p + q = 1.$$

The probability of *exactly r* successes and $n - r$ failures in n (fixed) independent Bernoulli trials *in a given order* is

$$P(r) = p^r q^{n-r}.$$

The probability of r successes and $n - r$ failures *in any order* is obtained by adding the probabilities of all sequences containing r successes and $n - r$ failures in some order. Each of these sequences has the probability $p^r q^{n-r}$, and the number of sequences is the number of combinations of n things taken r at a time. Thus,

$$P(r) = C_{n,r} p^r q^{n-r}. \tag{3.1}$$

But $C_{n,r} = \dfrac{n!}{r!\,(n-r)!}$. Hence, (3.1) can be written as

$$P(r) = \frac{n!}{r!\,(n-r)!} p^r q^{n-r}. \tag{3.2}$$

The *binomial distribution* is the probability distribution defined by (3.1) or (3.2). In fact, (3.1) or (3.2) defines a family of probability distributions, with each member of the family characterized by given values of the *parameters n* and *p*. Note that $q = 1 - p$.

PROBLEM 3.1 Find the probability density function of the binomial distribution.

Solution: The random variable r is the number of times event s occurs in n trials. Since r is an integer, the probability density function is discrete, and because $r \leqslant n$,

$$p(r) = P(0)\delta(r) + P(1)\delta(r-1) + \cdots + P(n)\delta(r-n) = \sum_{i=0}^{n} P(i)\delta(r-i).$$

Substituting (3.2), the probability density function is

$$p(r) = \sum_{i=1}^{n} \frac{n!}{i!\,(n-i)!} p^i q^{n-i} \delta(r-i).$$

PROBLEM 3.2 Determine $p(r)$ for $n = 3$ using the binomial expansion.

Solution: The probabilities $P(r)$, $r = 0,1,2,3$, are found from the appropriate terms of the expansion of $(p + q)^3$; i.e.,

$$(p + q)^3 = p^3 + 3p^2 q + 3pq^2 + q^3,$$

where

p^3 = probability that all three outcomes are $s = P(3)$,
$3p^2 q$ = probability that two outcomes are s and one is $f = P(2)$,
$3pq^2$ = probability that one outcome is s and two are $f = P(1)$,
q^3 = probability that outcome s does not occur, i.e., all three are $f = P(0)$.

Thus, the probability density function is

$$p(r) = P(0)\delta(r) + P(1)\delta(r - 1) + P(2)\delta(r - 2) + P(3)\delta(r - 3)$$
$$= q^3 \delta(r) + 3pq^2 \delta(r - 1) + 3p^2 q \delta(r - 2) + p^3 \delta(r - 3),$$

as shown in Fig. 3.1.

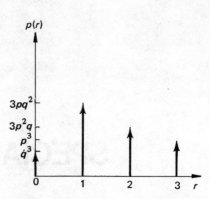

Fig. 3.1 Probability density function $p(r)$ for $n = 3$ for the binomial distribution.

PROBLEM 3.3 Determine the cumulative distribution function of the binomial distribution.

Solution: The probability that outcome s occurs at most r times in n trials is the cumulative distribution function; i.e.,

$$P*(r) = P(0) + P(1) + \cdots + P(r) = \sum_{n=0}^{r} P(n).$$

Substituting (3.2) yields

$$P*(r) = \sum_{n=0}^{r} \frac{n!}{r!\,(n - r)!} p^r q^{n-r}.$$

PROBLEM 3.4 Determine the mean and standard deviation of r successes in $n = 2$ Bernoulli trials.

Solution: For $n = 2$, $(p + q)^2 = p^2 + 2pq + q^2$. Thus, the probability density function is

$$p(r) = q^2\delta(r) + 2pq\delta(r - 1) + p^2\delta(r-2),$$

as shown in Fig. 3.2.

The mean value of r is

$$\overline{r} = \int_{-\infty}^{\infty} r\,p(r)\,dr$$

$$= \int_{-\infty}^{\infty} r[q^2 \delta(r) + 2pq\delta(r - 1) + p^2\delta(r - 2)]\,dr.$$

Using the sifting property of $\delta(r)$,

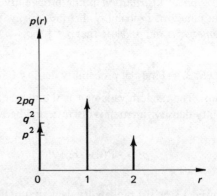

Fig. 3.2 Probability density function $p(r)$ for Bernoulli trials with $n = 2$ successes.

$$\overline{r} = (1)(2pq) + (2)(p^2).$$

Since there are only two mutually exclusive outcomes, $p + q = 1$. Thus,

$$\overline{r} = 2p(1 - p) + 2p^2 = 2p.$$

Similarly,

$$\bar{r^2} = \int_{-\infty}^{\infty} r^2 p(r)\,dr = \int_{-\infty}^{\infty} r^2 \left[q^2 \delta(r) + 2pq\,\delta(r-1) + p^2\,\delta(r-2) \right] dr = 2pq + 4p^2.$$

Thus, the standard deviation is

$$\sigma = \sqrt{\bar{r^2} - \bar{r}^2} = \sqrt{2pq + 4p^2 - 4p^2} = \sqrt{2pq}.$$

In general, it is shown in Chap. 5, that for n trials,

$$\bar{r} = np, \tag{3.3}$$

$$\sigma^2 = npq. \tag{3.4}$$

PROBLEM 3.5 Find the probability of obtaining either four or five heads if a fair coin is tossed six times.

Solution: From (3.2), with $n = 6$ and $p = q = \frac{1}{2}$,

$$P(4) = \frac{6!}{4!2!} \left(\frac{1}{2} \right)^4 \left(\frac{1}{2} \right)^2 = \frac{6 \cdot 5}{2} \cdot \frac{1}{2^6} = \frac{15}{64}, \qquad P(5) = \frac{6!}{5!1!} \left(\frac{1}{2} \right)^5 \left(\frac{1}{2} \right) = 6 \cdot \frac{1}{2^6} = \frac{6}{64}.$$

Thus, because $P(4 \text{ or } 5) = P(4) + P(5)$,

$$P(4 \text{ or } 5) = \tfrac{15}{64} + \tfrac{6}{64} = \tfrac{21}{64}.$$

PROBLEM 3.6 Find the probability of obtaining at least one head if a fair coin is tossed 100 times.

Solution: The probability of at least one head plus the probability of less than one head (i.e., no heads) in 100 tosses is equal to one. Therefore, the probability of obtaining at least one head is

$$P(\text{at least one head}) = 1 - P(\text{no heads}) = 1 - \left(\tfrac{1}{2} \right)^{100}.$$

PROBLEM 3.7 A radar system has a probability of 0.1 of detecting a certain target during a single scan. Find the probability that the target will be detected (a) at least two times in four consecutive scans and (b) at least once in twenty scans.

Solution: Let p represent the probability of detecting the target in a single scan, and q, the probability of not detecting the target.

(a) The probability P_D of detecting the target in at least two of four scans is found from

$$P_D = \sum_{m=2}^{4} C_{4,m}\, p^m q^{4-m}.$$

Since $C_{n,r} = \dfrac{n!}{r!\,(n-r)!}$,

$$C_{4,2} = \frac{4!}{2!2!} = 6, \qquad C_{4,3} = \frac{4!}{3!1!} = 4, \qquad C_{4,4} = \frac{4!}{4!0!} = 1.$$

Thus,

$$P_D = 6p^2 q^2 + 4p^3 q + p^4.$$

With $p = 0.1$ and $q = 1 - p = 1 - 0.1 = 0.9$,

$$P_D = 0.052.$$

(b) To determine the probability of detecting the target at least once in 20 scans, the same procedure can be followed. This, however, involves evaluating 20 binomial coefficients and corresponding powers of p and q. For a simpler procedure, note that the probability of detecting the target at least once out of 20 is $1 - q$, where q is the probability of not detecting the target in all 20 scans. The latter quantity is found from (3.2), with

$n = 20$ and $r = 0$. Thus,

$$P_D = 1 - \frac{20!}{0!20!} p^0 q^{20} = 1 - q^{20} = 1 - (1 - p)^{20}.$$

Since $p = 0.1$, $P_D = 1 - (0.9)^{20}$. The quantity $(0.9)^{20}$ is evaluated by logarithms; i.e.,

$$(0.9)^{20} = \text{antilog } [20 \log (0.9)] = 0.121.$$

The table of logarithms is given in Table II of the Appendix. Thus, the probability is $P_D = 0.879$.

PROBLEM 3.8 The probability that a defective soldered connection is made on any given connection is 10^{-4}. Find the expected number and standard deviation of defective joints in a system with 5×10^4 soldered connections. Also, find the probability that there are no defects in the system.

Solution: Using (3.3-4), with $n = 5 \times 10^4$, $p = 10^{-4}$ and $q = 1 - p = 1 - 10^{-4}$, the expected number $\bar{r}$ and the standard deviation σ_r of defective joints are

$$(\bar{r}) = np = 5, \qquad \sigma = \sqrt{npq} = \sqrt{5(1 - 10^{-4})} \approx \sqrt{5} \left[1 - \tfrac{1}{2}(10^{-4})\right] \approx \sqrt{5}.$$

The probability of no defects on any one connection is $q = 1 - p$. The probability of no defects on all n connections is q^n or $(1 - p)^n$, where $p = 10^{-4}$ and $n = 5 \times 10^4$. Hence, $(1 - p)^n = (1 - 10^{-4})^{5 \times 10^4}$. This can be evaluated by logarithms since

$$\log_e (1 - p)^n = n \log_e (1 - p) \approx -np \quad \text{for } p \ll 1.$$

$$\approx -5.$$

Since $\log_e x = 2.3 \log_{10} x$,

$$\log_{10} (1 - p)^n = \frac{-5}{2.3} = -2.174.$$

Hence, $(1 - p)^n = 6.7 \times 10^{-3}$.

3.2 Poisson Distribution

The *Poisson process* consists of independent events that occur *randomly* in time, where the probability of an event occurring in an interval dt is νdt and ν is the average number of events that occur per second. The probability of *exactly* k events occurring during a given time interval of length T is

$$P(k) = \frac{(\nu T)^k}{k!} e^{-\nu T}. \tag{3.5}$$

The *Poisson distribution* is the probability distribution defined by (3.5).

The *average number* of events occurring during the interval T is νT while the *standard deviation* is $\sqrt{\nu T}$. A typical random sequence of Poisson distributed events is shown in Fig. 3.3 (the events occur at the location of the delta functions).

Examples of independent events that occur randomly in time are emissions of electrons from a hot cathode, or failures or malfunctions in certain complex systems. In the latter case, such a model often ac-

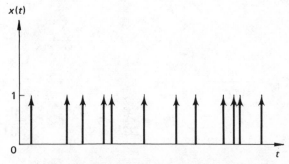

Fig. 3.3 A typical random sequence of Poisson distributed events.

curately predicts the reliability of a system during the time after the initial break-in period, when the "bugs" are removed, and prior to the "wearout" of the components.

The Poisson distribution also is a good approximation to the binomial distribution when $p \ll 1$ and $n \gg 1$. In this approximation, $\nu T = np$. Then,

$$P(k) \approx \frac{(np)^k}{k!} e^{-np}. \tag{3.6}$$

PROBLEM 3.9 Electrons are emitted from a hot cathode at an average rate of 10^{13} electrons/sec. Find the probability that no electron will be emitted for an interval of T sec if the emissions are independent events which occur randomly in time.

Solution: From (3.5), the probability of zero events in T sec is $P(0) = e^{-\nu T}$, as shown in Fig. 3.4. Since $\nu = 10^{13}$, $P(0) = \exp(-10^{13} T)$; thus, at $T = 10^{-13}$ sec, $P(0) = \dfrac{1}{e}$.

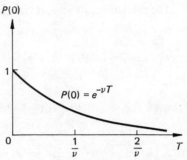

Fig. 3.4 Poisson distributed electrons for the probability of zero events in T sec.

PROBLEM 3.10 Assume that telephone calls are placed randomly and independently in time with an average frequency of ν calls/sec. Find the probability that exactly one call is made in a $3/\nu$ sec interval.

Solution: From (3.5), the probability of one call in T sec is $P(1) = \nu T e^{-\nu T}$, as shown in Fig. 3.5. When $T = 3/\nu$,

$$P(1) = \nu \left(\frac{3}{\nu}\right) e^{-\nu\left(\frac{3}{\nu}\right)} = 3e^{-3}.$$

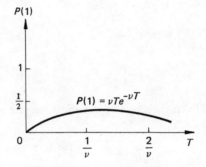

Fig. 3.5 Poisson distribution of a telephone call placed once in T sec.

PROBLEM 3.11 From (3.5), graph the general form of $P(k)$.

Solution: From (3.5),

$$P(k) = \frac{(\nu T)^k}{k!} e^{-\nu T}.$$

For fixed k, the maximum value occurs when $dP(k)/d(\nu T) = 0$. Thus,

$$\frac{(\nu T)^k}{k!} (-1) e^{-\nu T} + \frac{k(\nu T)^{k-1}}{k!} e^{-\nu T} = 0;$$

hence, $-\nu T + k = 0$, or $\nu T = k$. The value of $P(k)$ at this point is $\dfrac{k^k}{k!} e^{-k}$.

For small values of νT, that is $\nu T \ll 1$, $e^{-\nu T} \approx 1$, and, hence,

$$P(k) \approx \frac{(\nu T)^k}{k!}.$$

The Poisson distribution $P(k)$ is graphed in Fig. 3.6.

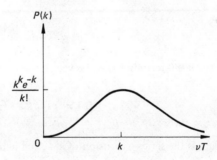

Fig. 3.6 General form of the Poisson distribution $P(k) \approx (\nu T)^k/k!$.

PROBLEM 3.12 From Prob. 3.10, determine the probability that less than three calls occur in an interval of $1/\nu$ sec.

Solution: Since $T = 1/\nu$, using (3.5), the probability that less than three calls occur in T sec is

$$P(k < 3) = P(0) + P(1) + P(2) = e^{-\nu T} + \nu T e^{-\nu T} + \frac{(\nu T)^2}{2} e^{-\nu T}$$

$$= e^{-\nu T} \left[1 + \nu T + \frac{(\nu T)^2}{2}\right]$$

$$= e^{-1} \left(1 + 1 + \tfrac{1}{2}\right)$$

$$= \frac{5}{2e}.$$

PROBLEM 3.13 Automobiles are randomly distributed with an average spacing of 1000 ft along a highway. Determine the probability that at least two cars are present in a 1000-ft interval selected at random.

Solution: The probability of at least two cars is

$$P(k > 1) = 1 - P(0) - P(1) = 1 - e^{-\nu T} - \nu T e^{-\nu T}.$$

For an average spacing of 1000 ft, $\nu = 1/1000$. Therefore, in a 1000-ft interval, that is $T = 1000$, $\nu T = 1$, and, hence,

$$P(k > 1) = 1 - e^{-1} - e^{-1} = 1 - \frac{2}{e} = 0.264.$$

PROBLEM 3.14 Show that the average number of Poisson-distributed events is νT.

Solution: The average number of Poisson-distributed events is

$$E[k] = \int_{-\infty}^{\infty} k p(k) dk.$$

Since $p(k)$ is discrete,

$$p(k) = \sum_{n=0}^{\infty} P(n) \delta(k - n),$$

where $P(n)$ is given by (3.5). Substituting for $p(k)$,

$$E[k] = \sum_{n=0}^{\infty} P(n) \int_{-\infty}^{\infty} k \delta(k - n) dk = \sum_{n=0}^{\infty} n P(n).$$

Substituting for $P(n)$, from (3.5),

$$E[k] = \sum_{n=0}^{\infty} n \frac{(\nu T)^n}{n!} e^{-\nu T}.$$

Since the $n = 0$ term in the series vanishes,

$$E[k] = \sum_{n=1}^{\infty} \nu T e^{-\nu T} \frac{(\nu T)^{n-1}}{(n - 1)!} = \nu T e^{-\nu T} \sum_{n=1}^{\infty} \frac{(\nu T)^{n-1}}{(n - 1)!}.$$

This sum is the series expansion of $e^{\nu T}$, and hence,

$$E[k] = \nu T e^{-\nu T} e^{\nu T} = \nu T.$$

(Cf., Table III of the Appendix for a tabulation of infinite series.)

PROBLEM 3.15 Show that the standard deviation of Poisson-distributed events is $(\nu T)^{1/2}$.

Solution: The standard deviation is

$$\sigma = (E[k^2] - E^2[k])^{1/2},$$

where from Prob. 3.14, $E[k] = \nu T$, and

$$E[k^2] = \sum_{n=0}^{\infty} n^2 \frac{(\nu T)^n}{n!} e^{-\nu T}$$

$$= \sum_{n=1}^{\infty} \frac{n}{(n - 1)!} (\nu T)^n e^{-\nu T},$$

that is,

$$E[k^2] = \sum_{n=1}^{\infty} \frac{(n-1)+1}{(n-1)!} (\nu T)^n\, e^{-\nu T}$$

$$= \nu T e^{-\nu T} \sum_{n=1}^{\infty} \frac{(\nu T)^{n-1}}{(n-1)!} + (\nu T)^2\, e^{-\nu T} \sum_{n=2}^{\infty} \frac{(\nu T)^{n-2}}{(n-2)!}.$$

As in Prob. 3.14, each of the sums is the series expansion of $e^{\nu T}$, and hence,

$$E[k^2] = \nu T e^{-\nu T}\, e^{\nu T} + (\nu T)^2\, e^{-\nu T}\, e^{\nu T} = \nu T + (\nu T)^2.$$

Thus, the standard deviation is

$$\sigma = [\nu T + (\nu T)^2 - (\nu T)^2]^{1/2} = (\nu T)^{1/2}.$$

PROBLEM 3.16 Show that the probability of 0 or more Poisson events occurring with average frequency ν in an interval T is 1.

Solution: To show that $\sum_{k=0}^{\infty} P(k) = 1$, note that

$$\sum_{k=0}^{\infty} P(k) = \sum_{k=0}^{\infty} \frac{(\nu T)^k}{k!}\, e^{-\nu T}.$$

Since the exponential is not dependent on k,

$$\sum_{k=0}^{\infty} P(k) = e^{-\nu T} \sum_{k=0}^{\infty} \frac{(\nu T)^k}{k!}.$$

The sum $\sum_{k=0}^{\infty} \frac{(\nu T)^k}{k!}$ is the series expansion of $e^{\nu T}$,

and hence,

$$\sum_{k=0}^{\infty} P(k) = e^{-\nu T} e^{\nu T} = 1.$$

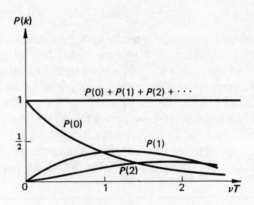

Fig. 3.7 Probability of 0 or more Poisson events occurring with average frequency ν in an interval T.

This is illustrated in Fig. 3.7.

PROBLEM 3.17 A certain system has a mean time between failures (MTBF) of 100 hr. Assuming that the times of failures are Poisson distributed, find the probability of at least one failure occurring in 1-, 100-, and 1000-hr periods. Also, find the probability that exactly one failure occurs in each of these periods.

Solution: From (3.5), the probability of at least one failure in time T is

$$P(\text{at least } 1) = 1 - e^{-\nu T}.$$

The average number of failures per unit of time is

$$\nu = \frac{1}{\text{MTBF}} = \frac{1}{100}.$$

Then $P(\text{at least } 1) = 1 - e^{-T/100}$. Thus, for $T = 1$, 100, and 1000,

$$P_1(\text{at least } 1) = 1 - e^{-0.01} \approx 0.01,$$

$$P_{100}(\text{at least } 1) = 1 - e^{-1} \approx 0.632,$$

$$P_{1000}(\text{at least } 1) = 1 - e^{-10} \approx 0.999955.$$

The probability of exactly one failure is obtained from

$$P(1) = \nu T e^{-\nu T} = \frac{T}{100} e^{-T/100}.$$

For $T = 1$, 100, and 1000, the probability of exactly one failure is

$$P_1(1) = 0.01\, e^{-.01} \approx 0.0099, \quad P_{100}(1) = e^{-1} \approx 0.368, \quad P_{1000}(1) = 10\, e^{-10} \approx 0.00045.$$

3.3 Uniform Distribution

The *uniform distribution* with parameters a and b is defined by the probability density function

$$p(x) = \frac{1}{b} \quad \text{for } a \leqslant x \leqslant a + b$$

$$\hspace{4cm} = 0 \quad \text{elsewhere}$$

(3.7)

of the random variable x, and is shown graphically in Fig. 3.8. Note that all values of x from a to $a + b$ are equally likely in the sense that the probability that x lies in a narrow interval of width Δx, entirely contained in the interval from a to $a + b$, is equal to $\Delta x/(b - a)$, regardless of the exact location of the interval.

The graph of the cumulative distribution function $P^*(x)$ that corresponds to the uniform distribution is shown in Fig. 3.9.

The uniform distribution occurs frequently when dealing with the phase of a sine wave that arises due to a random disturbance. Since usually it is not possible to distinguish between multiples of 2π nor reasonable to expect any preferred values of phase, a uniform distribution of phase between 0 and 2π is frequently assumed.

Similarly, the uniform distribution describes the errors that occur when numbers are rounded off.

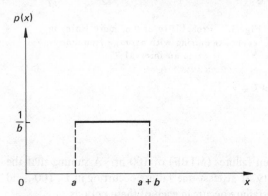

Fig. 3.8 Uniform distribution.

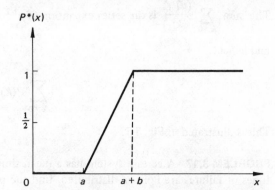

Fig. 3.9 Cumulative distribution function $P^*(x)$ corresponding to a uniform distribution.

PROBLEM 3.18 Determine the standard deviation for the uniform probability density function (3.7).

Solution: The mean value of $p(x)$ is

$$\bar{x} = \int_{-\infty}^{\infty} x p(x) dx = \frac{1}{b} \int_a^{a+b} x dx = \frac{1}{b} \frac{x^2}{2} \Big|_a^{a+b} = a + \frac{1}{2} b.$$

Similarly, the mean value of x^2 is

$$\bar{x^2} = \int_a^{a+b} x^2 p(x) dx = \frac{1}{b} \frac{x^3}{3} \Big|_a^{a+b} = a^2 + ab + \frac{1}{3} b^2.$$

Thus, the standard deviation is

$$\sigma = (\overline{x^2} - \overline{x}^2)^{1/2} = [a^2 + ab + \tfrac{1}{3}b^2 - (a^2 + ab + \tfrac{1}{4}b^2)]^{1/2} = \sqrt{\tfrac{1}{12}b^2} = \tfrac{1}{6}\sqrt{3}\,b .$$

Thus, σ is $\tfrac{1}{6}\sqrt{3}$ times the peak-to-peak deviation.

PROBLEM 3.19 A real number between 0 and 100 is randomly selected and rounded-off to the nearest integer. For example, 8.501 is rounded off to 9, $\sqrt{2}$ is rounded off to 1, and so forth. Determine $\overline{x^2}$ if a random variable x is defined by

$$x = (\text{number selected}) - (\text{nearest integer}).$$

Solution: Since x varies from -0.5 to 0.5, with all values in the interval equally probable,

$$p(x) = 1 \quad \text{for} -0.5 \leqslant x \leqslant 0.5$$
$$\quad\quad = 0 \quad \text{elsewhere,}$$

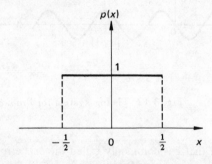

as shown in Fig. 3.10. Using the results of Prob. 3.18,

$$\overline{x^2} = a^2 + ab + \tfrac{1}{3}b^2 ,$$

where $a = -0.5$ and $b = 1.0$. Thus,

$$\overline{x^2} = 0.25 - 0.5 + \tfrac{1}{3}(1^2) = \tfrac{1}{12}.$$

Fig. 3.10 Solution to Prob. 3.19.

PROBLEM 3.20 A noninteger between 0 and 100 is randomly selected and rounded-off to the nearest lower integer. For example, 8.501 is rounded off to 8, $\sqrt{2}$ is rounded-off to 1, and so forth. Determine $\overline{x^2}$ if a random variable x is defined by

$$x = (\text{number selected}) - (\text{nearest lower integer}).$$

Solution: Since x varies from -0.5 to 0.5, with all values in the interval equally probable,

$$p(x) = 1 \quad \text{for } 0 \leqslant x \leqslant 1$$
$$\quad\quad = 0 \quad \text{elsewhere,}$$

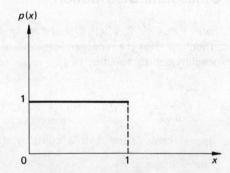

as shown in Fig. 3.11. Using the results of Prob. 3.18,

$$\overline{x^2} = a^2 + ab + \tfrac{1}{3}b^2 ,$$

where $a = 0$ and $b = 1.0$. Thus,

$$\overline{x^2} = 0 + 0(1) + \tfrac{1}{3}(1^2) = \tfrac{1}{3}.$$

Fig. 3.11 Solution to Prob. 3.20.

The difference between $\overline{x^2}$ in Probs. 3.19–20 is due to the fact that $\overline{x} = 0$ in Prob. 3.19 and $\overline{x} \neq 0$ in Prob. 3.20 even though the variance is the same for both. Since

$$\overline{x^2} = \sigma^2 + \overline{x}^2,$$

the $\overline{x^2}$ of Prob. 3.20 is larger by $\overline{x}^2 = \tfrac{1}{4}$.

PROBLEM 3.21 A timing system is actuated by a positive-going zero crossing of an oscillator generating $\sin w_0 t$, as shown in Fig. 3.12. The time between the start and finish is assumed to be arbitrary and is measured by counting the number of positive-going zero crossings in the interval $0 < t \leqslant T$ and multiplying this by $2\pi/w_0$. Find the expected value and standard deviation of the timing error.

Solution: Figure 3.12 shows that the measurement is always low, and the error ϵ is uniformly distributed between 0 and $2\pi/w_0$, as shown in Fig. 3.13. From Prob. 3.18, the expected value of ϵ is $\overline{\epsilon} = \pi/w_0$.

Similarly, the standard deviation is obtained by using the above value of $\overline{\epsilon}$ and the results of Prob. 3.18; thus, $\sigma_\epsilon = \pi/(\sqrt{3}\,w_0)$.

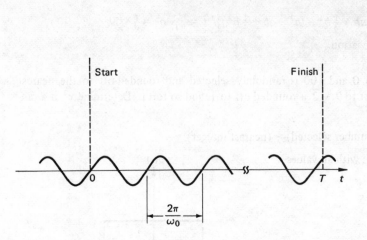

Fig. 3.12 Timing system for Prob. 3.21.

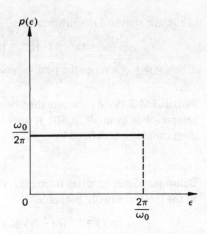

Fig. 3.13 Uniform distribution of the error ϵ between 0 and $2\pi/w_0$ for the timing system of Fig. 3.12.

Note that $\bar{\epsilon}$ is commonly called the *bias* error which, in this case, is of known value and therefore, can be removed from the measurement, thereby reducing the mean-squared error.

3.4 Sinusoidal Distribution

A variable $y = A \sin \theta$, where θ is uniformly distributed over the range $0 \leqslant \theta < 2\pi$, is said to have a *sinusoidal* distribution. If A is an independent random variable with probability density function $p(A)$,

$$p(y) = \int_y^\infty \frac{p(A)}{\pi\sqrt{A^2 - y^2}} dA \quad \text{for } -A \leqslant y \leqslant A. \quad (3.8)$$

In the special case where A is a constant, (3.8) reduces to

$$p(y) = \frac{1}{\pi\sqrt{A^2 - y^2}} \quad \text{for } -A \leqslant y \leqslant A, \quad (3.9)$$

as shown in Fig. 3.14.

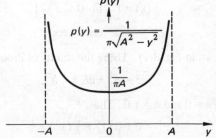

Fig. 3.14 A sinusoidal distribution for $A = $ const.

PROBLEM 3.22 Show that when A is a constant, (3.8) reduces to (3.9).

Solution: If $A = A_0$ is a constant, the probability density function is $p(A) = \delta(A - A_0)$. Hence,

$$p(y) = \int_y^\infty \frac{\delta(A - A_0)}{\pi\sqrt{A_0^2 - y^2}} dA = \frac{1}{\pi\sqrt{A_0^2 - y^2}},$$

or by replacing A_0 with A,

$$p(y) = \frac{1}{\pi\sqrt{A^2 - y^2}}. \quad [3.9]$$

PROBLEM 3.23 Using the definition of the sinusoidal distribution, show that if A is constant, (3.9) gives the probability density function for y.

Solution: Using Fig. 3.15, (3.9) is obtained by noting that the probability of obtaining a value of y lying between y and $y + dy$ is $p(y)dy$. But this is equal to the probability of obtaining values of θ between θ and $\theta + d\theta$ and, also, values of θ between $(\pi - \theta - d\theta)$ and $\pi - \theta$. Since θ is uniformly distributed between 0 and 2π, this latter probability is $p(\theta)(2d\theta)$, where

$$p(\theta) = \frac{1}{2\pi} \quad \text{for } 0 \leqslant \theta < 2\pi$$

$$= 0 \quad \text{elsewhere.}$$

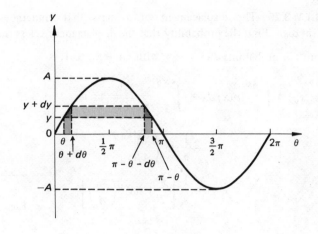

Fig. 3.15 Solution to Prob. 3.23.

Thus,

$$p(y)\, dy = \frac{1}{\pi}\, d\theta\,;$$

therefore,

$$p(y) = \frac{1}{\pi\, dy/d\theta} = \frac{1}{\pi A \cos\theta}.$$

Since $\sin\theta = y/A$ and $\cos^2\theta + \sin^2\theta = 1$,

$$\cos\theta = \sqrt{1 - (y/A)^2}\,,$$

and hence,

$$p(y) = \frac{1}{\pi A \sqrt{1 - (y/A)^2}} = \frac{1}{\pi\sqrt{A^2 - y^2}}\,.$$

PROBLEM 3.24 Determine $\overline{y}$ and $\overline{y^2}$ for the probability density function given in (3.9).

Solution: Since $p(y)$ is an even function of y, and the integrand is, thus, an odd function,

$$\overline{y} = \int_{-\infty}^{\infty} y\, p(y)\, dy = \int_{-A}^{A} \frac{y}{\pi\sqrt{A^2 - y^2}}\, dy = 0.$$

By definition,

$$\overline{y^2} = \int_{-\infty}^{\infty} y^2\, p(y)\, dy = \int_{-A}^{A} \frac{y}{\pi\sqrt{A^2 - y^2}}\, dy.$$

From Table 1 of the Appendix,

$$\overline{y^2} = \frac{1}{\pi}\left[-\frac{y}{2}\sqrt{A^2 - y^2} + \frac{A^2}{2}\sin^{-1}\left(\frac{y}{A}\right) \right]_{-A}^{A}$$

$$= \frac{1}{\pi}\frac{A^2}{2}\left[\sin^{-1}(1) - \sin^{-1}(-1)\right]$$

$$= \frac{1}{\pi}\frac{A^2}{2}\left[\frac{\pi}{2} - \left(-\frac{\pi}{2}\right)\right]$$

$$= \tfrac{1}{2}A^2.$$

PROBLEM 3.25 The displacement of a mass that undergoes simple harmonic motion is given by $x = A \sin \omega_0 t$. Find the probability that the displacement is less than x_0, $-A \leqslant x_0 \leqslant A$, at an arbitrary time t.

Solution: The probability $P(x < x_0)$, with $-A \leqslant x_0 \leqslant A$, is

$$P(x < x_0) = \int_{-\infty}^{x_0} p(x)\, dx = \int_{-A}^{x_0} \frac{1}{\pi \sqrt{A^2 - x^2}}\, dx$$

$$= \frac{1}{\pi} \sin \left(\frac{x}{A} \right) \Big|_{-A}^{x_0}$$

$$= \frac{1}{\pi} \left[\frac{\pi}{2} + \sin^{-1} \left(\frac{x_0}{A} \right) \right].$$

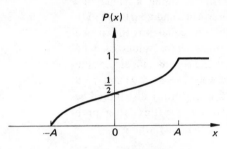

Fig. 3.16 Cumulative distribution function of sinusoidal distribution.

Note that the above expression, shown in Fig. 3.16, is, by definition, the *cumulative distribution function*.

3.5 Normal Distribution

If a random variable has the values x and a distribution with mean $\overline{x}$ and variance σ^2, the corresponding *standardized random variable* is

$$z = \frac{x - \overline{x}}{\sigma},$$

and its distribution has *zero mean* and *unit variance*.

If the probability density function of the standardized random variable is given by

$$p(z) = \frac{1}{\sqrt{2\pi}}\, e^{-z^2/2} \quad \text{for } -\infty < z < \infty,$$

the density is called the *standard normal density*, or *standard normal distribution*. The term *Gaussian* is also used interchangeably with *normal*.

If z represents a random variable having the standard normal distribution, $x = \sigma z + \overline{x}$ is a random variable whose density is

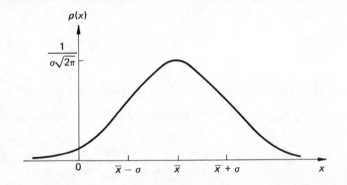

Fig. 3.17 General form of the normal distribution.

$$p(x) = \frac{1}{\sqrt{2\pi}\, \sigma}\, e^{-(x-\overline{x})^2/2\sigma^2} \quad \text{for } -\infty < x < \infty, \tag{3.10}$$

which is the general form of the normal distribution, and its graph is shown in Fig. 3.17.

PROBLEM 3.26 Show that the variance of x in (3.10) is σ^2.

Solution: Since σ^2 does not depend on $\overline{x}$, for convenience let the mean value of x be zero. From the definition of variance,

$$\text{Var}(x) = \int_{-\infty}^{\infty} (x - \overline{x})^2\, p(x) dx = \frac{1}{\sigma \sqrt{2\pi}} \int_{-\infty}^{\infty} x^2 e^{-x^2/2\sigma^2}\, dx = \frac{2}{\sigma \sqrt{2\pi}} \int_{0}^{\infty} x^2 e^{-x^2/2\sigma^2}\, dx.$$

From Table II of the Appendix,

$$\int_0^\infty x^2 \, e^{-x^2/2\sigma^2} \, dx = \frac{1}{2^2 \, (1/2\sigma^2)} \, \sqrt{\frac{\pi}{(1/2\sigma^2)}}.$$

Since the integrand is an even function of x, by substitution,

$$\text{Var}(x) = \frac{2}{\sigma\sqrt{2\pi}} \, \frac{\sigma^2}{2} \, \sqrt{2\pi\sigma^2} = \sigma^2.$$

The error function or *erf* is defined to be the integral

$$\text{erf } y = \frac{2}{\sqrt{\pi}} \int_0^y e^{-z^2} \, dz.$$

PROBLEM 3.27 Find the cumulative distribution function of a Gaussian random variable.

Solution: By definition, the cumulative distribution function is

$$P^*(x) = \int_{-\infty}^x p(x)dx = \frac{1}{\sigma\sqrt{2\pi}} \int_{-\infty}^x e^{-(x-\bar{x})^2/2\sigma^2} \, dx. \tag{3.11}$$

Let $z = \dfrac{x - \bar{x}}{\sqrt{2\sigma^2}}$; then, $dz = \dfrac{1}{\sqrt{2\sigma^2}} dx$. Hence,

$$P^*(x) = \frac{1}{\sqrt{\pi}} \int_{-\infty}^{(x-\bar{x})/\sqrt{2\sigma^2}} e^{-z^2} \, dz.$$

Since $p(x)$ is symmetrical about $x = \bar{x}$, that is, $z = 0$, the area under $p(x)$, in the interval $-\infty < x \leqslant \bar{x}$, is one-half the total area. Therefore,

$$P^*(x) = \frac{1}{\sqrt{\pi}} \int_{-\infty}^0 e^{-z^2} \, dz + \frac{1}{\sqrt{\pi}} \int_0^{(x-\bar{x})/\sqrt{2\sigma^2}} e^{-z^2} \, dz = \frac{1}{2} + \frac{1}{\sqrt{\pi}} \int_0^{(x-\bar{x})/\sqrt{2\sigma^2}} e^{-z^2} \, dz.$$

$$= \frac{1}{2} \left[1 + \frac{2}{\sqrt{\pi}} \int_0^{(x-\bar{x})/\sqrt{2\sigma^2}} e^{-z^2} \, dz \right].$$

From the definition of erf y,

$$\text{erf } y = \frac{2}{\sqrt{\pi}} \int_0^y e^{-z^2} \, dz, \tag{3.12}$$

the cumulative distribution function is

$$P^*(x) = \frac{1}{2} \left[1 + \text{erf} \left(\frac{x - \bar{x}}{\sqrt{2\sigma^2}} \right) \right], \tag{3.13}$$

as shown in Fig. 3.18.

A table of values for $P^*(x)$ is given in Table IV of the Appendix.

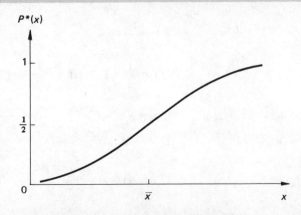

Fig. 3.18 Cumulative distribution function of a Gaussian random variable.

PROBLEM 3.28 Determine $P(\bar{x} - 3\sigma \geqslant x \geqslant \bar{x} + 3\sigma)$.

Solution: From Table IV of the Appendix,

$$P(x \leqslant \overline{x} - 3\sigma) = P^*(x)\big|_{x=\overline{x}-3\sigma} = 0.0013, \qquad P(x \geqslant \overline{x} + 3\sigma) = 1 - P^*(x)\big|_{x=\overline{x}+3\sigma} = 1 - 0.9987 = 0.0013.$$

Thus,

$$P(\overline{x} - 3\sigma \geqslant x \geqslant \overline{x} + 3\sigma) = P(x \leqslant \overline{x} - 3\sigma) + P(x \geqslant \overline{x} - 3\sigma) = 0.0013 + 0.0013 = 0.0026.$$

PROBLEM 3.29   Determine k if $P(\overline{x} - k\sigma \leqslant x \leqslant \overline{x} + k\sigma) = 0.16$.

Solution: Since

$$P(\overline{x} - k\sigma \leqslant x \leqslant \overline{x} + k\sigma) = P^*(x)\big|_{x=\overline{x}+k\sigma} - P^*(x)\big|_{x=\overline{x}-k\sigma},$$

from Table IV, $k = 0.2$.

PROBLEM 3.30   A structure is tested for metal fatigue. The logarithm (base 10) of the time until failure, in hours, is normally distributed with average value 3 and standard deviation 1. Determine the probability of a failure as a function of the test duration T. Express the result in terms of the error function.

Solution: Denoting $\log T$ by v, the probability distribution function is

$$p(v) = \frac{1}{\sigma\sqrt{2\pi}}\, e^{-(v-\overline{v})^2/2\sigma^2} = \frac{1}{\sqrt{2\pi}}\, e^{-(v-3)^2/2}$$

since $\sigma = 1$ and $\overline{v} = 3$. The probability of failure in a time T is

$$P(T) = \int_{\log 0}^{\log T} p(v)\,dv = \int_{-\infty}^{\log T} p(v)\,dv = \int_{-\infty}^{\log T} \frac{1}{\sqrt{2\pi}}\, e^{-(v-3)^2/2}\,dv.$$

Substituting $w = \dfrac{v-3}{\sqrt{2}}$ and, hence, $dw = \dfrac{1}{\sqrt{2}}\,dv$,

$$P(T) = \int_{-\infty}^{\frac{1}{\sqrt{2}}(\log T - 3)} \frac{1}{\sqrt{\pi}}\, e^{-w^2}\,dw = \int_{-\infty}^{0} \frac{1}{\sqrt{\pi}}\, e^{-w^2}\,dw + \int_{0}^{\frac{1}{\sqrt{2}}(\log T - 3)} \frac{1}{\sqrt{\pi}}\, e^{-w^2}\,dw.$$

The first integral is equal to $\frac{1}{2}$ because comparison with (3.11) shows that this is the value of the cumulative distribution function evaluated at $x = 0$ with $\overline{x} = 0$ and $\sigma = 1/\sqrt{2}$, that is, $P^*(0)$. Since $P^*(\infty) = 1$, from the symmetry of the normal distribution, $P^*(0) = \frac{1}{2} P^*(\infty) = \frac{1}{2}$.

Using (3.12), the second integral becomes

$$\int_{0}^{\frac{1}{\sqrt{2}}(\log T - 3)} \frac{1}{\sqrt{\pi}}\, e^{-w^2}\,dw = \frac{1}{2}\,\mathrm{erf}\left[\frac{1}{\sqrt{2}}(\log T - 3)\right].$$

Thus,

$$P(T) = \frac{1}{2}\left\{1 + \mathrm{erf}\left[\frac{1}{\sqrt{2}}(\log T - 3)\right]\right\}.$$

PROBLEM 3.31   Express $\mathrm{erf}(-y)$ in terms of $\mathrm{erf}\, y$.

Solution: Using (3.12),

$$\mathrm{erf}(-y) = \frac{2}{\sqrt{\pi}} \int_{0}^{-y} e^{-z^2}\,dz.$$

Substituting $u = -z$ and, hence, $du = -dz$,

$$\mathrm{erf}(-y) = \frac{-2}{\sqrt{\pi}} \int_{0}^{y} e^{-u^2}\,du = -\mathrm{erf}(y).$$

PROBLEM 3.32 A random variable s is added to a second independent random variable n to form the random variable $y = s + n$, where s can have the value 0 or 1 with equal likelihood, and n is normally distributed with $\bar{n} = 0$ and $\overline{n^2} = \sigma^2$. Determine the probability of measuring a value of y (a) greater than 0.5 when $s = 0$, and (b) greater than 1 if the value of s is unknown. Express the results in terms of the error function.

Solution: (a) The probability of measuring a value of y greater than 0.5 when $s = 0$ is

$$P(y > 0.5)\big|_{s=0} = P(n > 0.5) = \int_{0.5}^{\infty} p(n)dn$$

$$= \int_{0.5}^{\infty} \frac{1}{\sigma\sqrt{2\pi}} \, e^{-n^2/2\sigma^2} \, dn$$

$$= \int_{0}^{\infty} \frac{1}{\sigma\sqrt{2\pi}} \, e^{-n^2/2\sigma^2} \, dn - \int_{0}^{0.5} \frac{1}{\sigma\sqrt{2\pi}} \, e^{-n^2/2\sigma^2} \, dn$$

$$= \frac{1}{2} - \int_{0}^{0.5} \frac{1}{\sigma\sqrt{2\pi}} \, e^{-n^2/2\sigma^2} \, dn.$$

Substituting $z = n/\sigma\sqrt{2}$ and, hence, $dz = 1/\sigma\sqrt{2} \, dn$,

$$P(n > 0.5) = \frac{1}{2} - \frac{1}{\sqrt{\pi}} \int_{0}^{1/2\sigma\sqrt{2}} e^{-z^2} \, dz = \frac{1}{2}\left[1 - \mathrm{erf}\left(\frac{1}{2\sigma\sqrt{2}}\right)\right].$$

(b) To find $P(y > 1)$, note that

$$P(y > 1) = \tfrac{1}{2} P(y > 1)\big|_{s=0} + \tfrac{1}{2} P(y > 1)\big|_{s=1}.$$

The first term is

$$P(y > 1)\big|_{s=0} = P(n > 1) = \frac{1}{2} - \int_{0}^{1} \frac{1}{\sigma\sqrt{2\pi}} \, e^{-n^2/2\sigma^2} \, dn.$$

Substituting $z = n/\sigma\sqrt{2}$,

$$P(n > 1) = \frac{1}{2}\left[1 - \mathrm{erf}\left(\frac{1}{\sigma\sqrt{2}}\right)\right].$$

The quantity $P(y > 1)\big|_{s=1}$ is

$$P(y > 1)\big|_{s=1} = P(1 + n > 1) = P(n > 0).$$

Since $\bar{n} = 0$, $P(n > 0) = 0.5$. Thus,

$$P(y > 1) = \frac{1}{4}\left[1 - \mathrm{erf}\left(\frac{1}{\sigma\sqrt{2}}\right)\right] + \frac{1}{4} = \frac{1}{2} - \frac{1}{4}\,\mathrm{erf}\left(\frac{1}{\sigma\sqrt{2}}\right).$$

PROBLEM 3.33 A measurement of acidity is made on acid with pH = 3. Each measurement of pH is in error by δ, where δ is normally distributed, with $\bar{\delta} = 0$ and $\overline{\delta^2} = \sigma^2$. Determine the probability that if five independent measurements are made, all will be in error by more than 0.5.

Solution: Since the error δ is normally distributed, from Prob. 3.32(a),

$$P(-0.5 > \delta > 0.5) = 2 \int_{0.5}^{\infty} p(\delta)d\delta = 2 \cdot \frac{1}{2}\left[1 - \mathrm{erf}\left(\frac{1}{2\sigma\sqrt{2}}\right)\right] = 1 - \mathrm{erf}\left(\frac{1}{2\sigma\sqrt{2}}\right).$$

The probability that $|\delta| > 0.5$ on five successive independent measurements is

$$[P(|\delta| > 0.5)]^5 = \left[1 - \mathrm{erf}\left(\frac{1}{2\sigma\sqrt{2}}\right)\right]^5.$$

PROBLEM 3.34 A binomial distribution is to be approximated by a normal distribution. Use this approximation to find the probability of at least r successes in n trials if the probability of success is p. Assume that the mean and standard deviations of the two distributions are set equal to each other.

Solution: From (3.3-4), $\bar{r} = np$ and $\sigma = \sqrt{npq}$, where $q = 1 - p$. The normal approximation is

$$p(x) = \frac{1}{\sigma\sqrt{2\pi}} e^{-(x-\bar{x})^2/2\sigma^2} = \frac{1}{\sqrt{2\pi npq}} e^{-(x-np)^2/2npq},$$

where the continuous random variable x approximates the discrete random variable r. Thus, the probability of at least r successes is

$$P(x \geq r) = \int_r^\infty p(x)dx = \frac{1}{\sqrt{2\pi npq}} \int_r^\infty e^{-(x-np)^2/2npq}\,dx.$$

Substituting $z = \dfrac{x - np}{\sqrt{2npq}}$ and, hence, $dz = \dfrac{1}{\sqrt{2npq}}\,dx$,

$$P(x \geq r) = \frac{1}{\sqrt{\pi}} \int_{\frac{r-np}{\sqrt{2npq}}}^\infty e^{-z^2}\,dz = \frac{1}{\sqrt{\pi}} \int_0^\infty e^{-z^2}\,dz - \frac{1}{\sqrt{\pi}} \int_0^{\frac{r-np}{\sqrt{2npq}}} e^{-z^2}\,dz$$

$$= \frac{1}{2} - \frac{1}{2}\,\mathrm{erf}\left(\frac{r - np}{\sqrt{2npq}}\right)$$

$$= \frac{1}{2}\left[1 - \mathrm{erf}\left(\frac{r - np}{\sqrt{2npq}}\right)\right].$$

Note that the Gaussian approximation may not be accurate in the tail ends of the distribution, i.e., when $\dfrac{r - np}{\sqrt{2npq}} \gg 1$. This is evident from the above example because $P(x > n) = 0$, while the normal approximation will predict a finite probability for $P(x > n)$.

3.6 Rayleigh Distribution

A random variable whose probability density function is

$$p(x) = \frac{x}{\alpha^2} e^{-x^2/2\alpha^2} \quad \text{for } x \geq 0$$

$$= 0 \quad\quad\quad\quad \text{for } x < 0$$
$$(3.14)$$

is said to be *Rayleigh distributed*, as shown in Fig. 3.19. The first and second moments are

$$\bar{x} = \sqrt{\frac{\pi}{2}}\,\alpha, \quad (3.15)$$

$$\overline{x^2} = 2\alpha^2. \quad (3.16)$$

(Cf., Probs. 3.36–7.)

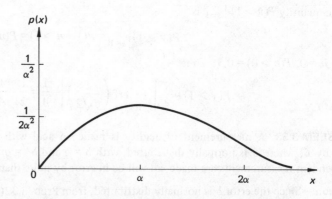

Fig. 3.19 Rayleigh-distributed random variable.

The Rayleigh distribution describes the distribution of the amplitude of the (vector) sum of a large number of independent two-dimensional vectors. It is not necessary for the amplitudes of the components of the vectors to follow any specific distribution. However, the phase, i.e., the angle, of each vector with respect to any arbitrary line in the plane must be uniformly distributed from 0 to 2π rad. The amplitude of any single two-dimensional vector whose components are normally distributed with mean zero and variance α^2 is also Rayleigh distributed.

This distribution describes, for example, the amplitude of the electromagnetic field scattered from a large number of small scatterers and, also, the amplitude of noise in an AM receiver when no signal is present.

PROBLEM 3.35 Determine the cumulative distribution function for a Rayleigh-distributed random variable.

Solution: The cumulative distribution function is

$$P^*(x) = \int_{-\infty}^{x} p(x)\, dx$$

$$= \int_{0}^{x} \frac{x}{\alpha^2} e^{-x^2/2\alpha^2}\, dx.$$

Substituting $u = x^2/2\alpha^2$, and, hence, $du = (x/\alpha^2)\, dx$,

$$P^*(x) = \int_{0}^{x^2/2\alpha^2} e^{-u}\, du$$

$$= -e^{-u} \Big|_{0}^{x^2/2\alpha^2}$$

$$= 1 - e^{-x^2/2\alpha^2}. \qquad (3.17)$$

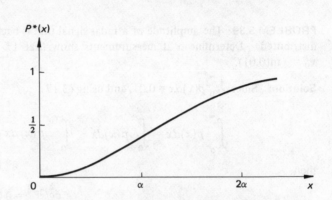

Fig. 3.20 Cumulative distribution function for a Rayleigh-distributed random variable.

The graph of $P^*(x)$, given in (3.17), is shown in Fig. 3.20.

PROBLEM 3.36 Show that $\bar{x} = \sqrt{\frac{\pi}{2}}\, \alpha$ for a Raleigh-distributed random variable.

Solution: By definition, the mean value of x is

$$\bar{x} = \int_{-\infty}^{\infty} x p(x)\, dx = \frac{1}{\alpha^2} \int_{0}^{\infty} x^2 e^{-x^2/2\alpha^2}\, dx.$$

Using Table II of the Appendix,

$$\bar{x} = \left(\frac{1}{\alpha^2}\right) \cdot \frac{1}{4(1/2\alpha^2)} \cdot \sqrt{\frac{\pi}{(1/2\alpha^2)}} = \sqrt{\frac{\pi}{2}}\, \alpha.$$

PROBLEM 3.37 Show that $\overline{x^2} = 2\alpha^2$ for a Rayleigh-distributed random variable.

Solution: By definition,

$$\overline{x^2} = \int_{-\infty}^{\infty} x^2\, p(x)\, dx = \frac{1}{\alpha^2} \int_{0}^{\infty} x^3 e^{-x^2/2\alpha^2}\, dx.$$

Substituting $u = x^2/2\alpha^2$ and $du = x/\alpha^2\, dx$,

$$\overline{x^2} = \int_{0}^{\infty} 2\alpha^2\, u e^{-u}\, du = 2\alpha^2 \int_{0}^{\infty} u e^{-u}\, du.$$

Since this integral is in the form of the gamma function, using Table II of the Appendix,

$$\overline{x^2} = 2\alpha^2\, \Gamma(2) = 2\alpha^2.$$

PROBLEM 3.38 Determine the probability that a Rayleigh-distributed random variable exceeds $3\bar{x}$.

Solution: The probability is obtained from

$$P(x > 3\bar{x}) = P\left(x > 3\sqrt{\frac{\pi}{2}}\,\alpha\right) = 1 - P^*(x)\Big|_{x=3\sqrt{\frac{\pi}{2}}\,\alpha}.$$

From (3.17), the probability is

$$P(x > 3\bar{x}) = e^{-x^2/2\alpha^2}\Big|_{x=3\sqrt{\frac{\pi}{2}}\,\alpha} = e^{-9\pi/4}.$$

PROBLEM 3.39 The amplitude of a radar signal that is back-scattered from the surface of the sea is Rayleigh distributed. Determine α if measurements show that 1% of the time the amplitude x exceeds x_0 where $x_0^2 = -\ln(0.01)$.

Solution: Since $\int_{x_0}^{\infty} p(x)\,dx = 0.01$, and using (3.17),

$$\int_{x_0}^{\infty} p(x)\,dx = \int_0^{\infty} p(x)\,dx - \int_0^{x_0} p(x)\,dx = 1 - \left[1 - e^{-x_0^2/2\alpha^2}\right] = e^{-x_0^2/2\alpha^2};$$

then,

$$e^{-x_0^2/2\alpha^2} = 0.01.$$

Taking the natural logarithm of both sides,

$$\frac{-x_0^2}{2\alpha^2} = \ln 0.01, \quad \text{or} \quad \alpha^2 = \frac{-x_0^2}{2\ln 0.01} = \frac{1}{2}.$$

Hence, $\alpha = \dfrac{1}{\sqrt{2}}$.

PROBLEM 3.40 If θ_1 and θ_2 are independent random variables with Gaussian probability density functions

$$p(\theta_1) = \frac{1}{\sqrt{2\pi}\,\sigma}\,e^{-\theta_1^2/2\sigma^2}, \qquad p(\theta_2) = \frac{1}{\sqrt{2\pi}\,\sigma}\,e^{-\theta_2^2/2\sigma^2},$$

the probability density function for $\theta_P = \sqrt{\theta_1^2 + \theta_2^2}$ is Rayleigh. Determine the probability that $\theta_1 \geqslant 0$ and $\theta_2 \geqslant 0$ and the most probable and the median values of θ_P. (Cf., Fig. 3.21.)

Solution: Since the distribution $p(\theta_P)$ is Rayleigh,

$$p(\theta_P) = \frac{\theta_P\, e^{-\theta_P^2/2\alpha^2}}{\alpha^2},$$

where from (3.16), $\overline{\theta_P^2} = 2\alpha^2$. Since $\theta_P^2 = \theta_1^2 + \theta_2^2$ and θ_1 and θ_2 are independent.

$$\overline{\theta_P^2} = 2\alpha^2 = \overline{\theta_1^2} + \overline{\theta_2^2} = \sigma^2 + \sigma^2 = 2\sigma^2.$$

Thus, $\alpha^2 = \sigma^2$, and, therefore,

$$p(\theta_P) = \frac{\theta_P\, e^{-\theta_P^2/2\sigma^2}}{\sigma^2}.$$

Referring to Fig. 3.21, because of symmetry,

$$P(\theta_1 \geqslant 0, \theta_2 \geqslant 0) = \tfrac{1}{4}.$$

The median value, i.e., the value that will be exceeded 50% of the time, of θ_P can be found using (3.17), with $P^*(\theta_P) = 0.5$. Thus,

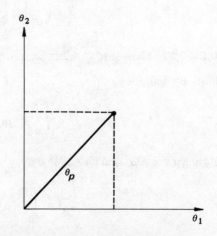

Fig. 3.21 Rayleigh distribution
for Prob. 3.40.

$$P^*(\theta_{P_m}) = \int_0^{\theta_{P_m}} p(\theta_P)\, d\theta_P = 0.5.$$

Therefore,

$$1 - e^{-\theta_{P_m}^2/2\sigma^2} = 0.5, \qquad \frac{-\theta_{P_m}^2}{2\sigma^2} = \ln\frac{1}{2}.$$

Hence, the median value of θ_P is

$$\theta_{P_m} = \sqrt{-2\sigma^2 \ln\frac{1}{2}} = 1.18\sigma.$$

To find the most probable value of θ_P, find the value of θ_P which maximizes $p(\theta_P)$. Thus,

$$\frac{dp(\theta_P)}{d\theta_P} = 0, \qquad \text{or} \qquad \frac{1}{\sigma^2}\left(e^{-\theta_{P_0}^2/2\sigma^2} - \frac{\theta_{P_0}^2}{\sigma^2} e^{-\theta_{P_0}^2/2\sigma^2}\right) = 0.$$

Hence, $\theta_{P_0} = \sigma$.

The quantity θ_{P_m} is commonly referred to as the *circular error probable* (cep).

3.7 Gamma Distribution

The *gamma distribution* with parameters α and β is defined by the density function

$$p(x) = \frac{1}{\beta^{\alpha+1}\,\Gamma(\alpha+1)} x^\alpha e^{-x/\beta}$$

$$\text{for } x > 0, \alpha > 0, \beta > 0$$

$$= 0 \quad \text{elsewhere}, \qquad (3.18a)$$

where $\Gamma(\alpha+1)$ is a value of the *gamma function*, defined by

$$\Gamma(\alpha+1) = \int_0^\infty x^\alpha e^{-x}\, dx. \qquad (3.18b)$$

Integration by parts shows that

$$\Gamma(\alpha+1) = \alpha\Gamma(\alpha)$$

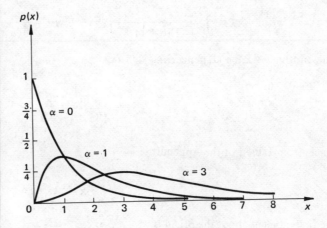

Fig. 3.22 Graphs of several gamma distributions for $\beta = 1$.

for any $\alpha > 0$ and, hence, that $\Gamma(\alpha+1) = \alpha!$ when α is a positive integer. Graphs of several gamma distributions are shown in Fig. 3.22 for $\beta = 1$.

PROBLEM 3.41 Show that the gamma distribution satisfies the condition $\int_{-\infty}^\infty p(x)\, dx = 1$.

Solution: Setting $I = \int_{-\infty}^\infty p(x)\, dx$, and using (3.18),

$$I = \int_0^\infty \frac{1}{\Gamma(\alpha+1)\,\beta^{\alpha+1}} x^\alpha\, e^{-x/\beta}\, dx.$$

Substituting $u = x/\beta$ and, hence, $du = 1/\beta\, dx$,

$$I = \frac{1}{\Gamma(\alpha + 1)} \int_0^\infty u^\alpha e^{-u} du.$$

From Table I of the Appendix,

$$\int_0^\infty x^{n-1} e^{-x} dx = \Gamma(n);$$

thus,

$$\int_0^\infty u^\alpha e^{-u} du = \Gamma(\alpha + 1),$$

and, therefore,

$$I = \frac{1}{\Gamma(\alpha + 1)} \Gamma(\alpha + 1) = 1.$$

PROBLEM 3.42 Calculate the first moment about the origin of the gamma distribution.

Solution: The first moment is

$$\overline{x} = \int_{-\infty}^\infty x p(x) dx.$$

Substituting (3.18),

$$\overline{x} = \int_0^\infty x \frac{1}{\Gamma(\alpha + 1) \beta^{\alpha+1}} x^\alpha e^{-x/\beta} dx = \frac{1}{\Gamma(\alpha + 1) \beta^{\alpha+1}} \int_0^\infty x^{\alpha+1} e^{-x/\beta} dx.$$

Substituting $u = x/\beta$ and, hence, $du = 1/\beta\, dx$,

$$\overline{x} = \frac{\beta}{\Gamma(\alpha + 1)} \int_0^\infty u^{\alpha+1} e^{-u} du.$$

Since, from Table I of the Appendix,

$$\int_0^\infty x^{n-1} e^{-x} dx = \Gamma(n),$$

the first moment about the origin is

$$\overline{x} = \frac{\beta}{\Gamma(\alpha + 1)} \Gamma(\alpha + 2) = \frac{\beta}{\alpha!} (\alpha + 1)! = \frac{\beta(\alpha + 1) \alpha!}{\alpha!} = \beta(\alpha + 1).$$

PROBLEM 3.43 Calculate the standard deviation σ of the gamma probability density function.

Solution: The standard deviation is obtained from

$$\sigma^2 = \overline{x^2} - \overline{x}^2,$$

where $\overline{x}$ has been calculated in Prob. 3.42 The second moment about the origin is

$$\overline{x^2} = \int_{-\infty}^\infty x^2 p(x) dx.$$

From (3.18), substituting for $p(x)$,

$$\overline{x^2} = \frac{1}{\Gamma(\alpha+1)\beta^{\alpha+1}} \int_0^\infty x^{\alpha+2} e^{-x/\beta} dx.$$

Substituting $u = x/\beta$ and, hence, $du = 1/\beta\, dx$,

$$\overline{x^2} = \frac{\beta^2}{\Gamma(\alpha+1)} \int_0^\infty u^{\alpha+2} e^{-u} du.$$

Since, from Table I of the Appendix,

$$\int_0^\infty x^{n-1} e^{-x} dx = \Gamma(n),$$

the second moment about the origin is

$$\overline{x^2} = \frac{\beta^2}{\Gamma(\alpha+1)} \Gamma(\alpha+3) = \frac{\beta^2}{\alpha!} (\alpha+2)(\alpha+1)\alpha! = \beta^2(\alpha+2)(\alpha+1).$$

Therefore, using the result of Prob. 3.42,

$$\sigma^2 = \overline{x^2} - \overline{x}^2 = \beta^2(\alpha+2)(\alpha+1) - \beta^2(\alpha+1)^2 = \beta^2[(\alpha^2+3\alpha+2) - (\alpha^2+2\alpha+1)] = \beta^2(\alpha+1);$$

hence, the standard deviation of the gamma distribution is

$$\sigma = \sqrt{\beta^2(\alpha+1)} = \beta\sqrt{\alpha+1}.$$

PROBLEM 3.44 Determine the cumulative distribution function for the gamma distribution when $\alpha = 1$.

Solution: When $\alpha = 1$, (3.18) becomes

$$p(x) = \frac{1}{\beta^2} x e^{-x/\beta} \quad \text{for } \beta > 0, \; x \geqslant 0$$

$$= 0 \qquad \text{for } x < 0.$$

The cumulative distribution function is

$$P^*(x) = \int_{-\infty}^x p(x)dx = \frac{1}{\beta^2} \int_0^x x e^{-x/\beta} dx.$$

Substituting $u = -x/\beta$ and, hence, $du = -1/\beta\, dx$,

$$P^*(x) = \int_0^{-x/\beta} u e^u du.$$

Using Table I of the Appendix,

$$\int u e^u du = e^u (u-1);$$

thus,

$$P^*(x) = e^u(u-1) \Big|_0^{-x/\beta} = e^{-x/\beta}\left(-\frac{x}{\beta} - 1\right) + 1 = 1 - \left(1 + \frac{x}{\beta}\right) e^{-x/\beta}.$$

In general, when α is not specified (although still subject to $\alpha > -1$),

$$P^*(x) = \int_0^x \frac{1}{\Gamma(\alpha + 1)\, \beta^{\alpha+1}}\, x^\alpha e^{-x/\beta}\, dx \quad \text{for } x \geqslant 0$$

$$= 0 \qquad\qquad\qquad\qquad \text{for } x < 0.$$

The function $P^*(x)$ is commonly known as the *incomplete gamma function*. In the case where α is a positive integer,

$$P^*(x) = 1 - \left[1 + \frac{x}{\beta} + \frac{1}{2!}\left(\frac{x}{\beta}\right)^2 + \cdots + \frac{1}{\alpha!}\left(\frac{x}{\beta}\right)^\alpha \right] e^{-x/\beta},$$

which reduces to the expression previously obtained when $\alpha = 1$.

3.8   Beta Distribution

A random variable is said to have a *beta distribution* if its density is

$$p(x) = \frac{(\alpha + \beta + 1)!}{\alpha!\, \beta!}\, x^\alpha (1 - x)^\beta$$

$$\text{for } 0 \leqslant x \leqslant 1, \alpha > -1, \beta > -1$$

$$= 0$$

$$\text{elsewhere.} \qquad (3.19)$$

Graphs of several beta distributions are shown in Fig. 3.23.

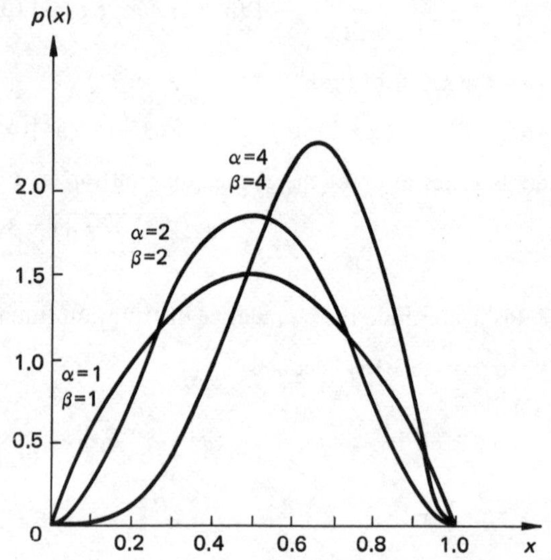

PROBLEM 3.45   Determine $\bar{x}$ for the beta distribution if $\alpha = 2$ and $\beta = 1$.

Solution: Substituting in (3.19),

$$p(x) = \frac{(2 + 1 + 1)!}{2!\, 1!}\, x^2\, (1 - x)$$

$$= 12 x^2 (1 - x) \quad \text{for } 0 \leqslant x \leqslant 1$$

$$= 0 \qquad\qquad \text{elsewhere.}$$

Fig. 3.23   Graphs of several beta distributions.

Hence, the mean value is

$$\bar{x} = \int_0^1 x p(x)\, dx = 12 \int_0^1 (x^3 - x^4)\, dx = 12 \left(\frac{x^4}{4} - \frac{x^5}{5}\right)\Bigg|_0^1 = 12\left(\frac{1}{4} - \frac{1}{5}\right) = \frac{3}{5}.$$

PROBLEM 3.46   (a)   Show that the moments of x about the origin for the beta distribution are

$$\overline{x^n} = \frac{(\alpha + \beta + 1)!\, (\alpha + n)!}{(\alpha + \beta + n + 1)!\, \alpha!}. \qquad (3.20)$$

(b)   Verify the result of Prob. 3.45.

Solution: (a)   The nth moment about the origin is

$$\overline{x^n} = \int_0^1 x^n\, p(x)\, dx.$$

Substituting (3.19) for $p(x)$,

$$\overline{x^n} = \int_0^1 \frac{(\alpha+\beta+1)!}{\alpha!\,\beta!}\, x^\alpha (1-x)^\beta\, x^n\, dx = \frac{(\alpha+\beta+1)!}{\alpha!\,\beta!} \int_0^1 x^{\alpha+n}(1-x)^\beta\, dx.$$

Letting $\alpha' = \alpha + n$,

$$\overline{x^n} = \frac{(\alpha+\beta+1)!}{\alpha!\,\beta!} \int_0^1 x^{\alpha'}(1-x)^\beta\, dx.$$

Since $\int_0^1 p(x)\,dx = 1$,

$$\int_0^1 \frac{(\alpha'+\beta+1)!}{\alpha'!\,\beta!}\, x^{\alpha'}(1-x)^\beta\, dx = 1, \quad \text{or} \quad \int_0^1 x^{\alpha'}(1-x)^\beta\, dx = \frac{\alpha'!\,\beta!}{(\alpha'+\beta+1)!}.$$

Thus,

$$\overline{x^n} = \frac{(\alpha+\beta+1)!}{\alpha!\,\beta!}\, \frac{\alpha'!\,\beta!}{(\alpha'+\beta+1)!} = \frac{(\alpha+\beta+1)!}{\alpha!}\, \frac{(\alpha+n)!}{(\alpha+n+\beta+1)!}.$$

(b) In the case where $\alpha = 2$ and $\beta = 1$,

$$\overline{x} = \frac{(2+1+1)!}{2!}\, \frac{(2+1)!}{(2+1+1+1)!} = \frac{4!}{2!}\, \frac{3!}{5!} = \frac{3}{5},$$

which agrees with the result of Prob. 3.45.

PROBLEM 3.47 Determine the cumulative distribution function for the beta distribution with $\alpha = 2$ and $\beta = 1$.

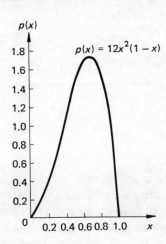

Fig. 3.24 Density function for the beta distribution with $\alpha = 2$ and $\beta = 1$.

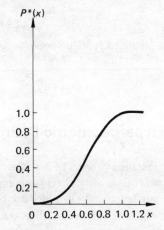

Fig. 3.25 Cumulative distribution function of the density function shown in Fig. 3.24.

Solution: From Prob. 3.45, the density function is

$$p(x) = 12x^2(1-x) \quad \text{for } 0 \leqslant x \leqslant 1$$
$$= 0 \quad \text{elsewhere,}$$

as shown in Fig. 3.24.

The cumulative distribution function is

$$P^*(x) = \int_0^x p(x)\,dx.$$

Thus, for $x < 0$, $P^*(x) = 0$, while for $x > 1$, $P^*(x) = 1$, and for $0 \leqslant x \leqslant 1$,

$$P*(x) = 12 \int_0^x (x^2 - x^3)dx = 12 \left(\frac{x^3}{3} - \frac{x^4}{4} \right) \Bigg|_0^x = 4x^3 - 3x^4.$$

Hence, the cumulative distribution function is

$$P*(x) = 4x^3 - 3x^4 \quad \text{for } 0 \leqslant x \leqslant 1$$
$$= 0 \qquad\qquad \text{for } x < 0$$
$$= 1 \qquad\qquad \text{for } x > 1.$$

This result is shown in Fig. 3.25.

In general, the cumulative distribution function is

$$P*(x) = \int_0^x p(x)dx \quad \text{for } 0 \leqslant x \leqslant 1$$
$$= 0 \qquad\qquad \text{for } x < 0$$
$$= 1 \qquad\qquad \text{for } x > 1.$$

Substituting (3.19),

$$P*(x) = \int_0^x \frac{(\alpha + \beta + 1)!}{\alpha! \, \beta!} x^\alpha (1 - x)^\beta dx \quad \text{for } 0 \leqslant x \leqslant 1$$
$$= 0 \qquad\qquad\qquad\qquad\qquad \text{for } x < 0$$
$$= 1 \qquad\qquad\qquad\qquad\qquad \text{for } x > 1, \qquad\qquad (3.21)$$

which is a tabulated function commonly known as the *incomplete beta function*.

3.9   Hypergeometric Distribution

If a population consists of n elements of which n_1 have attribute A, and $n_2 = n - n_1$ have attribute B, and r elements are taken without replacement, the sample space for this experiment is the $\binom{n}{r}$ possible outcomes; viz., the number of ways in which a subset of r objects can be selected from among a set of n objects. Furthermore, k elements can be selected from the n_1 elements with attribute A in $\binom{n_1}{k}$ ways, the $r - k$ elements can be selected from the n_2 elements with attribute B in $\binom{n-n_1}{r-k}$ ways, and the whole sample can be selected in $\binom{n_1}{k} \binom{n-n_1}{r-k}$ ways. Assuming that each of the $\binom{n}{r}$ samples has the same probability of being selected, the probability for k "successes" in r trials without replacement is

$$P_k = \frac{\binom{n_1}{k} \binom{n - n_1}{r - k}}{\binom{n}{r}} \quad \text{for } k = 0, 1, \cdots, r, \qquad\qquad (3.22)$$

where $k \leqslant r, k \leqslant n_1$, and $\binom{n_1}{k} = \frac{n_1!}{k! \, (n_1 - k)!}$. Equation (3.22) can be rewritten as

$$P_k = \frac{\binom{r}{k} \binom{n - r}{n_1 - k}}{\binom{n}{n_1}} \quad \text{for } k = 0, 1, \cdots, r, \qquad\qquad (3.23)$$

where $k \leqslant r$ and $k \leqslant n_1$. The probability distribution defined by these equations is called the *hypergeometric distribution;* the parameters of this family of distributions are the *sample size r*, the *population size n*, and the number of "successes" in the elements n_1 with attributes A, i.e., the number of elements, k, in r having the attribute A.

PROBLEM 3.48 An urn contains two black and four white balls, five of which are drawn at random. Find the probability that four of the five balls are white.

Solution: Since $n = 6, n_1 = 4, n_2 = 2, r = 5$, and $k = 4$, from (3.22), the probability is

$$P_4 = \frac{\binom{4}{4}\binom{2}{1}}{\binom{6}{5}} = \frac{\frac{4!}{4!\,0!} \cdot \frac{2!}{1!\,1!}}{\frac{6!}{5!\,1!}} = \frac{1}{3}.$$

Alternatively, (3.23) can be used to calculate P_k. Then,

$$P_4 = \frac{\binom{5}{4}\binom{1}{0}}{\binom{6}{4}} = \frac{\frac{5!}{4!\,1!} \cdot \frac{1!}{0!\,1!}}{\frac{6!}{4!\,2!}} = \frac{5 \cdot 1}{15} = \frac{1}{3},$$

which agrees with the previous calculation.

PROBLEM 3.49 In Prob. 3.48, determine the probability that four of the five balls drawn at random are black.

Solution: Then $P_4 = 0$ since there are only two black balls in the urn. In this case, $n_1 = 2$ and $k = 4$. Thus, the inequalities in (3.22) and (3.23) are exceeded. But (3.22) and (3.23) can still be used if one adopts the definition $\binom{r}{s} = 0$, where r and s are arbitrary positive integers and $s > r$.

PROBLEM 3.50 A group of 50 U.S. senators are chosen at random from a total of 100. Find the probability that the two New York senators are among them.

Solution: Substituting $n = 100, n_1 = 2, r = 50$, and $k = 2$ in (3.22), the probability is

$$P_2 = \frac{\binom{2}{2}\binom{98}{48}}{\binom{100}{50}} = \frac{1 \cdot \frac{98!}{48!\,50!}}{\frac{100!}{50!\,50!}} = \frac{50 \cdot 49}{100 \cdot 99} = \frac{49}{198}.$$

PROBLEM 3.51 In Prob. 3.50, determine the probability that no New York senator is among the senators that are chosen.

Solution: Substituting $n = 100, n_1 = 2, r = 50$, and $k = 0$ in (3.22), the probability is

$$P_0 = \frac{\binom{2}{0}\binom{98}{50}}{\binom{100}{50}} = \frac{\frac{2!}{2!\,0!} \cdot \frac{98!}{50!\,48!}}{\frac{100!}{50!\,50!}} = \frac{50 \cdot 49}{99 \cdot 100} = \frac{49}{198}.$$

3.10 Supplementary Problems

PROBLEM 3.52 Determine the probability that ten tosses of a coin produce five heads and five tails.
Answer: $\frac{63}{256}$.

PROBLEM 3.53 Determine the probability that five hundred tosses of a coin produce two hundred and fifty or more heads.
Answer: $\frac{1}{2}$.

PROBLEM 3.54 Show that if an experiment has three possible outcomes E_1, E_2, and E_3 with probabilities P_1, P_2, and P_3, respectively, then the probability that in n trials E_1 occurs n_1 times, E_2 occurs n_2 times, and E_3 occurs n_3 times is given by

$$\frac{n!}{n_1!n_2!n_3!} \; P_1^{n_1}P_2^{n_2}P_3^{n_3} \, .$$

PROBLEM 3.55 If the start of wars are assumed to be randomly distributed in time with an average frequency of occurrence of one every ten years, what is the probability of at least one war starting in the next ten years?
Answer: $1 - e^{-1}$.

PROBLEM 3.56 If the probability that an average driver in a certain city has an accident in a given year is 0.2, what is the average interval between accidents?
Answer: 5 yr.

PROBLEM 3.57 Under the conditions of Prob. 3.56, what is the probability of at least one accident in 5 yr?
Answer: 0.6733.

PROBLEM 3.58 A random variable is defined by the difference between a number selected at random and the nearest multiple of one hundred. Determine the mean and standard deviation of the random variable.
Answer: Mean = 0; Standard deviation = $50\sqrt{3}/3$.

PROBLEM 3.59 Determine the probability density function of a random variable $y = A \sin \theta$, where θ is uniformly distributed over the range $0 \leqslant \theta < 2\pi$. The probability density function of A is given by $p(A) = \frac{1}{2}\delta(x + 1) + \frac{1}{2}\delta(x - 1)$, where $\delta(x)$ is the Dirac delta function.
Answer: $p(y) = \dfrac{1}{\pi\sqrt{1 - y^2}}$ for $|y| \leqslant 1$

$\qquad\qquad = 0$ elsewhere.

PROBLEM 3.60 Determine the probability density function of a random variable $y = A \cos \theta$, where θ is uniformly distributed over the range $0 \leqslant \theta < 2\pi$ and A is constant.
Answer: $p(y) = \dfrac{1}{\pi\sqrt{A^2 - y^2}}$ for $|y| < |A|$

$\qquad\qquad = 0$ elsewhere.

PROBLEM 3.61 Determine the probability density function of a random variable $y = \cos \theta$, where θ is uniformly distributed over the range $0 \leqslant \theta < \frac{1}{2}\pi$.
Answer: $p(y) = \dfrac{2}{\pi\sqrt{A^2 - y^2}}$ for $0 \leqslant y \leqslant 1$

$\qquad\qquad = 0$ elsewhere.

PROBLEM 3.62 Determine the mean and variance of the probability density function

$$p(x) = \frac{e^{-\pi(x^2-2x)}}{e^\pi} \, .$$

Answer: Mean = 1; Variance = $1/2\pi$.

PROBLEM 3.63 Determine the mean value of the gamma distribution

$$p(x) = \frac{1}{10!(2048)} \, x^{10} e^{-(1/2)x} \quad \text{for } x \geqslant 0$$
$$= 0 \qquad\qquad\qquad \text{elsewhere.}$$

Answer: $\bar{x} = 22$.

PROBLEM 3.64 Determine the mean value for the beta distribution

$$p(x) = 66x^{10}(1-x) \quad \text{for } 0 \leqslant x \leqslant 1$$
$$= 0 \qquad\qquad \text{elsewhere.}$$

Answer: $\bar{x} = \frac{11}{13}$.

PROBLEM 3.65 Determine the mean-squared value for the beta distribution of Prob. 3.64.
Answer: $\frac{66}{91}$.

PROBLEM 3.66 Using the hypergeometric distribution, show that if a card is selected at random from a deck of 52 cards, the probability that it will be an ace is $\frac{1}{13}$.

PROBLEM 3.67 Determine the probability that if five cards are drawn at random from a deck of cards, they will all be either a jack, queen, king or an ace.
Answer: $\frac{1}{595}$.

PROBLEM 3.68 Determine the probability that if three cards are drawn at random from a deck of cards, that two of them will be deuces.
Answer: $\frac{72}{5525}$.

PROBLEM 3.69 Determine the *n*th moment of the distribution

$$p(x) = \frac{21!}{(10!)^2} \, x^{10}(1-x)^{10} \quad \text{for } 0 \leqslant x \leqslant 1$$
$$= 0 \qquad\qquad\qquad \text{elsewhere.}$$

Answer: $\dfrac{21!(10+n)!}{(21+n)!10!}$.

PROBLEM 3.70 A random variable with a mean of 18 and a standard deviation of 6 is distributed according to the gamma distribution. Determine its probability density function.
Answer: $p(x) = \dfrac{1}{2^{10}\Gamma(9)} \, x^8 e^{-(1/2)x} \quad \text{for } x \geqslant 0$
$$= 0 \qquad\qquad \text{elsewhere.}$$

PROBLEM 3.71 A random variable is said to be *exponentially distributed* if its probability density function is given by

$$p(x) = \frac{1}{a} \, e^{-x/a} \quad \text{for } x \geqslant 0$$
$$= 0 \qquad \text{for } x < 0,$$

where a is a constant. Show that this distribution is a special case of the gamma distribution.

4 CHAPTER | DERIVED AND TWO-DIMENSIONAL DISTRIBUTIONS

4.1 Transformation of Variables

A random variable x has the probability density function $p_x(x)$; and a variable y that is a function of x, given by $y = f(x)$, has the probability density function $p_y(y)$. Since the probability of finding a value of x in the interval from x to dx is equal to the probability of finding a value of y in the interval from y to dy,

$$p_y(y)\,dy = p_x(x)\,dx. \tag{4.1}$$

Assuming that x is a single-valued function of y,

$$p_y(y) = \frac{p_x(x)}{|dy/dx|} = p_x[x(y)]\left|\frac{dx(y)}{dy}\right|. \tag{4.2}$$

Note that (4.1-2) holds in general if $y = f(x)$ is monotonic.

PROBLEM 4.1 A random variable x has a probability density function $p_x(x)$. Determine $p_y(y)$ if $y = 3x$.

Solution: Using (4.2),

$$p_y(y) = \frac{p_x(x)}{|dy/dx|} = \tfrac{1}{3}\,p_x(x)\Big|_{x=y/3} = \tfrac{1}{3}\,p_x\left(\frac{y}{3}\right).$$

PROBLEM 4.2 Determine $p_y(y)$ for $y = e^x + 1$ if x is a random variable with a probability density function $p_x(x)$.

Solution: Since $x = \log(y - 1)$ and $dy/dx = e^x$, using (4.2),

$$p_y(y) = \frac{p_x(x)}{|dy/dx|} = \frac{p_x(x)}{e^x}\bigg|_{x=\log(y-1)} = \frac{p_x[\log(y-1)]}{e^{\log(y-1)}} = \frac{p_x[\log(y-1)]}{y-1}.$$

PROBLEM 4.3 Determine $p_y(y)$ if $y = e^{-x}$ and

$$p_x(x) = e^{-x} \quad \text{for } x \geqslant 0$$
$$= 0 \quad \text{for } x < 0.$$

Solution: Since $x = -\log y$ and

$$\left|\frac{dy}{dx}\right| = e^{-x} \quad \text{for } x \geqslant 0$$

$$= 0 \quad \text{for } x < 0,$$

using (4.2),

$$p_y(y) = \frac{p_x(x)}{|dy/dx|} = \frac{e^{-x}}{e^{-x}}\bigg|_{x=-\log y} \quad \text{for } x \geqslant 0$$

$$= 0 \quad \text{for } x < 0.$$

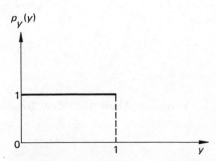

Fig. 4.1 Solution to Prob. 4.3.

Thus,

$$p_y(y) = 1 \quad \text{for } 0 \leqslant y \leqslant 1$$
$$= 0 \quad \text{elsewhere,}$$

as shown in Fig. 4.1.

PROBLEM 4.4 Determine $P[0.1 \leqslant y \leqslant 0.5]$ if $y = \sqrt{x}$ and

$$p_x(x) = 1 \quad \text{for } 0 \leqslant x \leqslant 1$$
$$= 0 \quad \text{elsewhere.}$$

Solution: From (4.2), $p_y(y) = 0$ when y is outside the interval $0 \leqslant y \leqslant 1$, and when y is inside this interval,

$$p_y(y) = \frac{p_x(x)}{|dy/dx|} = \frac{1}{1/(2\sqrt{x})} \bigg|_{\sqrt{x}=y} \quad \text{for } 0 \leqslant x \leqslant 1.$$

Thus,

$$p_y(y) = 2y \quad \text{for } 0 \leqslant y \leqslant 1$$
$$= 0 \quad \text{elsewhere,}$$

as shown in Fig. 4.2.

Then,

$$P[0.1 \leqslant y \leqslant 0.5] = \int_{0.1}^{0.5} p_y(y)dy = y^2 \bigg|_{0.1}^{0.5} = 0.25 - 0.01 = 0.24.$$

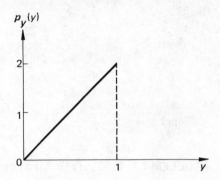

Fig. 4.2 Solution to Prob. 4.4.

PROBLEM 4.5 Find $p_y(y)$ if $y = x^2$ and x is Rayleigh distributed.

Solution: The probability density for a Rayleigh-distributed random variable is

$$p_x(x) = \frac{x}{\alpha^2} e^{-x^2/2\alpha^2} \quad \text{for } x \geqslant 0$$
$$= 0 \quad \text{for } x < 0.$$

Although x is not a single-valued function of y, only $x = +\sqrt{y}$ is an allowable solution because x does not take on negative values. Thus, (4.2) is applicable, and

$$p_y(y) = \frac{p_x(x)}{|dy/dx|} = \frac{\frac{x}{\alpha^2} e^{-x^2/2\alpha^2}}{2x} \bigg|_{x=\sqrt{y}}$$
$$= \frac{1}{2\alpha^2} e^{-y/2\alpha^2} \quad \text{for } y \geqslant 0.$$

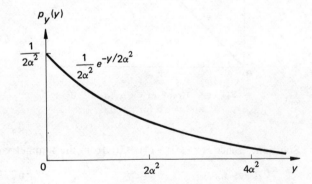

Fig. 4.3 The exponential probability density function of a transformed Rayleigh-distributed variable.

Thus, the square of a Rayleigh-distributed variable has an exponential probability density function, as shown in Fig. 4.3.

Problem 4.6 illustrates the procedure to be followed if y is not a monotonic function of x.

PROBLEM 4.6 Find $p_y(y)$ if $y = x^2$ and x is a normally distributed random variable with $p_x(x) = (1/\sqrt{2\pi}\,\sigma) e^{-x^2/2\sigma^2}$.

Solution: In this case, $x = \pm\sqrt{y}$ are both allowable solutions because x can have both positive and negative values in a normal distribution. Then,

$$p_y(y)dy = p_x(x)dx + p_x(-x)dx.$$

Since $p_x(x)$ is an even function of x, that is, $p_x(x) = p_x(-x)$,

$$p_y(y)dy = 2p_x(x)dx.$$

Hence,

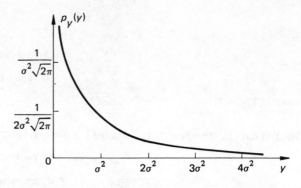

Fig. 4.4 The chi-squared density function.

$$p_y(y) \;=\; \frac{2p_x(x)}{|dy/dx|} \;=\; \left.\frac{\dfrac{2}{\sqrt{2\pi}\,\sigma}\,e^{-x^2/2\sigma^2}}{2x}\right|_{x=\sqrt{y}} \;=\; \frac{1}{\sqrt{2\pi}\,\sigma}\,\frac{e^{-y/2\sigma^2}}{\sqrt{y}}.$$

This density function with $y = x^2$ is a special case of the *chi-square density function* and is shown graphically in Fig. 4.4.

PROBLEM 4.7 Find $p_y(y)$ if x is a normally distributed random variable of zero mean and

$$y = x \quad \text{for } x \geqslant 0$$
$$= 0 \quad \text{for } x < 0.$$

The graph is shown in Fig. 4.5.

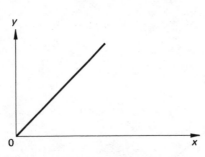

Fig. 4.5 Graph of $y = x$ for $x \geq 0$
and $y = 0$ for $x < 0$.

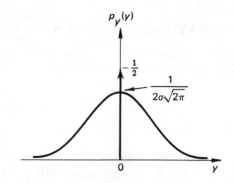

Fig. 4.6 Probability density function
of $y = x$ for $x \geq 0$.

Solution: Since $P(x < 0) = P(y = 0)$, from the symmetry of the normal distribution,

$$P(y = 0) = \int_{-\infty}^{0} p_x(x)dx = \frac{1}{2},$$

and, hence, $P(y = x) = \frac{1}{2}$. Thus,

$$p_y(y) = \tfrac{1}{2}\,\delta(x) + \tfrac{1}{2}\,p_x(x)\Big|_{x=y} = \tfrac{1}{2}\,\delta(y) + \tfrac{1}{2}\,p_x(y),$$

where $\delta(y)$ is the delta function at $y = 0$. Since the random variable has the general normal distribution,

$$p_x(x) = \frac{1}{\sqrt{2\pi}\,\sigma}\,e^{-x^2/2\sigma^2}.$$

(See Fig. 4.6.) Hence, the probability density function of y is

$$p_y(y) = \frac{1}{2}\,\delta(y) + \frac{1}{2\sqrt{2\pi}\,\sigma}\,e^{-y^2/2\sigma^2}.$$

PROBLEM 4.8 (a) Find $p_y(y)$ if $y = \ln x$ and

$$p_x(x) = (1/\sigma) e^{-x/\sigma} \quad \text{for } x \geqslant 0$$
$$= 0 \quad \text{for } x < 0.$$

(b) Calculate $P[1 < y < 2]$.

Solution: (a) Since $dy/dx = 1/x$, using (4.2), $p_y(y) = 0$ for $x < 0$, and for $x \geqslant 0$,

$$p_y(y) = \frac{p_x(x)}{dy/dx} = \frac{(1/\sigma) e^{-x/\sigma}}{1/x} \Bigg|_{x=e^y} = (1/\sigma) e^y e^{-e^y/\sigma} = (1/\sigma) e^{y-(e^y/\sigma)},$$

where $-\infty < y < \infty$.

(b) The quantity

$$P[1 < y < 2] = \int_1^2 p_y(y) dy.$$

However, because it is simpler to integrate the probability density function of x, $p_y(y)dy = p_x(x)dx$ and

$$P[1 < y < 2] = \int_e^{e^2} p_x(x) dx = (1/\sigma) \int_e^{e^2} e^{-x/\sigma} dx = -e^{-x/\sigma} \Bigg|_e^{e^2} = e^{-e/\sigma} - e^{-e^2/\sigma}.$$

4.2 Distribution of a Linear Combination of Random Variables

The *general linear combination* of the n independent random variables $x_1, x_2, \cdots, x_n$ is

$$y = a_1 x_1 + a_2 x_2 + \cdots + a_n x_n, \tag{4.3}$$

where $a_1, a_2, \cdots, a_n$ are constants. In particular, for the sum of independent random variables and $a_1 = a_2 = \cdots = a_n = 1$,

$$y = x_1 + x_2 + \cdots + x_n. \tag{4.4}$$

The probability density function $p_y(y)$ for the sum $y = x_1 + x_2$ of the random variables x_1 and x_2, having probability density functions $p_{x_1}(x)$ and $p_{x_2}(x)$, is

$$p_y(y) = \int_{-\infty}^{\infty} p_{x_2}(x_2) p_{x_1}(y - x_2) dx_2, \tag{4.5}$$

or, alternately,

$$p_y(y) = \int_{-\infty}^{\infty} p_{x_1}(x_1) p_{x_2}(y - x_1) dx_1. \tag{4.6}$$

Integrals of the form (4.5-6) are called *convolution integrals* and are abbreviated by

$$p_y(y) = p_{x_2} * p_{x_1}, \tag{4.5}$$

$$p_y(y) = p_{x_1} * p_{x_2}. \tag{4.6}$$

The probability density function $p_y(y)$ for the sum $y = x_1 + x_2 + \cdots + x_n$ of the independent random variables $x_1, x_2, \cdots, x_n$, having probability density functions $p_{x_1}(x), p_{x_2}(x), \cdots, p_{x_n}(x)$, is

$$p_y(y) = p_{x_1} * p_{x_2} * \cdots * p_{x_n}. \tag{4.7}$$

PROBLEM 4.9 Verify (4.5).

Solution: If the variable x_2 is assumed to be a constant, $p_y(y)\big|_{x_2=\text{const}}$ is determined by the procedure of Sec. 4.1. Then $p_y(y)$ is found by averaging $p_y(y)\big|_{x_2=\text{const}}$ over the variation of x_2. Therefore,

$$p_y(y)\,\Big|_{x_2=\text{const}} = \frac{p_{x_1}(x_1)}{\left|\dfrac{\partial y}{\partial x_1}\right|}\Bigg|_{x_1=y-x_2} = p_{x_1}(y-x_2)$$

since $\partial y/\partial x_1 = 1$. The statistical average of $p_y(y)\big|_{x_2=\text{const}}$ yields the probability density function of y; i.e.,

$$E\left[p_y(y)\,\big|_{x_2=\text{const}}\right] = \int_{-\infty}^{\infty} p_y(y)\,\Big|_{x_2=\text{const}}\cdot p_{x_2}(x)\,dx_2 = \int_{-\infty}^{\infty} p_{x_2}(x_2)p_{x_1}(y-x_2)\,dx_2.\qquad [4.5]$$

PROBLEM 4.10 Show that an alternate form of (4.5) is (4.6); that is, show that

$$p_y(y) = \int_{-\infty}^{\infty} p_{x_1}(x_1)\,p_{x_2}(y-x_1)\,dx_1.\qquad [4.6]$$

Solution: If the variable x_1 is assumed to be a constant, (4.6) is determined by the procedure of Prob. 4.9.

Alternatively, transform the variables in (4.5) by making the substitution $x_1 = y - x_2$ and, hence, $dx_1 = -dx_2$. Thus,

$$p_y(y) = \int_{+\infty}^{-\infty} p_{x_2}(y-x_1)\,p_{x_1}(x_1)\,(-dx_1) = -\int_{+\infty}^{-\infty} p_{x_1}(x_1)\,p_{x_2}(y-x_1)\,dx_1 = \int_{-\infty}^{\infty} p_{x_1}(x_1)\,p_{x_2}(y-x_1)\,dx_1.$$

Hence,

$$p_y(y) = p_{x_2} * p_{x_1} = p_{x_1} * p_{x_2}.$$

PROBLEM 4.11 Determine $p_y(y)$ if $y = x_1 + x_2$, and x_1 is a random variable with probability density function $p_{x_1}(x)$ and $x_2 = k$, where k is a constant.

Solution: Since $x_2 = k$ and, hence, $p_{x_2}(x) = \delta(x-k)$, from (4.5), the probability density function is

$$p_y(y) = \int_{-\infty}^{\infty} \delta(x-k)\,p_{x_1}(y-x)\,dx = p_{x_1}(y-k).$$

PROBLEM 4.12 Determine $p_y(y)$ if $y = x_1 + x_2$, and x_1 and x_2 are independent random variables with probability density functions p_{x_1} and p_{x_2}, as shown in Fig. 4.7.

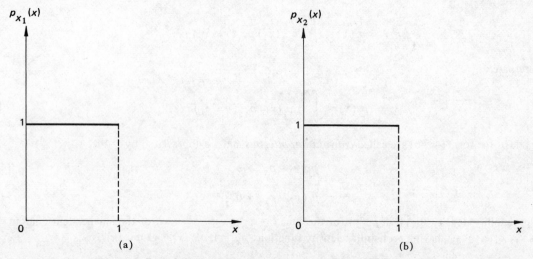

Fig. 4.7 Probability density functions p_{x_1} and p_{x_2} for Prob. 4.12.

Solution: Using (4.5),

$$p_y(y) = \int_{-\infty}^{\infty} p_{x_2}(x)\, p_{x_1}(y - x)\, dx.$$

The quantity $p_{x_1}(y - x)$ is shown in Fig. 4.8, and the corresponding product $p_{x_2}(x)\,p_{x_1}(y - x)$ for $0 < y < 1$ and for $1 < y < 2$ is shown in Figs. 4.9-10, respectively. Outside these two regions, the product is zero. Then,

$$
\begin{aligned}
p_y(y) &= 0 && \text{for } y < 0 \\
&= y && \text{for } 0 < y < 1 \\
&= 2 - y && \text{for } 1 < y < 2 \\
&= 0 && \text{for } y > 2,
\end{aligned}
$$

as shown in Fig. 4.11.

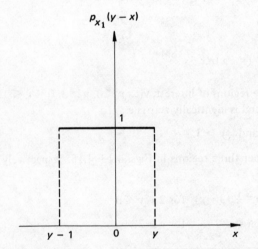

Fig. 4.8 Probability density function
$p_{x_1}(y - x)$.

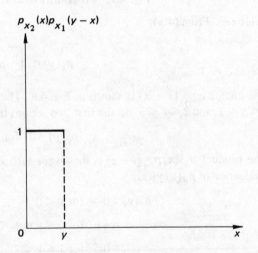

Fig. 4.9 Product $p_{x_2}(x)p_{x_1}(y-x)$
for $0 < y < 1$.

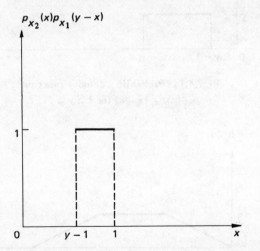

Fig. 4.10 Product $p_{x_2}(x)p_{x_1}(y-x)$
for $1 < y < 2$.

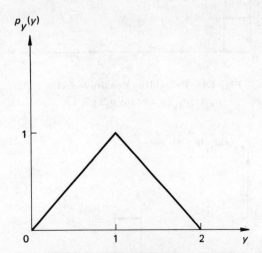

Fig. 4.11 Probability density function
$p_y(y)$ for $y = x_1 + x_2$, where p_{x_1} and
p_{x_2} are shown in Fig. 4.7.

PROBLEM 4.13   Determine $p_y(y)$ if $y = x_1 + x_2$, and x_1 and x_2 are random variables with probability density functions p_{x_1} and p_{x_2}, as shown in Fig. 4.12.

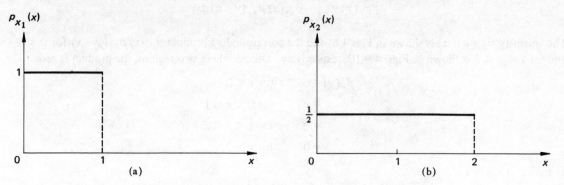

Fig. 4.12   Probability density functions p_{x_1} and p_{x_2} for Prob. 4.13.

Solution: From (4.5),

$$p_y(y) = \int_{-\infty}^{\infty} p_{x_2}(x) \, p_{x_1}(y - x) \, dx.$$

The quantity $p_{x_1}(y - x)$ is shown in Fig. 4.8. There are five regions of interest, viz., $y < 0$, $y > 3$, $0 \leqslant y \leqslant 1$, $1 \leqslant y \leqslant 2$, and $2 \leqslant y \leqslant 3$. In the first two regions the integrand is identically zero; i.e.,

$$p_y(y) = 0 \quad \text{for } y < 0 \quad \text{and} \quad y > 3.$$

The product $p_{x_2}(x) p_{x_1}(y - x)$ is shown for each of the other three regions in Figs. 4.13–4.15, respectively. Evaluation of $p_y(y)$ yields

$$
\begin{aligned}
p_y(y) &= 0 &&\text{for } y < 0 & \qquad p_y(y) &= \tfrac{1}{2}(3 - y) &&\text{for } 2 \leqslant y \leqslant 3 \\
&= \tfrac{1}{2}y &&\text{for } 0 \leqslant y \leqslant 1 & &= 0 &&\text{for } y > 3, \\
&= 0.5 &&\text{for } 1 \leqslant y \leqslant 2,
\end{aligned}
$$

as shown in Fig. 4.16.

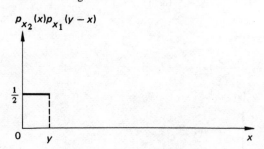

Fig. 4.13   Probability density function $p_{x_2}(x) p_{x_1}(y - x)$ for $0 \leq y \leq 1$.

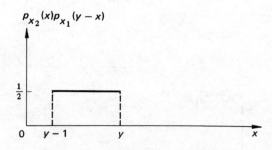

Fig. 4.14   Probability density function $p_{x_2}(x) p_{x_1}(y - x)$ for $1 \leq y \leq 2$.

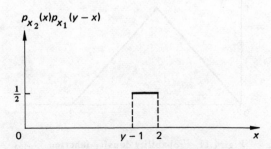

Fig. 4.15   Probability density function $p_{x_2}(x) p_{x_1}(y - x)$ for $2 \leq y \leq 3$.

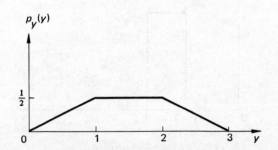

Fig. 4.16   Solution to Prob. 4.13.

PROBLEM 4.14 Prove (4.7).

Solution: From (4.5),

$$p_{x_1 + x_2}(x) = p_{x_1} * p_{x_2}.$$

(Cf., Prob. 4.9.) Accordingly, the probability density function of $x_1 + x_2 + x_3$ is

$$p_{x_1 + x_2 + x_3} = p_{x_1 + x_2} * p_{x_3} = p_{x_1} * p_{x_2} * p_{x_3}.$$

Successive application of (4.5) to the remaining random variables yields

$$p_y(y) = p_{x_1} * p_{x_2} * \cdots * p_{x_n}.$$

PROBLEM 4.15 Determine $p_y(y)$ for $y = a_1 x_1 + a_2 x_2 + \cdots + a_n x_n$ if $x_1, x_2, \cdots, x_n$ are independent random variables with probability density functions $p_{x_1}, p_{x_2}, \cdots, p_{x_n}$.

Solution: Defining a new set of variables $x_1', x_2', \cdots, x_n'$ given by

$$x_1' = a_1 x_1,$$
$$x_2' = a_2 x_2,$$
$$\vdots$$
$$x_n' = a_n x_n,$$

then, $y = x_1' + x_2' + \cdots + x_n'$. From (4.2),

$$p_{x_1'}(x) = \frac{1}{|a_1|} p_{x_1}\left(\frac{x}{a_1}\right),$$

$$p_{x_2'}(x) = \frac{1}{|a_2|} p_{x_2}\left(\frac{x}{a_2}\right),$$

$$\vdots$$

$$p_{x_n'}(x) = \frac{1}{|a_n|} p_{x_n}\left(\frac{x}{a_n}\right).$$

Using the result of Prob. 4.14,

$$p_y(y) = p_{x_1'} * p_{x_2'} * \cdots * p_{x_n'}$$

$$= \frac{1}{|a_1|} p_{x_1}\left(\frac{x}{a_1}\right) * \frac{1}{|a_2|} p_{x_2}\left(\frac{x}{a_2}\right) * \cdots * \frac{1}{|a_n|} p_{x_n}\left(\frac{x}{a_n}\right).$$

PROBLEM 4.16 The sum y of two independent random variables x_1 and x_2 is formed, where x_1 has the values -1, 0, $+1$ with probabilities $\frac{1}{4}$, $\frac{1}{3}$, and $\frac{5}{12}$. Express $p_y(y)$ in terms of p_{x_2}.

Solution: Since $y = x_1 + x_2$, its probability density function is

$$p_y(y) = p_{x_1}(x_1) * p_{x_2}(x_2).$$

Then $p_{x_1}(x_1)$ consists of three delta functions with areas as shown in Fig. 4.17. Thus,

$$p_{x_1}(x_1) = \tfrac{1}{4} \delta(x_1 + 1) + \tfrac{1}{3} \delta(x_1) + \tfrac{5}{12} \delta(x_1 - 1).$$

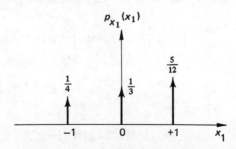

Fig. 4.17 The areas of the three delta functions which comprise $p_{x_1}(x_1)$ of Prob. 4.16.

Using (4.6),

$$p_y(y) = p_{x_1} * p_{x_2}$$

$$= \int_{-\infty}^{\infty} p_{x_1}(\alpha) \, p_{x_2}(y - \alpha) d\alpha$$

$$= \int_{-\infty}^{\infty} \left[\tfrac{1}{4} \delta(\alpha + 1) + \tfrac{1}{3} \delta(\alpha) + \tfrac{5}{12} \delta(\alpha - 1) \right] p_{x_2}(y - \alpha) d\alpha$$

$$= \tfrac{1}{4} p_{x_2}(y + 1) + \tfrac{1}{3} p_{x_2}(y) + \tfrac{5}{12} p_{x_2}(y - 1).$$

PROBLEM 4.17 The difference $y = x_1 - x_2$ of two random variables x_1 and x_2 is formed, where x_1 has the values $-1, 0, +1$, with probabilities $\tfrac{1}{4}, \tfrac{1}{3}$, and $\tfrac{5}{12}$ respectively. Express $p_y(y)$ in terms of p_{x_2}.

Solution: Since $y = x_1 + (-x_2)$, from (4.6), the probability density function is

$$p_y(y) = p_{x_1}(x_1) * p_{x_2}(-x_2)$$

$$= \int_{-\infty}^{\infty} p_{x_1}(\alpha) \, p_{x_2}(\alpha - y) d\alpha$$

$$= \int_{-\infty}^{\infty} \left[\tfrac{1}{4} \delta(\alpha + 1) + \tfrac{1}{3} \delta(\alpha) + \tfrac{5}{12} \delta(\alpha - 1) \right] p_{x_2}(\alpha - y) d\alpha$$

$$= \tfrac{1}{4} p_{x_2}(-1 - y) + \tfrac{1}{3} p_{x_2}(-y) + \tfrac{5}{12} p_{x_2}(1 - y).$$

PROBLEM 4.18 If $y = x_1 + x_2$, find $p_y(y)$ when

$$p_{x_1}(x_1) = a e^{-a x_1} \quad \text{for } x_1 \geqslant 0 \qquad p_{x_2}(x_2) = b e^{-b x_2} \quad \text{for } x_2 \geqslant 0$$
$$\qquad\qquad = 0 \qquad \text{for } x_1 < 0, \qquad\qquad\qquad = 0 \qquad \text{for } x_2 < 0.$$

Assume x_1 and x_2 are statistically independent.

Solution: From (4.6),

$$p_y(y) = p_{x_1} * p_{x_2}$$

$$= ab \int_0^y e^{-a\alpha} \, e^{-b(y-\alpha)} \, d\alpha.$$

As shown in Fig. 4.18, the lower limit is zero because $p_{x_1}(\alpha) = 0$ for $\alpha < 0$, and the upper limit is y because $p_{x_2}(y - \alpha) = 0$ for $\alpha > y$. Thus, on integration,

$$p_y(y) = abe^{-by} \int_0^y e^{-(a-b)\alpha} \, d\alpha$$

$$= \frac{ab}{a - b} e^{-by} \left(-e^{-(a-b)\alpha} \right) \Big|_0^y$$

$$= \frac{ab}{a - b} e^{-by} \left(1 - e^{-(a-b)y} \right)$$

$$= \frac{ab}{a - b} \left(e^{-by} - e^{-ay} \right).$$

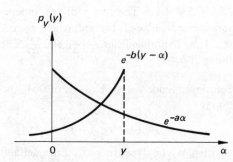

Fig. 4.18 Solution to Prob. 4.18.

4.3 Central Limit Theorem

The *central limit theorem* states that, under very general conditions, the distribution of the sum of a large number of independent random variables is asymptotically normal, regardless of the distribution of the individual variables. *Asymptotically normal* means that the sum will approach a normal distribution as the number of random variables that are summed becomes large. Thus, if

$$y = x_1 + x_2 + \cdots + x_n, \tag{4.8}$$

where $x_1, x_2, \cdots, x_n$ are independent random variables with probability density functions $p_{x_1}, p_{x_2}, \cdots, p_{x_n}$, the probability density function of the sum y is

$$p_y(y) = p_{x_1} * p_{x_2} * \cdots * p_{x_n}. \tag{4.9}$$

In the limit as $n \longrightarrow \infty$, the limiting Gaussian probability function is

$$\lim_{n \to \infty} p_y(y) \longrightarrow \frac{1}{\sqrt{2\pi}\,\sigma} e^{-(y-\bar{y})^2/2\sigma^2}, \tag{4.10}$$

where

$$\bar{y} = \bar{x}_1 + \bar{x}_2 + \cdots + \bar{x}_n + \cdots, \tag{4.11}$$

$$\sigma^2 = \sigma_1^2 + \sigma_2^2 + \cdots + \sigma_n^2 + \cdots. \tag{4.12}$$

In the special case where the component distributions are identical, the central limit theorem holds if there is a *finite second moment* for the common distribution.

PROBLEM 4.19 A sum of N identically distributed random variables is formed. Determine the limiting distribution of the sum as $N \longrightarrow \infty$ if each variable has a probability density function

$$p_{x_i}(x) = e^{-x} \quad \text{for } x \geqslant 0$$
$$= 0 \quad \text{for } x < 0,$$

where $i = 1, 2, \cdots, N$.

Solution: The first and second moments of each variable are

$$\bar{x}_i = \int_{-\infty}^{\infty} x p_{x_i}(x)dx = 1, \qquad \bar{x}_i^2 = \int_{-\infty}^{\infty} x^2 p_{x_i}(x) = \int_{-\infty}^{\infty} x^2 e^{-x}dx = \Gamma(3) = 2! = 2.$$

Hence, the variance of each variable is

$$\sigma_i^2 = \bar{x}_i^2 - \bar{x}_i^2 = 1,$$

where $i = 1, 2, \cdots, N$. From (4.11-2), the mean and variance of the sum are

$$\bar{y} = \bar{x}_1 + \bar{x}_2 + \cdots + \bar{x}_N = N, \qquad \sigma^2 = \sigma_1^2 + \sigma_2^2 + \cdots + \sigma_N^2 = N.$$

Therefore, from (4.10), the limiting probability density function is

$$p_y(y) = \frac{1}{\sqrt{2\pi N}} e^{-(y-N)^2/2N}.$$

PROBLEM 4.20 The sum of 100 identically distributed random variables is formed. Estimate $P[0 \leqslant x_1 + x_2 + \cdots + x_{100} \leqslant 0.1]$ if each variable has the probability density function

$$p_{x_i}(x) = 1 \quad \text{for } -0.5 \leqslant x \leqslant 0.5$$
$$= 0 \quad \text{elsewhere,}$$

where $i = 1, 2, \cdots, 100$.

Solution: Use the limiting Gaussian probability density function, given by (4.10), to estimate $P[0 \leqslant x_1 + x_2 + \cdots + x_{100} \leqslant 0.1]$. Since $\bar{x}_i = 0$ and

$$\sigma^2 = \overline{x_i^2} = \int_{-\infty}^{\infty} x^2 \, p_{x_i}(x) \, dx = \left. \frac{x^3}{3} \right|_{-0.5}^{0.5} = \frac{1}{12},$$

from (4.10-2), the mean and variance of the sum are

$$\overline{y} = 0, \qquad \sigma^2 = 100 \left(\tfrac{1}{12} \right) = \tfrac{25}{3},$$

and, hence, the probability density function is

$$p_y(y) = \frac{1}{\sqrt{\dfrac{50\pi}{3}}} \, e^{-3y^2/50},$$

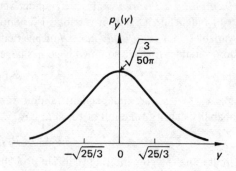

Fig. 4.19 Solution to Prob. 4.20.

where $y = x_1 + x_2 + \cdots + x_{100}$. Its graph is shown in in Fig. 4.19. In the region $0 \leqslant y \leqslant 0.1$, $p_y(y) \approx \sqrt{\frac{3}{50\pi}}$; hence,

$$P[0 \leqslant y \leqslant 0.1] \approx \tfrac{1}{10} \sqrt{\frac{3}{50\pi}}.$$

PROBLEM 4.21 In (4.8), $x_1, x_2, \cdots, x_n$ are normally distributed with common mean zero and standard deviations $\sigma_1, \sigma_2, \cdots, \sigma_n$. Show that the distribution of y is exactly normal with mean zero and standard deviation $\sqrt{\sigma_1^2 + \sigma_2^2 + \cdots + \sigma_n^2}$.

Solution: For the distribution $w = x_1 + x_2$, the probability density function is

$$p_w(w) = p_{x_1}(x_1) * p_{x_2}(x_2) = \int_{-\infty}^{\infty} \frac{1}{\sqrt{2\pi}\,\sigma_1} e^{-\alpha^2/2\sigma_1^2} \frac{1}{\sqrt{2\pi}\,\sigma_2} e^{-(w-\alpha)^2/2\sigma_2^2} \, d\alpha$$

$$= \frac{1}{2\pi\sigma_1\sigma_2} \int_{-\infty}^{\infty} e^{-\alpha^2/2\sigma_1^2} \, e^{-(w^2-2w\alpha+\alpha^2)/2\sigma_2^2} \, d\alpha$$

$$= \frac{1}{2\pi\sigma_1\sigma_2} \int_{-\infty}^{\infty} \exp\left[-\left(\frac{1}{2\sigma_1^2} + \frac{1}{2\sigma_2^2} \right)\alpha^2 + \frac{1}{\sigma_2^2} w\alpha - \frac{1}{2\sigma_2^2} w^2 \right] d\alpha.$$

Completing the square in the exponent of the exponential,

$$-\left(\frac{1}{2\sigma_1^2} + \frac{1}{2\sigma_2^2} \right)\alpha^2 + \frac{1}{\sigma_2^2} w\alpha - \frac{1}{2\sigma_2^2} w^2 = -\frac{\sigma_1^2 + \sigma_2^2}{2\sigma_1^2\sigma_2^2} \left(\alpha^2 - \frac{2\sigma_1^2}{\sigma_1^2 + \sigma_2^2} w\alpha + \frac{\sigma_1^2}{\sigma_1^2 + \sigma_2^2} w^2 \right)$$

$$= -\frac{\sigma_1^2 + \sigma_2^2}{2\sigma_1^2\sigma_2^2} \left[\left(\alpha - \frac{\sigma_1^2}{\sigma_1^2 + \sigma_2^2} w \right)^2 + \frac{\sigma_1^2}{\sigma_1^2 + \sigma_2^2} w^2 - \left(\frac{\sigma_1^2}{\sigma_1^2 + \sigma_2^2} \right)^2 w^2 \right]$$

$$= -\frac{\sigma_1^2 + \sigma_2^2}{2\sigma_1^2\sigma_2^2} \left[\left(\alpha - \frac{\sigma_1^2}{\sigma_1^2 + \sigma_2^2} w \right)^2 + \frac{\sigma_1^2}{\sigma_1^2 + \sigma_2^2} w^2 \left(1 - \frac{\sigma_1^2}{\sigma_1^2 + \sigma_2^2} \right) \right]$$

$$= -\frac{\sigma_1^2 + \sigma_2^2}{2\sigma_1^2\sigma_2^2} \left[\left(\alpha - \frac{\sigma_1^2}{\sigma_1^2 + \sigma_2^2} w \right)^2 + \frac{\sigma_1^2}{\sigma_1^2 + \sigma_2^2} w^2 \left(\frac{\sigma_2^2}{\sigma_1^2 + \sigma_2^2} \right) \right]$$

$$= -\frac{\sigma_1^2 + \sigma_2^2}{2\sigma_1^2\sigma_2^2} \left(\alpha - \frac{\sigma_1^2}{\sigma_1^2 + \sigma_2^2} w \right)^2 - \frac{w^2}{2(\sigma_1^2 + \sigma_2^2)}.$$

Thus, the probability density function is

$$p_w(w) = \frac{1}{2\pi\sigma_1\sigma_2} \, e^{-w^2/2(\sigma_1^2 + \sigma_2^2)} \int_{-\infty}^{\infty} \exp\left[\frac{-(\sigma_1^2 + \sigma_2^2)}{2\sigma_1^2\sigma_2^2} \left(\alpha - \frac{\sigma_1^2}{\sigma_1^2 + \sigma_2^2} w \right)^2 \right] d\alpha.$$

The term $e^{-w^2/2(\sigma_1^2 + \sigma_2^2)}$ has been brought out from the integrand because it is not a function of the variable of integration α. The integral is proportional to the area under a Gaussian of mean $\dfrac{\sigma_1^2}{\sigma_1^2 + \sigma_2^2} w$ and standard deviation $\dfrac{\sigma_1 \sigma_2}{\sqrt{\sigma_1^2 + \sigma_2^2}}$. Since

$$\frac{1}{\sqrt{2\pi} \dfrac{\sigma_1 \sigma_2}{\sqrt{\sigma_1^2 + \sigma_2^2}}} \int_{-\infty}^{\infty} \exp\left[-\frac{\sigma_1^2 + \sigma_2^2}{2\sigma_1^2 \sigma_2^2}\left(\alpha - \frac{\sigma_1^2}{\sigma_1^2 + \sigma_2^2}\,w\right)^2 d\alpha\right] = 1,$$

the probability density function $p_w(w)$ becomes

$$p_w(w) = \frac{1}{2\pi\sigma_1\sigma_2}\, e^{-w^2/2(\sigma_1^2 + \sigma_2^2)}\, \sqrt{2\pi}\,\frac{\sigma_1 \sigma_2}{\sqrt{\sigma_1^2 + \sigma_2^2}} = \frac{1}{\sqrt{2\pi(\sigma_1^2 + \sigma_2^2)}}\, e^{-w^2/2(\sigma_1^2 + \sigma_2^2)}.$$

Hence, $p_w(w)$ is normal with mean zero and standard deviation $\sqrt{\sigma_1^2 + \sigma_2^2}$.

Since $p_y(y) = p_{x_1} * p_{x_2} * \cdots * p_{x_n}$, p_y must also be normal, since from the previous calculations, successive convolutions of normal distributions result in a normal distribution. In each convolution the new variance is the sum of the component variances; thus,

$$p_y(y) = \frac{1}{\sqrt{2\pi(\sigma_1^2 + \sigma_2^2 + \cdots + \sigma_n^2)}}\, \exp\left[\frac{-y^2}{2(\sigma_1^2 + \sigma_2^2 + \cdots + \sigma_n^2)}\right].$$

Hence, if the component distributions are initially normal, the resulting distribution is exactly normal, even for finite n. This statement also applies to the general case where the mean values of the component normal distributions are nonzero.

4.4   Two-Dimensional Distributions

A *joint probability density function of two random variables* x, y is a function $p(x, y)$ that possesses the properties

$$p(x, y) \geqslant 0,$$

$$\int_{-\infty}^{\infty} \int_{-\infty}^{\infty} p(x, y)dx\,dy = 1,$$

$$P[x_1 \leqslant x \leqslant x_2, y_1 \leqslant y \leqslant y_2] = \int_{y_1}^{y_2} \int_{x_1}^{x_2} p(x, y)dx\,dy, \qquad (4.13)$$

where $P[x_1 \leqslant x \leqslant x_2, y_1 \leqslant y \leqslant y_2]$ is the probability that $x_1 \leqslant x \leqslant x_2$ and $y_1 \leqslant y \leqslant y_2$.

The *cumulative distribution function* is

$$P^*(x, y) = \int_{-\infty}^{y} \int_{-\infty}^{x} p(x, y)dx\,dy, \qquad (4.14)$$

so that $p(x, y) = \dfrac{\partial^2 P^*(x, y)}{\partial x \partial y}$.

Two random variables x, y with probability density functions $p_x(x)$ and $p_y(y)$ are *independent* if and only if the joint probability density function $p(x, y)$ is equal to the product of $p_x(x)$ and $p_y(y)$; i.e.,

$$p(x, y) = p_x(x) \cdot p_y(y).$$

The *marginal probability density functions* of the variables x and y are defined to be

$$p_1(x) = \int_{-\infty}^{\infty} p(x, y)dy, \qquad (4.15)$$

$$p_2(y) = \int_{-\infty}^{\infty} p(x, y)dx. \qquad (4.16)$$

PROBLEM 4.22　Determine the resulting probability density function if one of the variables in a two-dimensional probability density function $p(x,y)$ is disregarded.

Solution:　If the variable y in $p(x, y)$ is disregarded, the new density function is found by integrating out the variable y. The result is the marginal probability density function. Thus,

$$p_1(x) = \int_{-\infty}^{\infty} p(x,y)\,dy. \qquad [4.15]$$

Similarly, if the variable x is disregarded,

$$p_2(y) = \int_{-\infty}^{\infty} p(x,y)\,dy. \qquad [4.16]$$

PROBLEM 4.23　Determine the marginal cumulative distribution functions corresponding to (4.15) and (4.16).

Solution:　The two marginal cumulative distribution functions are

$$P_1^*(x) = \int_{-\infty}^{x} p_1(x)\,dx = \int_{-\infty}^{x} dx \int_{-\infty}^{\infty} p(x,y)\,dy, \qquad (4.17)$$

$$P_2^*(y) = \int_{-\infty}^{y} p_2(y)\,dy = \int_{-\infty}^{y} dy \int_{-\infty}^{\infty} p(x,y)\,dx. \qquad (4.18)$$

PROBLEM 4.24　Find k for the two-dimensional density function

$$p(x,y) = ke^{-2x-3y} \quad \text{for } x \geq 0, y \geq 0$$
$$= 0 \quad \text{elsewhere.}$$

Solution:　Since $\int_{-\infty}^{\infty} \int_{-\infty}^{\infty} p(x,y)\,dx\,dy = 1$, on substitution,

$$k \int_{0}^{\infty} e^{-2x}\,dx \int_{0}^{\infty} e^{-3y}\,dy = 1.$$

On integration,

$$k \cdot \tfrac{1}{2} \cdot \tfrac{1}{3} = 1.$$

Hence, $k = 6$.

PROBLEM 4.25　Calculate the cumulative distribution function for the probability density function of Prob. 4.24.

Solution:　Using (4.14), the cumulative distribution function is

$$P^*(x, y) = \int_{-\infty}^{x} \int_{-\infty}^{y} p(x,y)\,dy\,dx = 6 \int_{0}^{x} e^{-2x}\,dx \int_{0}^{y} e^{-3y}\,dy = (1 - e^{-2x})(1 - e^{-3y}).$$

PROBLEM 4.26　Calculate the marginal cumulative distribution functions and the marginal probability density functions for the probability density function of Prob. 4.24.

Solution:　Using (4.17-18), the marginal cumulative distribution functions are

$$P_1^*(x) = \int_{-\infty}^{x} dx \int_{-\infty}^{\infty} p(x,y)\,dy = 6 \int_{0}^{x} e^{-2x}\,dx \int_{0}^{\infty} e^{-3y}\,dy = 1 - e^{-2x},$$

$$P_2^*(y) = \int_{-\infty}^{y} dy \int_{-\infty}^{\infty} p(x,y)\,dx = 6 \int_{0}^{y} e^{-3y}\,dy \int_{0}^{\infty} e^{-2x}\,dx = 1 - e^{-3y}.$$

Using (4.15–16), the marginal probability density functions are

$$P_1^*(x) = \int_{-\infty}^{\infty} p(x,y)\,dy = 6e^{-2x} \int_0^{\infty} e^{-3y}\,dy = 2e^{-2x},$$

$$P_2^*(y) = \int_{-\infty}^{\infty} p(x,y)\,dx = 6e^{-3y} \int_0^{\infty} e^{-2x}\,dx = 3e^{-3y}.$$

Note that $p_1(x)$ and $p_2(y)$ can also be obtained by differentiating $P_1^*(x)$ and $P_2^*(y)$, respectively.

PROBLEM 4.27 Express $E[F(x,y)]$ in terms of $p(x,y)$ if $F(x,y)$ is an arbitrary function of the random variables x and y, having the two-dimensional probability density function $p(x,y)$.

Solution: In the case of one-dimensional probability density functions considered in earlier chapters,

$$E[f(x)] = \int_{-\infty}^{\infty} f(x)\,p(x)\,dx.$$

Analogous to this expression, for the two-dimensional case,

$$E[F(x,y)] = \int_{-\infty}^{\infty} \int_{-\infty}^{\infty} F(x,y)\,p(x,y)\,dx\,dy. \tag{4.19}$$

4.5 Moments of Two-Dimensional Distributions

Moments of a joint probability distribution are called *joint moments*, and are defined as

$$\mu_{ij}' = E[x^i y^j] \tag{4.20}$$

$$= \int_{-\infty}^{\infty} \int_{-\infty}^{\infty} x^i y^j\, p(x,y)\,dx\,dy, \tag{4.21}$$

where $i, j = 0, 1, 2, \cdots$. The *order* of any moment is the sum $i + j$.
In particular, the *expectation*

$$E(x) = \overline{x} = \mu_{10}' = \int_{-\infty}^{\infty} \int_{-\infty}^{\infty} x\,p(x,y)\,dx\,dy, \tag{4.22}$$

$$E(y) = \overline{y} = \mu_{01}' = \int_{-\infty}^{\infty} \int_{-\infty}^{\infty} y\,p(x,y)\,dx\,dy. \tag{4.23}$$

The corresponding *central moments*, i.e., moments about the mean, are defined by

$$\mu_{ij} = E[(x - \overline{x})^i (y - \overline{y})^j] = \int_{-\infty}^{\infty} \int_{-\infty}^{\infty} (x - \overline{x})^i (y - \overline{y})^j\, p(x,y)\,dx\,dy. \tag{4.24}$$

The moment μ_{11} is the *covariance* of the two variables x and y.
Note that in (4.20-4), x and y are, in general, not statistically independent.

PROBLEM 4.28 Determine the three second-order joint central moments of the random variables x and y.

Solution: From (4.24), the three second-order moments, or those for which $i + j = 2$, are μ_{20}, μ_{02}, and μ_{11}; thus,

$$\mu_{20} = E[(x - \overline{x})^2] = \overline{x^2} - \overline{x}^2 = \sigma_x^2, \tag{4.25}$$

$$\mu_{02} = E[(y - \overline{y})^2] = \overline{y^2} - \overline{y}^2 = \sigma_y^2, \tag{4.26}$$

$$\mu_{11} = E[(x - \overline{x})(y - \overline{y})] = E[xy] - E[x]\,E[y] = \overline{xy} - \overline{x}\,\overline{y}. \tag{4.27}$$

PROBLEM 4.29   Determine the covariance μ_{11} of x and y if they are statistically independent random variables.

Solution: When x and y are statistically independent random variables,

$$p(x, y) = p_1(x) \cdot p_2(y). \qquad (4.28)$$

In other words, their joint probability density function is separable into the product of the two one-dimensional probability density functions of x and y. Thus,

$$E[xy] = \overline{xy}$$

$$= \int_{-\infty}^{\infty} \int_{-\infty}^{\infty} xy\, p(x, y)\, dx\, dy$$

$$= \int_{-\infty}^{\infty} \int_{-\infty}^{\infty} xy\, p_1(x)\, p_2(y)\, dx\, dy$$

$$= \int_{-\infty}^{\infty} xp_1(x)\, dx \int_{-\infty}^{\infty} yp_2(y)\, dy$$

$$= \overline{x} \cdot \overline{y}.$$

Therefore, from (4.27-8), $\mu_{11} = \overline{xy} - \overline{x}\,\overline{y} = 0$.

Thus, if x and y are independent, $\mu_{11} = 0$. The converse of this statement, however, is not necessarily true. If $\mu_{11} = 0$, x and y are *linearly independent* or *uncorrelated* but not necessarily statistically independent because higher order cross moments are not necessarily zero. An important special case, discussed in Sec. 4.6, occurs when $p(x, y)$ is a two-dimensional Gaussian distribution. In this case, if $\mu_{11} = 0$, x and y are statistically independent.

The numerical measure of the dependence between x and y is the *normalized correlation coefficient* and is defined by

$$\rho = \frac{\mu_{11}}{\sqrt{\mu_{20}\,\mu_{02}}}. \qquad (4.29)$$

The value of ρ is restricted to $-1 \leqslant \rho \leqslant 1$, and $|\rho| \approx 1$ signifies high correlation, whereas $\rho \ll 1$ signifies low correlation.

PROBLEM 4.30   Determine μ_{11} for the density function

$$p(x, y) = e^{-(x+y)} \quad \text{for } x \geqslant 0, y \geqslant 0$$
$$= 0 \qquad\qquad \text{elsewhere.}$$

Solution: Since

$$p(x, y) = e^{-x}\, e^{-y} = p_1(x) \cdot p_2(y),$$

$p(x, y)$ is separable; hence, x and y are independent. From Prob. 4.29, $E[xy] = \overline{x} \cdot \overline{y}$; thus, from (4.27),

$$\mu_{11} = \overline{xy} - \overline{x}\,\overline{y} = 0.$$

PROBLEM 4.31   Determine the normalized correlation coefficient ρ if $y = bx$, where x is a random variable with zero mean and b is a nonzero constant.

Solution: Using (4.25-7), with $\overline{x} = \overline{y} = 0$,

$$\mu_{20} = \overline{x^2}, \qquad \mu_{02} = \overline{y^2} = \overline{(bx)^2} = b^2\,\overline{x^2}, \qquad \mu_{11} = \overline{xy} = b\overline{x^2}.$$

Then, from (4.29), the normalized correlation coefficient is

$$\rho = \frac{\mu_{11}}{\sqrt{\mu_{20}\,\mu_{02}}} = \frac{b\overline{x^2}}{\sqrt{b^2\,\overline{x^2}\,\overline{x^2}}}\,.$$

Hence,

$$\cdot\ \rho = 1 \quad \text{if } b > 0$$
$$= -1 \quad \text{if } b < 0.$$

Note that there is total correlation between x and y and that the same result is obtained even if the mean of x is not zero.

PROBLEM 4.32 Determine the normalized correlation coefficient for x and y if $y = x + z$, where x and z are statistically independent random variables with zero mean and unit variance.

Solution: Since $\overline{y} = \overline{x} = \overline{z} = 0$, the three second-order joint central moments are

$$\mu_{11} = \overline{xy} = \overline{x^2 + xz} = \overline{x^2} + \overline{xz} = \overline{x^2} = 1,$$

$$\mu_{20} = \overline{x^2} = 1,$$

$$\mu_{02} = \overline{y^2} = \overline{(x + z)^2} = \overline{x^2} + \overline{z^2} + \overline{2xz} = \overline{x^2} + \overline{z^2} = 2.$$

Because x and z are statistically independent, $\overline{xz} = 0$. Hence, the normalized correlation coefficient is

$$\rho = \frac{\mu_{11}}{\sqrt{\mu_{20}\,\mu_{02}}} = \frac{1}{\sqrt{2}} = \frac{\sqrt{2}}{2}\,.$$

PROBLEM 4.33 The sum and difference of two statistically independent random variables x and y are formed. Find the conditions under which u and v are uncorrelated if $u = x + y$ and $v = x - y$.

Solution: Since the variances of x and y are $\sigma_x^2 = \overline{x^2} - \overline{x}^2$ and $\sigma_y^2 = \overline{y^2} - \overline{y}^2$, the covariance is

$$\begin{aligned}
\mu_{11} &= E\left[(u - \overline{u})(v - \overline{v})\right]\\
&= E\left[\{(x + y) - (\overline{x} + \overline{y})\}\{(x - y) - (\overline{x} - \overline{y})\}\right]\\
&= E\left[x^2 - y^2 + \overline{x}^2 - \overline{y}^2 - (x - y)(\overline{x} + \overline{y}) - (x + y)(\overline{x} - \overline{y})\right]\\
&= \overline{x^2} - \overline{y^2} + \overline{x}^2 - \overline{y}^2 - (\overline{x} - \overline{y})(\overline{x} + \overline{y}) - (\overline{x} + \overline{y})(\overline{x} - \overline{y})\\
&= \overline{x^2} - \overline{y^2} - (\overline{x}^2 - \overline{y}^2)\\
&= \sigma_x^2 - \sigma_y^2.
\end{aligned}$$

Thus, $\mu_{11} = 0$ if $\sigma_x = \sigma_y$.

PROBLEM 4.34 A random variable x is uniformly distributed between -1 and $+1$. Determine the normalized correlation coefficient for x and y if $y = x^2$.

Solution: The covariance is

$$\mu_{11} = \overline{xy} - \overline{x}\,\overline{y} = \overline{x^3} - \overline{x}\,\overline{x^2}.$$

The quantities $\overline{x}$ and $\overline{x^3}$ are

$$\overline{x} = \int_{-\infty}^{\infty} x\,p(x)dx, \qquad \overline{x^3} = \int_{-\infty}^{\infty} x^3\,p(x)dx.$$

Since $p(x)$ is an even function of x, both integrands are odd functions of x, integrated over symmetric limits. Therefore,

$$\overline{x} = \overline{x^3} = 0.$$

Accordingly, $\mu_{11} = 0$, and, hence, the normalized correlation coefficient is also zero; that is, $\rho = 0$.

PROBLEM 4.35   A random variable x is uniformly distributed between -1 and $+1$. Find the normalized correlation coefficient for x and y if $y = x^3$.

Solution: The density function for a random variable uniformly distributed between -1 and $+1$ is

$$p(x) = \tfrac{1}{2} \quad \text{for } |x| < 1$$
$$= 0 \quad \text{elsewhere.}$$

The mean values of x, x^2, y, x^4 and y^2 are

$$\overline{x} = \int_{-1}^{1} x \left(\tfrac{1}{2}\right) dx = 0, \qquad \overline{x^2} = \int_{-1}^{1} x^2 \left(\tfrac{1}{2}\right) dx = \tfrac{1}{3}, \qquad \overline{y} = \overline{x^3} = \int_{-1}^{1} x^3 \left(\tfrac{1}{2}\right) dx = 0,$$

$$\overline{x^4} = \int_{-1}^{1} x^4 \left(\tfrac{1}{2}\right) dx = \tfrac{1}{5}, \qquad \overline{y^2} = \overline{x^6} = \int_{-1}^{1} x^6 \left(\tfrac{1}{2}\right) dx = \tfrac{1}{7}.$$

Therefore, the three second-order joint central moments are

$$\mu_{20} = \overline{x^2} - \overline{x}^2 = \tfrac{1}{3}, \qquad \mu_{02} = \overline{y^2} - \overline{y}^2 = \tfrac{1}{7}, \qquad \mu_{11} = \overline{xy} - \overline{x}\,\overline{y} = \overline{x^4} - \overline{x}\,\overline{x^3} = \tfrac{1}{5}.$$

Hence, the normalized correlation coefficient for x and y is

$$\rho = \frac{\mu_{11}}{\sqrt{\mu_{20}\,\mu_{02}}} = \frac{\tfrac{1}{5}}{\sqrt{\left(\tfrac{1}{3}\right)\left(\tfrac{1}{7}\right)}} = \frac{\sqrt{21}}{5}.$$

PROBLEM 4.36   Show that if the probability density function $p(x)$ of a random variable is an even function of x with mean zero, x^2 and x are uncorrelated.

Solution: From (4.29), $\rho = 0$ if $\mu_{11} = 0$. Since $\overline{x} = 0$, $\mu_{11} = \overline{x^3} - \overline{x}\,\overline{x^2} = \overline{x^3} = \int_{-\infty}^{\infty} x^3 p(x)dx$. If $p(x)$ is even, that is, $p(x) = p(-x)$, $x^3 p(x)$ is odd. An odd function integrated between symmetric limits yields zero, that is, $\mu_{11} = 0$, and, therefore, $\rho = 0$.

4.6   Two-Dimensional Normal Distributions

If two random variables x and y are *normally* or *Gaussian* distributed with mean zero and, in addition, are independently distributed, their joint probability density function $p(x, y)$ is the product of the two (normal) marginal probability density functions; i.e.,

$$p(x, y) = \frac{1}{2\pi\sqrt{\mu_{20}\,\mu_{02}}} \exp\left[-\frac{1}{2}\left(\frac{x^2}{\mu_{20}} + \frac{y^2}{\mu_{02}}\right)\right]. \tag{4.30}$$

If the variables x and y are *not* independent, the above equation is modified by introducing a cross-product term in the exponent that has a coefficient of 0 when x and y are independent. Thus, the normal probability density function of two variables is

$$p(x, y) = \frac{1}{2\pi M} \exp\left[\frac{-1}{2M^2}\left(\mu_{02}x^2 - 2\mu_{11}xy + \mu_{20}y^2\right)\right], \tag{4.31}$$

where

$$M^2 = \mu_{20}\,\mu_{02} - \mu_{11}^2, \tag{4.32}$$

and $\mu_{20}, \mu_{02}, \mu_{11}$ are defined in (4.27-9) with $\overline{x} = \overline{y} = 0$. Since, from (4.29),

$$\rho^2 = \frac{\mu_{11}^2}{\mu_{20}\,\mu_{02}},$$

then

$$M^2 = \mu_{20}\,\mu_{02}\,(1 - \rho^2). \tag{4.33}$$

Using (4.29) and (4.33), (4.31) can be rewritten as

$$p(x, y) = \frac{1}{2\pi M} \exp \left[\frac{-1}{2(1-\rho^2)} \left(\frac{x^2}{\mu_{20}} - \frac{2\rho\, xy}{\sqrt{\mu_{20}\,\mu_{02}}} + \frac{y^2}{\mu_{02}} \right) \right]. \tag{4.34}$$

Since from (4.25-6), $\mu_{20} = \sigma_x{}^2$ and $\mu_{02} = \sigma_y{}^2$, (4.34) becomes

$$p(x, y) = \frac{1}{2\pi M} \exp \left[\frac{-1}{2(1-\rho^2)} \left(\frac{x^2}{\sigma_x^2} - \frac{2\rho}{\sigma_x \sigma_y} xy + \frac{y^2}{\sigma_y^2} \right) \right]. \tag{4.35}$$

If $\overline{x}$ and $\overline{y}$ are not equal to zero, x and y in (4.35) are replaced by $(x - \overline{x})$ and $(y - \overline{y})$, respectively.

PROBLEM 4.37 Show that if two jointly normal random variables x and y are uncorrelated, they are statistically independent.

Solution: If x and y are uncorrelated, $\rho = 0$.

Since x and y are jointly normal, their joint probability density function is given by (4.34). Setting $\rho = 0$ in (4.34),

$$p(x, y) = \frac{1}{2\pi\sigma_x\sigma_y} \exp \left[-\frac{1}{2} \left(\frac{x^2}{\sigma_x^2} + \frac{y^2}{\sigma_y^2} \right) \right]$$

$$= \left(\frac{1}{\sqrt{2\pi}\,\sigma_x} e^{-x^2/2\sigma_x^2} \right) \left(\frac{1}{\sqrt{2\pi}\,\sigma_y} e^{-y^2/2\,\sigma_y^2} \right)$$

$$= p_x(x) \cdot p_y(y),$$

showing that x and y are statistically independent because their joint probability density function is separable into the product of the two one-dimensional probability density functions.

PROBLEM 4.38 Two random variables x and y are jointly normal. Determine $p(x, y)$ if $\overline{x^2} = \overline{y^2} = 2$, $\overline{x} = \overline{y} = 0$, and $\rho = 1/\sqrt{2}$.

Solution: Using (4.25-6)

$$\mu_{20} = \overline{x^2} - \overline{x}^2 = 2, \qquad \mu_{02} = \overline{y^2} - \overline{y}^2 = 2.$$

From (4.33),

$$M^2 = \mu_{20}\,\mu_{02}\,(1 - \rho^2) = 2 \cdot 2 \left(1 - \tfrac{1}{2} \right) = 2.$$

From (4.34), the joint probability density function is

$$p(x, y) = \frac{1}{2\pi M} \exp \left[\frac{-1}{2(1-\rho^2)} \left(\frac{x^2}{\mu_{20}} - \frac{2\rho\, xy}{\sqrt{\mu_{20}\,\mu_{02}}} + \frac{y^2}{\mu_{02}} \right) \right].$$

Substituting for M, ρ, μ_{20}, and μ_{02},

$$p(x, y) = \frac{1}{2\pi\sqrt{2}} \exp \left[-\left(\frac{x^2}{2} - \frac{1}{\sqrt{2}} xy + \frac{y^2}{2} \right) \right].$$

PROBLEM 4.39 Two random variables x and y are jointly normal. Determine $p(x, y)$ if $\overline{x^2} = \overline{y^2} = 2$, $\overline{x} = \overline{y} = 1$, and $\rho = 1/\sqrt{2}$.

Solution: The joint probability density function when $\overline{x} = \overline{y} \neq 0$ is found from (4.35) on replacing x by $x - \overline{x}$ and y by $y - \overline{y}$. Thus,

$$p(x, y) = \frac{1}{2\pi M} \exp \left\{ \frac{-1}{2(1-\rho^2)} \left[\frac{(x - \overline{x})^2}{\sigma_x^2} - \frac{2\rho(x - \overline{x})\,(y - \overline{y})}{\sigma_x\sigma_y} + \frac{(y - \overline{y})^2}{\sigma_y^2} \right] \right\},$$

where

$$\mu_{20} = \overline{x^2} - \overline{x}^2 = 2 - 1 = 1, \qquad \mu_{02} = \overline{y^2} - \overline{y}^2 = 2 - 1 = 1, \qquad M^2 = \mu_{20}\mu_{02}(1 - \rho^2) = 1 \cdot 1 \left(1 - \tfrac{1}{2} \right) = \tfrac{1}{2}.$$

Substituting these values,

$$p(x, y) = \frac{1}{\pi\sqrt{2}} \exp\{-[(x - 1)^2 - \sqrt{2}\,(x - 1)(y - 1) + (y - 1)^2]\}.$$

PROBLEM 4.40 The joint normal probability density function of two random variables x and y is

$$p(x, y) = \frac{1}{1.6\pi} \exp\left[-\left(\frac{x^2}{1.28} + \frac{0.6xy}{0.64} + \frac{y^2}{1.28}\right)\right].$$

Calculate ρ.

Solution: From (4.34),

$$p(x, y) = \frac{1}{2\pi M} \exp\left[\frac{-1}{2(1 - \rho^2)}\left(\frac{x^2}{\mu_{20}} - \frac{2\rho\,xy}{\sqrt{\mu_{20}\,\mu_{02}}} + \frac{y^2}{\mu_{02}}\right)\right],$$

where $M^2 = \mu_{20}\,\mu_{02}\,(1 - \rho^2)$. Therefore,

$$2\pi M = 1.6\pi,$$

and equating the coefficients of xy in the exponent of the exponential of the calculated and given values of $p(x,y)$,

$$\frac{\rho}{(1 - \rho^2)\,\sqrt{\mu_{20}\,\mu_{02}}} = \frac{-0.6}{0.64}.$$

Since $M = \sqrt{\mu_{20}\,\mu_{02}\,(1 - \rho^2)} = 0.8$,

$$\frac{\rho}{\sqrt{1 - \rho^2}\,(0.8)} = \frac{-0.6}{0.64}.$$

Solving for ρ,

$$\rho = -0.6.$$

PROBLEM 4.41 Show that for $p(x,y)$, as given by (4.34),

$$\int_{-\infty}^{\infty}\int_{-\infty}^{\infty} p(x, y)\,dx\,dy = 1.$$

Assume $\overline{x} = \overline{y} = 0$.

Solution: Let

$$I = \int_{-\infty}^{\infty}\int_{-\infty}^{\infty} p(x, y)\,dx\,dy.$$

On substitution of the value of $p(x,y)$, from (4.35),

$$I = \frac{1}{2\pi\sigma_x\sigma_y\,\sqrt{1 - \rho^2}} \int_{-\infty}^{\infty}\int_{-\infty}^{\infty} \exp\left[\frac{-1}{2(1 - \rho^2)}\left(\frac{x^2}{\sigma_x^2} - \frac{2\rho xy}{\sigma_x\sigma_y} + \frac{y^2}{\sigma_y^2}\right)\right] dx\,dy.$$

Substituting $u = x/\sigma_x$ and $v = y/\sigma_y$,

$$I = \frac{1}{2\pi\sqrt{1 - \rho^2}} \int_{-\infty}^{\infty}\int_{-\infty}^{\infty} \exp\left[\frac{-1}{2(1 - \rho^2)}\,(u^2 - 2\rho uv + v^2)\right] du\,dv.$$

Completing the square in the exponent of the exponential, i.e.,

$$u^2 - 2\rho uv + v^2 = (u - \rho v)^2 + (1 - \rho^2)v^2,$$

the above integral becomes

$$I = \frac{1}{2\pi\sqrt{1 - \rho^2}} \int_{-\infty}^{\infty}\int_{-\infty}^{\infty} \exp\left\{\frac{-1}{2(1 - \rho^2)}\,[(u - \rho v)^2 + (1 - \rho^2)\,v^2]\right\} du\,dv.$$

Substituting $z = \dfrac{u - \rho v}{\sqrt{1 - \rho^2}}$ and, hence, $dz = \dfrac{du}{\sqrt{1 - \rho^2}}$,

$$I = \frac{1}{2\pi} \int_{-\infty}^{\infty} \int_{-\infty}^{\infty} \exp\left[-\frac{1}{2}(z^2 + v^2) \right] dz\, dv = \left(\frac{1}{\sqrt{2\pi}} \int_{-\infty}^{\infty} e^{-z^2/2}\, dz \right) \left(\frac{1}{\sqrt{2\pi}} \int_{-\infty}^{\infty} e^{-v^2/2}\, dv \right).$$

Each of the parenthetical terms represents the total area under a normal distribution curve of mean zero and unit standard deviation and is, therefore, equal to unity. Thus $I = 1$.

PROBLEM 4.42 Find the marginal probability density function $p_1(x)$ for the two-dimensional normal distribution. Assume $\overline{x} = \overline{y} = 0$.

Solution: From (4.15), the marginal probability density function is

$$p_1(x) = \int_{-\infty}^{\infty} p(x, y)\, dy = \frac{1}{2\pi\sigma_x\sigma_y\sqrt{1 - \rho^2}} \int_{-\infty}^{\infty} \exp\left[\frac{-1}{2(1 - \rho^2)} \left(\frac{x^2}{\sigma_x^2} - \frac{2\rho x y}{\sigma_x\sigma_y} + \frac{y^2}{\sigma_y^2} \right) \right] dy.$$

Substituting $u = y/\sigma_y$ and, hence, $du = dy/\sigma_y$,

$$p_1(x) = \frac{1}{2\pi\sigma_x\sqrt{1 - \rho^2}} \int_{-\infty}^{\infty} \exp\left[\frac{-1}{2(1 - \rho^2)} \left(\frac{x^2}{\sigma_x^2} - \frac{2\rho x u}{\sigma_x} + u^2 \right) \right] du.$$

Completing the square in the exponent of the exponential, i.e.,

$$\frac{x^2}{\sigma_x^2} - \frac{2\rho x u}{\sigma_x} + u^2 = \left(u - \frac{\rho x}{\sigma_x} \right)^2 + (1 - \rho^2) \left(\frac{x}{\sigma_x} \right)^2,$$

the above integral becomes

$$p_1(x) = \frac{1}{2\pi\sigma_x\sqrt{1 - \rho^2}} \int_{-\infty}^{\infty} \exp\left\{ \frac{-1}{2(1 - \rho^2)} \left[\left(u - \frac{\rho x}{\sigma_x} \right)^2 + (1 - \rho^2) \left(\frac{x}{\sigma_x} \right)^2 \right] \right\} du.$$

Substituting $z = \dfrac{u - \rho x/\sigma_x}{\sqrt{1 - \rho^2}}$ and $dz = \dfrac{du}{\sqrt{1 - \rho^2}}$,

$$p_1(x) = \frac{1}{2\pi\sigma_x} \int_{-\infty}^{\infty} \exp\left[-\frac{1}{2}\left(z^2 + \frac{x^2}{\sigma_x^2} \right) \right] dz = \frac{1}{\sqrt{2\pi}\,\sigma_x} e^{-x^2/2\sigma_x^2} \left(\frac{1}{\sqrt{2\pi}} \int_{-\infty}^{\infty} e^{-z^2/2}\, dz \right).$$

The parenthetical quantity is the total area under a normal distribution curve of mean zero and unit standard deviation and is, therefore, equal to unity. Thus,

$$p_1(x) = \frac{1}{\sqrt{2\pi}\,\sigma_x} e^{-x^2/2\sigma_x^2},$$

which is a normal distribution of mean zero and standard deviation σ_x.

PROBLEM 4.43 The error of an inertial navigation system, used for determining the latitude and longitude of a vehicle, is represented by a two-dimensional normal distribution. Let the errors in the east-west and north-south directions have mean zero and standard deviations σ_e and σ_n miles, respectively.

If $\rho = 0$, determine the probability that the true location is more than (a) k_1 miles east of the indicated location and (b) k_1 miles east and k_2 miles north of the indicated location. (c) Repeat part (b) for the case $\sigma_e = \sigma_n = \sigma$ and $\rho = 1$.

Solution: The probability density function for the error can be represented by

$$p(x, y) = \frac{1}{2\pi\sigma_e\sigma_n\sqrt{1 - \rho^2}} \exp\left[\frac{-1}{2(1 - \rho^2)} \left(\frac{x^2}{\sigma_e^2} - \frac{2\rho}{\sigma_e\sigma_n} xy + \frac{y^2}{\sigma_n^2} \right) \right],$$

where x and y are the errors in the east-west and north-south directions, respectively.

(a) The required probability is

$$P(x > k_1) = \int_{k_1}^{\infty} dx \int_{-\infty}^{\infty} p(x, y) dy.$$

The inner integral is just the marginal probability density function that is evaluated in Prob. 4.42 as

$$\int_{-\infty}^{\infty} p(x, y) dy = \frac{1}{\sqrt{2\pi}\,\sigma_e}\, e^{-x^2/2\sigma_e^2}.$$

Thus, the probability is

$$P(x > k_1) = \frac{1}{\sqrt{2\pi}\,\sigma_e} \int_{k_1}^{\infty} e^{-x^2/2\sigma_e^2}\, dx = 1 - \frac{1}{\sqrt{2\pi}\,\sigma_e} \int_{-\infty}^{k_1} e^{-x^2/2\sigma_e^2}\, dx.$$

Since

$$\frac{1}{\sqrt{2\pi}\,\sigma_e} \int_{-\infty}^{\infty} e^{-x^2/2\sigma_e^2}\, dx = 1,$$

then

$$P(x > k_1) = 1 - P^*(k_1) = \frac{1}{2}\left[1 - \operatorname{erf}\left(\frac{k_1}{\sqrt{2}\sigma_e}\right)\right].$$

(b) The required probability is

$$P(x > k_1, y > k_2) = \int_{k_1}^{\infty} dx \int_{k_2}^{\infty} p(x, y) dy$$

$$= \int_{k_1}^{\infty} \frac{1}{\sqrt{2\pi}\,\sigma_e}\, e^{-x^2/2\sigma_e^2}\, dx \int_{k_2}^{\infty} \frac{1}{\sqrt{2\pi}\,\sigma_n}\, e^{-y^2/2\sigma_n^2}\, dy$$

$$= \frac{1}{2}\left[1 - \operatorname{erf}\left(\frac{k_1}{\sqrt{2}\,\sigma_e}\right)\right] \cdot \frac{1}{2}\left[1 - \operatorname{erf}\left(\frac{k_2}{\sqrt{2}\,\sigma_n}\right)\right]$$

$$= \frac{1}{4}\left[1 - \operatorname{erf}\left(\frac{k_1}{\sqrt{2}\,\sigma_e}\right)\right] \left[1 - \operatorname{erf}\left(\frac{k_2}{\sqrt{2}\,\sigma_n}\right)\right].$$

(c) Calculate $P(x > k_1, y > k_2)$ for $\rho = 1$ and $\sigma_e = \sigma_n$. Thus, $\rho = 1$ implies that $y = ax + b$. But since $\overline{x} = \overline{y} = 0$, the constant $b = 0$. Since $\sigma_e = \sigma_n$, the constant $a = 1$. Thus, $x = y$.

Hence,

$$P(x > k_1, y > k_2) = P(x > k_1) \qquad \text{for } k_1 \geqslant k_2$$

$$= P(y > k_2) \qquad \text{for } k_1 < k_2.$$

Then, from part (b),

$$P(x > k_1, y > k_2) = \frac{1}{2}\left[1 - \operatorname{erf}\left(\frac{k_1}{\sqrt{2}\,\sigma}\right)\right] \qquad \text{for } k_1 \geqslant k_2$$

$$= \frac{1}{2}\left[1 - \operatorname{erf}\left(\frac{k_2}{\sqrt{2}\,\sigma}\right)\right] \qquad \text{for } k_1 < k_2.$$

4.7 Supplementary Problems

PROBLEM 4.44 Show that the square of a Rayleigh-distributed random variable is exponentially distributed.

PROBLEM 4.45 Show that if x and y are statistically independent random variables with probability density functions $p_x(x)$ and $p_y(y)$, respectively, that the distribution of the product $z = xy$ is given by

$$p_z(z) = \int_{-\infty}^{\infty} \frac{p_y(y)p_x(z/y)dy}{y}.$$

PROBLEM 4.46 Show that the distribution of the product of two statistically independent random variables is normal if one of the variables is Rayleigh distributed and the other is sinusoidally distributed.

PROBLEM 4.47 Show that the distribution of the product $z = 3x$, obtained using the result of Prob. 4.45, agrees with that obtained using (4.2). (Cf., Prob. 4.1.)

PROBLEM 4.48 Determine the probability density function of the random variable $x = \sin(\phi_1 + \phi_2 + \cdots + \phi_n)$, where $\phi_1, \phi_2, \cdots, \phi_n$ are independent random variables with probability density functions

$$p_{\phi_1}(\phi) = p_{\phi_2}(\phi) = \cdots = p_{\phi_n}(\phi) = 1/2\pi \quad \text{for } 0 \leqslant \phi < 2\pi$$
$$= 0 \quad \text{elsewhere.}$$

Answer: $p_x(x) = \dfrac{1}{\pi\sqrt{1-x^2}}$.

PROBLEM 4.49 If $y = ax + b$, express the probability density function of the random variable y in terms of the probability density function of x.

Answer: $p_y(y) = \dfrac{1}{|a|} \, p_x\left[\dfrac{1}{a}(y - b)\right]$.

PROBLEM 4.50 A random variable x has a probability density function

$$p_x(x) = 1 \quad \text{for } -\tfrac{1}{2} \leqslant x \leqslant \tfrac{1}{2}$$
$$= 0 \quad \text{elsewhere.}$$

Determine $p_y(y)$ if

$$y = x \quad \text{for } -\tfrac{1}{4} \leqslant x \leqslant \tfrac{1}{4}$$
$$= 0 \quad \text{elsewhere.}$$

Answer: $p_y(y) = p_x(y) + \tfrac{1}{2}\delta(y) \quad \text{for } -\tfrac{1}{4} \leqslant y \leqslant \tfrac{1}{4}$
$= 0 \qquad\qquad\qquad \text{elsewhere.}$

PROBLEM 4.51 A random variable x has a probability density function

$$p_x(x) = e^{-x} \quad \text{for } x \geqslant 0$$
$$= 0 \qquad \text{elsewhere.}$$

Determine the probability density function of x^3.
Answer: $p_{x^3}(x) = e^{-y^{1/3}}/3y^{2/3}$.

PROBLEM 4.52 Show that the sum of n independent normally distributed random variables is normally distributed. Assume an arbitrary mean and variance for each variable.

PROBLEM 4.53 Show that the sum $y = a_1 x_1 + a_2 x_2 + \cdots + a_n x_n$ is normally distributed if the variables $x_1, x_2, \cdots, x_n$ are independently normally distributed.

5 CHAPTER

CHARACTERISTIC FUNCTIONS

5.1 Moment Generating Functions

The *moment-generating function* of a random variable x is defined by

$$M(\xi) = E[e^{x\xi}] \tag{5.1}$$

$$= \int_{-\infty}^{\infty} e^{x\xi} p(x)dx, \tag{5.2}$$

where $p(x)$ is the probability density function of x. Since the Maclaurin series expansion of $e^{x\xi}$ about $x\xi = 0$ is

$$e^{x\xi} = 1 + x\xi + \frac{1}{2!}(x\xi)^2 + \frac{1}{3!}(x\xi)^3 + \cdots,$$

the moment-generating function (5.2) can be written as

$$M(\xi) = \int_{-\infty}^{\infty}\left[1 + x\xi + \frac{1}{2!}(x\xi)^2 + \cdots\right]p(x)dx = \int_{-\infty}^{\infty}p(x)dx + \xi\int_{-\infty}^{\infty}xp(x)dx + \frac{1}{2!}\xi^2\int_{-\infty}^{\infty}x^2 p(x)dx + \cdots.$$

Since $\int_{-\infty}^{\infty}p(x)dx = 1$, and $\int_{-\infty}^{\infty}xp(x)dx$, $\int_{-\infty}^{\infty}x^2 p(x)dx, \cdots$ are the moments $\mu_1, \mu_2, \cdots$,

$$M(\xi) = 1 + \mu_1\xi + \frac{1}{2!}\mu_2\xi^2 + \cdots. \tag{5.3}$$

If $p(x,y)$ is the joint probability density function of two random variables x and y, the *joint moment-generating function* is

$$M(\xi,\eta) = E[e^{\xi x + \eta y}] \tag{5.4}$$

$$= \int_{-\infty}^{\infty}\int_{-\infty}^{\infty} e^{\xi x + \eta y} p(x,y)dxdy. \tag{5.5}$$

PROBLEM 5.1 Determine the moment-generating function for the distribution with moments $\mu_n = \frac{1}{n+1}$.

Solution: Since the moments of the distribution are

$$\mu_1 = \frac{1}{1+1} = \frac{1}{2},$$

$$\mu_2 = \frac{1}{2+1} = \frac{1}{3},$$

$$\vdots$$

$$\mu_n = \frac{1}{n+1},$$

$$\vdots$$

94

its moment-generating function is

$$M(\xi) = 1 + \mu_1 \xi + \frac{1}{2!}\mu_2\xi^2 + \cdots + \frac{1}{n!}\mu_n\xi^n + \cdots$$

$$= 1 + \frac{1}{2}\xi + \frac{1}{2!3}\xi^2 + \frac{1}{3!4}\xi^3 + \cdots + \frac{1}{n!(n+1)}\xi^n + \cdots$$

$$= 1 + \frac{1}{2!}\xi + \frac{1}{3!}\xi^2 + \frac{1}{4!}\xi^3 + \cdots + \frac{1}{(n+1)!}\xi^n + \cdots$$

$$= \frac{e^\xi - 1}{\xi}.$$

PROBLEM 5.2 Determine the moment-generating function for the probability density function

$$p(x) = 1 \quad \text{for } 0 \leqslant x \leqslant 1$$

$$= 0 \quad \text{elsewhere.}$$

Solution: Using (5.2), the moment-generating function is

$$M(\xi) = \int_{-\infty}^{\infty} e^{x\xi} p(x)dx = \int_0^1 e^{x\xi}dx = \frac{1}{\xi}e^{x\xi}\Big|_0^1 = \frac{1}{\xi}(e^\xi - 1).$$

If the exponential is expanded in a series,

$$M(\xi) = \frac{1}{\xi}\left(1 + \xi + \frac{1}{2!}\xi^2 + \frac{1}{3!}\xi^2 + \cdots - 1\right) = 1 + \frac{1}{2!}\xi + \frac{1}{3!}\xi^2 + \cdots,$$

which is identical with the moment-generating function obtained in Prob. 5.1.

Under very general conditions, if two random variables have the same moment-generating function, they have the same density function. Similarly, density functions with identical sets of moments are equivalent.

PROBLEM 5.3 Express the derivatives of the moment-generating function at $\xi = 0$ in terms of the moments of the distribution.

Solution: From (5.2), the moment-generating function is

$$M(\xi) = \int_{-\infty}^{\infty} e^{x\xi} p(x)dx.$$

Differentiating with respect to ξ,

$$\frac{dM(\xi)}{d\xi} = \frac{d}{d\xi}\int_{-\infty}^{\infty} e^{x\xi} p(x)dx.$$

Since the integration is with respect to x,

$$\frac{dM(\xi)}{d\xi} = \int_{-\infty}^{\infty} \frac{d}{d\xi}e^{x\xi} p(x)dx = \int_{-\infty}^{\infty} xe^{x\xi} p(x)dx.$$

At $\xi = 0$, $\dfrac{dM(0)}{d\xi} = \displaystyle\int_{-\infty}^{\infty} xp(x)dx = \mu_1$; that is, the first derivative of the moment-generating function at $\xi = 0$ is the first moment of the distribution. In general, the nth derivative is

$$\frac{d^n M(\xi)}{d\xi^n} = \int_{-\infty}^{\infty} \frac{d^n}{d\xi^n}(e^{x\xi}) p(x)dx = \int_{-\infty}^{\infty} x^n e^{x\xi} p(x)dx.$$

At $\xi = 0$, the moment-generating function is

$$\frac{d^n M(0)}{d\xi^n} = \int_{-\infty}^{\infty} x^n \, p(x) dx = \mu_n.$$

Hence, the nth derivative of the moment-generating function at $\xi = 0$ is the nth moment of the distribution. This result can also be obtained by differentiating (5.3). Thus, the moments of a distribution can be obtained by successive differentiation of the moment-generating function and by setting $\xi = 0$.

PROBLEM 5.4   Determine the variance of the Poisson distribution from its moment-generating function

$$M(\xi) = e^{-a} \, e^{ae^\xi}.$$

Solution: Differentiating the moment-generating function,

$$\frac{dM}{d\xi} = \frac{d}{d\xi}(e^{-a} \, e^{ae^\xi}) = e^{-a} \frac{d}{d\xi}(e^{ae^\xi}) = e^{-a} \, e^{ae^\xi} \, ae^\xi.$$

Thus, the first moment of the distribution is

$$\mu_1 = \frac{dM(0)}{d\xi} = e^{-a} \, e^a \, a = a.$$

The second derivative of the moment-generating function is

$$\frac{d^2 M}{d\xi^2} = \frac{d}{d\xi}\left(\frac{dM}{d\xi}\right) = ae^{-a} \frac{d}{d\xi}(e^{ae^\xi} e^\xi) = ae^{-a}\left[e^\xi \frac{d}{d\xi}(e^{ae^\xi}) + e^{ae^\xi} \frac{d}{d\xi}(e^\xi) \right] = ae^{-a}(e^\xi e^{ae^\xi} ae^\xi + e^{ae^\xi} e^\xi);$$

therefore, the second moment is

$$\mu_2 = \frac{d^2 M(0)}{d\xi^2} = ae^{-a}(e^a \, a + e^a) = a\,(1 + a).$$

The variance $\sigma^2 = \mu_2 - \mu_1^2 = a\,(1 + a) - a^2 = a$.

The *cumulants* of a distribution are

$$\gamma_n = \left. \frac{d^n c(\xi)}{d\xi^n} \right|_{\xi=0} \qquad \text{for } n = 1, 2, 3, \cdots, \tag{5.6}$$

where $c(\xi) = \log M(\xi)$ and $M(\xi)$ is the moment-generating function.

PROBLEM 5.5   Express the first cumulant in terms of the moments of the distribution.

Solution: By definition, the first cumulant is

$$\gamma_1 = \left. \frac{dc(\xi)}{d\xi} \right|_{\xi=0} = \left. \frac{d}{d\xi} \log M(\xi) \right|_{\xi=0} = \left. \frac{1}{M(\xi)} \frac{dM(\xi)}{d\xi} \right|_{\xi=0} = \frac{M'(0)}{M(0)}.$$

From (5.3), $\dfrac{dM(0)}{d\xi} = M'(0) = \mu_1$ and $M(0) = 1$. Hence the first cumulant is $\gamma_1 = \mu_1$.

PROBLEM 5.6   Express the second cumulant of a distribution in terms of its moments.

Solution: The second cumulant is

$$\gamma_2 = \left. \frac{d^2 c(\xi)}{d\xi^2} \right|_{\xi=0} = \left. \frac{d^2}{d\xi^2} \log M(\xi) \right|_{\xi=0}.$$

Differentiating once,

$$\gamma_2 = \frac{d}{d\xi}\left(\frac{dM(\xi)/d\xi}{M(\xi)}\right)\Bigg|_{\xi=0}.$$

On differentiating a second time,

$$\gamma_2^2 = \left\{-\frac{[dM(\xi)/d\xi]^2}{M^2(\xi)} + \frac{d^2 \cdot M(\xi)/d\xi^2}{M(\xi)}\right\}_{\xi=0} = -\frac{[dM(0)/d\xi]^2}{M^2(0)} + \frac{d^2 M(0)/d\xi^2}{M(0)}.$$

Since, from (5.3), $M(0) = 1$ and the nth derivative of the moment-generating function is the nth moment,

$$\gamma_2 = -\mu_1^2 + \mu_2 = \sigma^2.$$

5.2 Characteristic Functions

The *characteristic function* of a random variable x with probability density function $p(x)$ is

$$C(\xi) = \int_{-\infty}^{\infty} e^{j\xi x} p(x)dx \tag{5.7}$$

$$= E\left[e^{j\xi x}\right], \tag{5.8}$$

where ξ is a real-valued parameter and $j = \sqrt{-1}$. The characteristic function $C(\xi)$ has both real and imaginary parts.

The *joint characteristic function* of two random variables x and y with joint probability density function $p(x,y)$ is

$$C(\xi,\eta) = \int_{-\infty}^{\infty} \int_{-\infty}^{\infty} e^{j(\xi x + \eta y)} p(x, y)dxdy \tag{5.9}$$

$$= E\left[e^{j(\xi x + \eta y)}\right]. \tag{5.10}$$

Thus, because of (5.7) and (5.9), the characteristic functions $C(\xi)$ and $C(\xi,\eta)$ are *Fourier transforms* of the corresponding probability density functions. The Fourier inversion formula for $p(x)$ in terms of $C(\xi)$ is

$$p(x) = \frac{1}{2\pi} \int_{-\infty}^{\infty} e^{-j\xi x} C(\xi)d\xi. \tag{5.11}$$

Note that the characteristic function is more useful than the moment-generating function since the integral in (5.7) exists for all $p(x)$ because $|e^{j\xi x}| = 1$. However, the integral in (5.2) does not exist for all $p(x)$ because in the interval $-\infty < x < \infty$ the function $e^{x\xi}$ is unbounded.

PROBLEM 5.7 Calculate the characteristic function for the probability density function $p(x) = \delta(x - x_0)$, as shown in Fig. 5.1.

Solution: From (5.7), the characteristic function is

$$C(\xi) = \int_{-\infty}^{\infty} e^{j\xi x} p(x)dx = \int_{-\infty}^{\infty} e^{j\xi x} \delta(x - x_0)dx.$$

Using the sifting property of the delta function, $C(\xi) = e^{j\xi x_0}$.

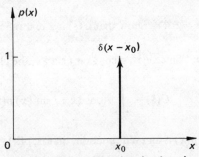

Fig. 5.1 Probability density function $p(x) = \delta(x - x_0)$.

PROBLEM 5.8   Evaluate the characteristic function $C(\xi)$ at $\xi = 0$ for the probability density function $p(x) = \delta(x - x_0)$. (Cf., Prob. 5.7.)

Solution: From (5.7), the characteristic function at $\xi = 0$ is

$$C(0) = \int_{-\infty}^{\infty} p(x)dx = 1.$$

PROBLEM 5.9   Find the characteristic function that corresponds to a general discrete probability density function of the form

$$p(x) = \sum_{k=0}^{n} P(x_k)\,\delta(x - x_k).$$

Solution: Using (5.7), the characteristic function is

$$C(\xi) = \int_{-\infty}^{\infty} e^{j\xi x}\, p(x)dx = \int_{-\infty}^{\infty} e^{j\xi x} \sum_{k=0}^{n} P(x_k)\,\delta(x - x_k)dx.$$

Interchanging the order of summation and integration,

$$C(\xi) = \sum_{k=0}^{n} P(x_k) \int_{-\infty}^{\infty} e^{j\xi x}\,\delta(x - x_k)dx \ .$$

Using the sifting property of the delta function, $C(\xi) = \sum_{k=0}^{n} P(x_k)\, e^{j\xi x_k}$.

PROBLEM 5.10   Show that $|C(\xi)| \leqslant 1$.

Solution: From (5.7), the magnitude of the characteristic function is

$$|C(\xi)| = \left| \int_{-\infty}^{\infty} e^{j\xi x}\, p(x)dx \right| \leqslant \int_{-\infty}^{\infty} |e^{j\xi x}|\, |p(x)|dx.$$

The magnitude of $e^{j\xi x}$ is unity since $e^{j\xi x} = \cos \xi x + j \sin \xi x$, and hence,

$$|e^{j\xi x}| = \sqrt{\cos^2 \xi x + \sin^2 \xi x} = 1.$$

Therefore, since $|p(x)| = p(x)$,

$$|C(\xi)| \leqslant \int_{-\infty}^{\infty} p(x)dx \leqslant 1.$$

PROBLEM 5.11   Show that $C(\xi)$ is a real function of ξ if $p(x)$ is an even function of x.

Solution: Since $e^{j\xi x} = \cos \xi x + j \sin \xi x$, the characteristic function is

$$C(\xi) = \int_{-\infty}^{\infty} (\cos \xi x + j \sin \xi x)\, p(x)dx = \int_{-\infty}^{\infty} \cos \xi x\, p(x)dx + j \int_{-\infty}^{\infty} \sin \xi x\, p(x)dx.$$

Because $p(x)$ is an even function, that is, $p(x) = p(-x)$, then $(\sin \xi x)p(x)$ is an odd function of x since

$$\sin \xi x\, p(x) = - [\sin (-\xi x)\, p(-x)].$$

Accordingly, the second integral vanishes and

$$C(\xi) = \int_{-\infty}^{\infty} \cos \xi x \, p(x) dx = 2 \int_{0}^{\infty} \cos \xi x \, p(x) dx,$$

which is purely real.

PROBLEM 5.12 Find the characteristic function of the uniform probability density function

$$p(x) = \frac{1}{2a} \quad \text{for } -a \leqslant x \leqslant a$$

$$= 0 \quad \text{elsewhere.}$$

Solution: Using (5.7),

$$C(\xi) = \int_{-a}^{a} e^{j\xi x} \left(\frac{1}{2a} \right) dx = \frac{1}{2a} \frac{1}{j\xi} e^{j\xi x} \Big|_{-a}^{a} = \frac{1}{2ja\xi} [e^{j\xi a} - e^{-j\xi a}].$$

Since $e^{j\theta} = \cos \theta + j \sin \theta$,

$$\frac{e^{j\xi a} - e^{-j\xi a}}{2ja\xi} = \frac{\sin \xi a}{\xi a}.$$

Hence, the characteristic function is

$$C(\xi) = \frac{\sin \xi a}{\xi a},$$

as shown in Fig. 5.2.

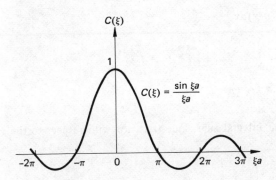

Fig. 5.2 Solution to Prob. 5.12.

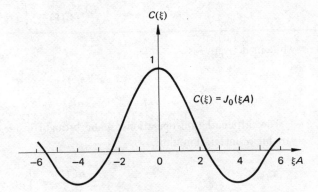

Fig. 5.3 Characteristic function of the sinusoidal distribution.

PROBLEM 5.13 Find the characteristic function of the sinusoidal distribution.

Solution: The density function of the sinusoidal distribution is

$$p(x) = \frac{1}{\pi \sqrt{A^2 - x^2}} \quad \text{for } |x| \leqslant A$$

$$= 0 \quad \text{elsewhere.}$$

Hence, the characteristic function is

$$C(\xi) = \int_{-A}^{A} e^{j\xi x} p(x) dx = \int_{-A}^{A} \frac{e^{j\xi x} \, dx}{\pi \sqrt{A^2 - x^2}} = \frac{1}{\pi} \int_{-\frac{\pi}{2}}^{\frac{\pi}{2}} e^{jA\xi \sin \theta} \, d\theta.$$

The latter integral which is obtained by making the substitution $x = A \sin \theta$, can also be written in the form

$$C(\xi) = J_0 (A\xi),$$

where $J_0 (A\xi)$ is the *zero-order Bessel function* of the first kind. The characteristic function $C(\xi)$ is shown in Fig. 5.3.

PROBLEM 5.14   Find the characteristic function of a Poisson-distributed random variable x.

Solution: Since x is Poisson distributed,

$$P(k) = \frac{(\nu T)^k}{k!} \, e^{-\nu T}, \quad k = 0, 1, 2, \cdots,$$

where $P(k)$ is the probability of k events occurring in interval T and ν is the average number of events per second.

Using the results of Prob. 5.9, the characteristic function is

$$C(\xi) = \sum_{k=0}^{\infty} P(k) \, e^{j\xi k} = \sum_{k=0}^{\infty} \frac{(\nu T)^k}{k!} e^{-\nu T} e^{j\xi k} = e^{-\nu T} \sum_{k=0}^{\infty} \frac{(\nu T)^k}{k!} e^{j\xi k} = e^{-\nu T} \sum_{k=0}^{\infty} \frac{(\nu T e^{j\xi})^k}{k!}.$$

The summation is the Maclaurin series expansion of $e^{(\nu T e^{j\xi})}$; hence,

$$C(\xi) = e^{-\nu T} e^{(\nu T e^{j\xi})} = e^{\nu T (e^{j\xi} - 1)}.$$

PROBLEM 5.15   Show that the moments of an arbitrary probability density function are related to the derivatives of the corresponding characteristic function, evaluated at the origin.

Solution: The characteristic function is

$$C(\xi) = \int_{-\infty}^{\infty} e^{j\xi x} p(x) dx,$$

while its derivative is

$$\frac{dC(\xi)}{d\xi} = \frac{d}{d\xi} \int_{-\infty}^{\infty} e^{j\xi x} p(x) dx.$$

The differentiation operation can be brought inside the integral sign since it is not with respect to the variable of integration; thus,

$$\frac{dC(\xi)}{d\xi} = \int_{-\infty}^{\infty} jx e^{j\xi x} p(x) dx.$$

Similarly, the second derivative is

$$\frac{d^2 C(\xi)}{d\xi^2} = \int_{-\infty}^{\infty} (jx)^2 \, e^{j\xi x} p(x) dx,$$

and, in general, the nth derivative is

$$\frac{d^n C(\xi)}{d\xi^n} = \int_{-\infty}^{\infty} (jx)^n \, e^{j\xi x} p(x) dx.$$

When $\xi = 0$, the nth derivative is

$$\frac{d^n C(0)}{d\xi^n} = \int_{-\infty}^{\infty} (jx)^n \, p(x) dx.$$

Because the nth moment is

$$\mu_n = \int_{-\infty}^{\infty} x^n \, p(x) dx,$$

then,

$$\frac{d^n C(0)}{d\xi^n} = j^n \mu_n,$$

or, hence,

$$\mu_n = \frac{1}{j^n} \frac{d^n C(0)}{d\xi^n}. \tag{5.12}$$

A similar result was obtained in Prob. 5.3 using derivatives of the *moment-generating function $E\left[e^{\xi x}\right]$* rather than $E\left[e^{j\xi x}\right]$.

PROBLEM 5.16 Determine the characteristic function of the normal probability density function with mean $\overline{x}$ and standard deviation σ.

Solution: The characteristic function of the normal density is

$$C(\xi) = \int_{-\infty}^{\infty} p(x) \, e^{j\xi x} \, dx$$

$$= \frac{1}{\sqrt{2\pi}\sigma} \int_{-\infty}^{\infty} e^{-(x-\overline{x})^2/2\sigma^2} \, e^{j\xi x} \, dx.$$

Substituting $u = x - \overline{x}$ and $du = dx$,

$$C(\xi) = \frac{1}{\sqrt{2\pi}\sigma} \int_{-\infty}^{\infty} e^{-u^2/2\sigma^2} \, e^{j\xi(u+\overline{x})} \, du$$

$$= \frac{1}{\sqrt{2\pi}\sigma} e^{j\xi\overline{x}} \int_{-\infty}^{\infty} e^{-u^2/2\sigma^2} \, e^{j\xi u} \, du.$$

Since $e^{j\xi u} = \cos \xi u + j \sin \xi u$,

$$C(\xi) = \frac{1}{\sqrt{2\pi}\sigma} e^{j\xi\overline{x}} \left(\int_{-\infty}^{\infty} e^{-u^2/2\sigma^2} \cos \xi u \, du + \int_{-\infty}^{\infty} e^{-u^2/2\sigma^2} \sin \xi u \, du \right).$$

The second term on the right-hand side integrates to zero since the integrand is an odd function of u, integrated over symmetric limits. Hence, using a standard table of definite integrals,

$$\int_{-\infty}^{\infty} e^{-u^2/2\sigma^2} \cos \xi u \, du = \sqrt{2\pi} \, \sigma \, e^{-\sigma^2 \xi^2/2}.$$

Therefore, the characteristic function is

$$C(\xi) = e^{j\xi\overline{x}} \, e^{-\sigma^2 \xi^2/2}. \tag{5.13}$$

Thus, the form of $C(\xi)$ is also Gaussian (excepting the factor $e^{j\xi\overline{x}}$ due to the nonzero mean value).

PROBLEM 5.17 When a fair coin is tossed, the possible outcomes, heads and tails, are represented by a random variable x which has the value 1 or 0, respectively. Find the characteristic function of the corresponding probability density function $p(x)$.

Solution: As shown in Fig. 5.4, the probability density function is

$$p(x) = \tfrac{1}{2}\,\delta(x) + \tfrac{1}{2}\,\delta(x-1),$$

where $\delta(x)$ is the Dirac delta function at $x = 0$.

Hence, the characteristic function is

$$C(\xi) = \tfrac{1}{2} \int_{-\infty}^{\infty} e^{j\xi x}\,[\delta(x) + \delta(x-1)]\,dx$$

$$= \tfrac{1}{2}\,(e^{j\xi x}\big|_{x=0} + e^{j\xi x}\big|_{x=1})$$

$$= \tfrac{1}{2}\,(1 + e^{j\xi}).$$

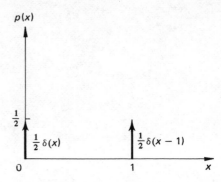

Fig. 5.4 Probability density function for Prob. 5.17.

PROBLEM 5.18 Find the first moment of the Gaussian probability density function from its characteristic function.

Solution: From Prob. 5.16, the characteristic function for the Gaussian probability density function is

$$C(\xi) = e^{j\xi\bar{x}}\,e^{-\sigma^2 \xi^2/2}, \qquad\qquad [5.12]$$

and its first derivative is

$$\frac{dC}{d\xi} = (j\bar{x} - \sigma^2 \xi)\,e^{j\xi\bar{x}}\,e^{-\sigma^2 \xi^2/2}.$$

Hence, using (5.12), the first moment is

$$\mu_1 = \frac{1}{j}\,\frac{dC(0)}{d\xi} = \frac{1}{j}\,(j\bar{x}) = \bar{x}.$$

PROBLEM 5.19 Determine the second moment for the characteristic function $C(\xi) = \dfrac{\sin \xi}{\xi}$.

Solution: Since, in series form, $\sin \xi = \xi - \dfrac{\xi^3}{3!} + \dfrac{\xi^5}{5!} - \cdots$, the characteristic function is

$$C(\xi) = \frac{1}{\xi}\left(\xi - \frac{\xi^3}{3!} + \frac{\xi^5}{5!} - \cdots\right) = 1 - \frac{1}{3!}\,\xi^2 + \frac{1}{5!}\,\xi^4 - \cdots$$

and its first and second derivatives are

$$\frac{dC(\xi)}{d\xi} = -\frac{1}{3}\,\xi + \frac{4}{5!}\,\xi^3 - \cdots,$$

$$\frac{d^2 C(\xi)}{d\xi^2} = -\frac{1}{3} + \frac{1}{10}\,\xi^2 - \cdots.$$

Therefore, from (5.12), the second moment is

$$\mu_2 = \frac{1}{j^2}\,\frac{d^2 C(0)}{d\xi^2}$$

$$= -\frac{d^2 C(0)}{d\xi^2} = \frac{1}{3}.$$

5.3 Characteristic Function of The Sum of Random Variables

The probability density function $p(z)$ of the sum $z = x + y$, where the random variables x and y have probability density functions $p_x(x)$ and $p_y(y)$, is

$$p_z(z) = p_x(x) * p_y(y) \tag{5.14a}$$

$$= \int_{-\infty}^{\infty} p_x(\alpha)\, p_y(z - \alpha)\, d\alpha \tag{5.14b}$$

$$= \int_{-\infty}^{\infty} p_y(\alpha)\, p_x(z - \alpha)\, d\alpha. \tag{5.14c}$$

(Cf., Chap. 4.)

Since the characteristic functions $C_x(\xi)$ and $C_y(\xi)$ are the Fourier transforms of $p_x(x)$ and $p_y(y)$, the Fourier transform of $p_z(z)$ is

$$C_z(\xi) = C_x(\xi) C_y(\xi)\;, \tag{5.15}$$

where the *characteristic function* $C_z(\xi)$ is

$$C_z(\xi) = \int_{-\infty}^{\infty} e^{j\xi z}\, p_z(z)\, dz. \tag{5.16}$$

Thus, $p_z(z)$ can be evaluated by using the product of $C_x(\xi)$ and $C_y(\xi)$ as follows:
(1) Using (5.7), calculate $C_x(\xi)$ and $C_y(\xi)$ from $p_x(x)$ and $p_y(y)$.
(2) Using (5.15), calculate $C_z(z)$.
(3) Using (5.11), calculate $p_z(z)$.

PROBLEM 5.20 Determine the characteristic function corresponding to the random variable $z = x_1 + x_2 + \cdots + x_n$, where $x_1, x_2, \cdots, x_n$ are independent random variables with probability density functions $p_{x_1}(x)$, $p_{x_2}(x), \cdots, p_{x_n}(x)$.

Solution: The characteristic functions corresponding to $p_{x_1}(x)$, $p_{x_2}(x), \cdots, p_{x_n}(x)$ are denoted by $C_{x_1}(\xi), C_{x_2}(\xi), \cdots, C_{x_n}(\xi)$, where

$$C_{x_1}(\xi) = \int_{-\infty}^{\infty} p_{x_1}(x)\, e^{j\xi x} dx,$$

$$\vdots \qquad\qquad \vdots$$

$$C_{x_k}(\xi) = \int_{-\infty}^{\infty} p_{x_k}(x)\, e^{j\xi x} dx.$$

$$\vdots \qquad\qquad \vdots$$

Successively applying (5.15) to $x_1 + x_2$, $(x_1 + x_2) + x_3, \cdots,$

$$C_z(\xi) = C_{x_1}(\xi)\, C_{x_2}(\xi) \cdots C_{x_n}(\xi). \tag{5.17}$$

The probability density function of z is obtained from (5.11); i.e.,

$$p_z(z) = \frac{1}{2\pi} \int_{-\infty}^{\infty} C_z(\xi)\, e^{-j\xi z} dx$$

$$= \frac{1}{2\pi} \int_{-\infty}^{\infty} C_{x_1}(\xi)\, C_{x_2}(\xi) \cdots C_{x_n}(\xi)\, e^{-j\xi z} d\xi.$$

PROBLEM 5.21 Determine the characteristic function corresponding to $p_z(z)$, where $z = x + y$, and the independent random variables x and y have the probability density functions

$$p_x(x) = \delta(x - x_0), \qquad p_y(y) = \delta(y - y_0).$$

(See Fig. 5.5.)

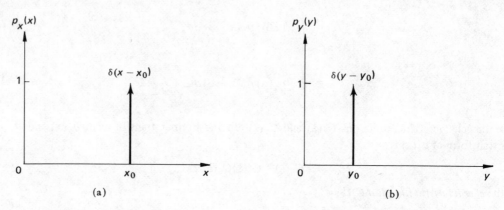

Fig. 5.5 Probability density functions (a) $p_x(x)$ and (b) $p_y(y)$ of Prob. 5.21.

Solution: From Prob. 5.7, the characteristic functions corresponding to $p_x(x)$ and $p_y(y)$ are

$$C_x(\xi) = \int_{-\infty}^{\infty} e^{j\xi x} p_x(x)dx = \int_{-\infty}^{\infty} e^{j\xi x} \delta(x - x_0)dx = e^{j\xi x_0},$$

$$C_y(\xi) = \int_{-\infty}^{\infty} e^{j\xi x} p_y(y)dy = \int_{-\infty}^{\infty} e^{j\xi x} \delta(y - y_0)dy = e^{j\xi y_0}.$$

Then from (5.15), the characteristic function corresponding to $p_z(z)$ is

$$C_z(\xi) = C_x(\xi) C_y(\xi) = e^{j\xi(x_0 + y_0)}.$$

PROBLEM 5.22 Using characteristic functions, show that the sum of n independent normal variables $x_1, x_2, \cdots, x_n$ with mean values $\bar{x}_1, \bar{x}_2, \cdots, \bar{x}_n$ and standard deviations $\sigma_1, \sigma_2, \cdots, \sigma_n$ yields a normal variable z with mean and variance

$$\bar{z} = \bar{x}_1 + \bar{x}_2 + \cdots + \bar{x}_n, \qquad \sigma_z^2 = \sigma_1^2 + \sigma_2^2 + \cdots \sigma_n^2.$$

Solution: Using the results of Prob. 5.16,

$$C_{x_i}(\xi) = e^{j\xi\bar{x}_i - e^{-\sigma_i^2\xi^2/2}}.$$

Since $z = x_1 + x_2 + \cdots + x_n$, the characteristic function is

$$C_z(\xi) = \prod_{i=1}^{n} C_{x_i}(\xi) = e^{\sum_{i=1}^{n}(j\xi\bar{x}_i - \sigma_i^2\xi^2/2)} = e^{j\xi(\bar{x}_1 + \bar{x}_2 + \cdots + \bar{x}_n) - (\sigma_1^2 + \sigma_2^2 + \cdots + \sigma_n^2)\xi^2/2} = e^{j\xi\bar{z} - \sigma_z^2\xi^2/2},$$

which is the characteristic function of a normal variable of mean $\bar{z}$ and variance σ_z^2.

PROBLEM 5.23 Show that the distribution of the sum of n independent uniformly distributed random variables $x_1, x_2, \cdots, x_n$ can be approximated by a normal distribution. Assume that $p_{x_1} = p_{x_2} = \cdots = p_{x_n} = p_x$, where

$$p_x = \frac{1}{2a} \quad \text{for } -a \leqslant x \leqslant a$$

$$= 0 \quad \text{elsewhere.}$$

Use an exponential approximation to the series expansion of the characteristic function of $x_1 + x_2 + \cdots + x_n$.

Solution: Using the results of Prob. 5.12.

$$C_1(\xi) = C_2(\xi) = \cdots = C_n(\xi) = \frac{\sin \xi a}{\xi a}.$$

If $y = x_1 + x_2 + \cdots + x_n$, the characteristic function is

$$C_y(\xi) = \frac{\sin^n \xi a}{(\xi a)^n}.$$

Expanding $\sin^n \xi a$ in a Taylor series about $\xi = 0$,

$$C_y(\xi) = \frac{\left[\xi a - \frac{(\xi a)^3}{3!} + \cdots \right]^n}{(\xi a)^n} = \left[1 - \frac{(\xi a)^2}{3!} + \cdots \right]^n.$$

When $\xi a \ll 1$, the higher order terms can be neglected. Then,

$$1 - \frac{(\xi a)^2}{3!} + \cdots \approx e^{-(\xi a)^2/6};$$

hence, the characteristic function is

$$C_y(\xi) \approx e^{-n(\xi a)^2/6}.$$

Using the results of Prob. 5.16, $C_y(\xi)$ is approximately the characteristic function of a normal variable of mean zero and variance $\frac{na^2}{3}$. This is as expected since

$$\bar{y} = x_1 + x_2 + \cdots + \overline{x}_n = n\overline{x}_1 = 0, \qquad \sigma_y^2 = \sigma_{x_1}^2 + \sigma_{x_2}^2 + \cdots + \sigma_{x_n}^2 = n\sigma_{x_1}^2 = n\left(\frac{a^2}{3} \right).$$

PROBLEM 5.24 Show that (5.15) correctly gives the characteristic function of the sum of two independent random variables x and y.

Solution: If $z = x + y$, and $p_x(x)$ and $p_y(y)$ are the probability density functions of x and y, the characteristic function is

$$
\begin{aligned}
C_z(\xi) &= E[e^{j\xi z}] \\
&= E[e^{j(x+y)\xi}] \\
&= \int_{-\infty}^{\infty} \int_{-\infty}^{\infty} e^{j(x+y)\xi} p_x(x) p_y(y) \, dx \, dy \\
&= \int_{-\infty}^{\infty} e^{jx\xi} p_x(x) \, dx \int_{-\infty}^{\infty} e^{jy\xi} p_y(y) \, dy \\
&= C_x(\xi) C_y(\xi).
\end{aligned}
$$

PROBLEM 5.25 When a biased coin is tossed, the possible outcome, heads or tails, is represented by a random variable x which has the value 1 or 0, respectively. Find the probability of r heads in n tosses if the probability of a 1 is p and that of a 0 is q. (Cf., Prob. 2.32.)

Solution: This problem, previously discussed in Chap. 2, leads to the binomial distribution which can be shown using characteristic functions as follows:
The probability density function of x is

$$p(x) = q \delta(x) + p \delta(x - 1).$$

The number of heads occuring in n tosses is

$$y = x_1 + x_2 + \cdots + x_n,$$

where $x_1, x_2, \cdots, x_n$ denote the values of x on each of the tosses. The characteristic functions of x and y are

$$C_x(\xi) = \int_{-\infty}^{\infty} e^{j\xi x} \left[q\delta(x) + p\delta(x-1)\right] dx = q + pe^{j\xi},$$

$$C_y(\xi) = C_x^n(\xi) = (q + pe^{j\xi})^n = q^n + nq^{n-1}pe^{j\xi} + \frac{n(n-1)}{2!} q^{n-2}p^2 e^{2j\xi} + \cdots + p^n e^{nj\xi}$$

on using the binomial theorem.

Since a term of the form $Ae^{mj\xi}$ in the characteristic function corresponds to an impulse of area A located at $y = m$ in the probability density function $p_y(y)$, the probability of r heads, or $y = r$, is just the coefficient of $e^{rj\xi}$; i.e.,

$$\frac{n(n-1)(n-2)\cdots(n-r+1)}{r!} q^{n-r}p^r = \frac{n!}{r!(n-r)!} p^r q^{n-r}.$$

Hence, the probability of r heads in n tosses is

$$P[y = r] = \frac{n!}{r!(n-r)!} q^{n-r}p^r.$$

PROBLEM 5.26 An object undergoes a random walk motion in which it is constrained to move along the x-axis. Periodically (as shown in Fig. 5.6), its position changes either by one unit to the left or one unit to the right with the respective probabilities q and p. Determine the probability that it will be at the origin after n steps if the object starts at $x = 0$.

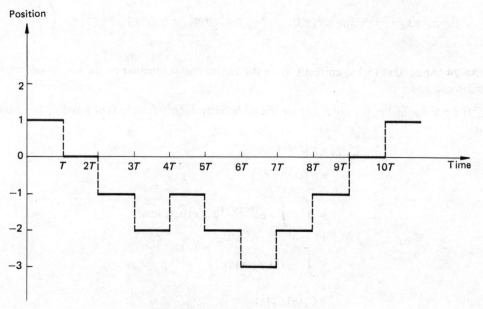

Fig. 5.6 Random walk along the x-axis.

Solution: If x_i denotes the change in x at the ith step and x_i has the value 1 with probability p or the value -1 with probability q, the position of the object after n steps is

$$x_t = x_1 + x_2 + \cdots + x_n.$$

Using the results of Prob. 5.25, the density of x_i is

$$p_{x_i} = q\delta(x+1) + p\delta(x-1).$$

Hence, the characteristic function of x_i is

$$C_{x_i}(\xi) = \int_{-\infty}^{\infty} e^{j\xi x} \left[q\delta(x+1) + p\delta(x-1)\right] dx = qe^{-j\xi} + pe^{j\xi}.$$

Thus, the characteristic function of x_t is

$$C_{x_t}(\xi) = C_x^n(\xi)$$

$$= (qe^{-j\xi} + pe^{j\xi})^n$$

$$= q^n e^{-jn\xi} + nq^{n-1} e^{-j(n-1)\xi} pe^{j\xi} + \frac{n(n-1)}{2!} q^{n-2} e^{-j(n-2)\xi} p^2 e^{2j\xi}$$

$$+ \frac{n(n-1)(n-2)}{3!} q^{n-3} e^{-j(n-3)\xi} p^3 e^{3j\xi} + \cdots$$

$$= q^n e^{-jn\xi} + nq^{n-1} pe^{-j(n-2)\xi} + \frac{n(n-1)}{2!} q^{n-2} p^2 e^{-j(n-4)\xi}$$

$$+ \frac{n(n-1)(n-2)}{3!} q^{n-3} p^3 e^{-j(n-6)\xi} + \cdots$$

$$+ \frac{n(n-1)(n-2)\cdots(n-k+1)}{k!} q^{n-k} p^k e^{-j(n-2k)\xi} + \cdots .$$

The probability $P(x_t = 0)$ that $x_t = 0$ is equal to the coefficient of e^{j0}. Thus, setting $n - 2k = 0$,

$$P(x_t = 0) = \frac{n(n-1)\cdots(n-k+1)}{k!} q^{n-k} p^k \bigg|_{k=\frac{n}{2}} .$$

Since n must be even, k must be an integer. When n is odd it is not possible to obtain $x = 0$. Therefore,

$$P(x_t = 0) = \frac{n(n-1)\cdots(\frac{1}{2}n+1)}{(\frac{1}{2}n)!} q^{n/2} p^{n/2} \quad \text{for } n \text{ even}$$

$$= 0 \quad \text{for } n \text{ odd.}$$

5.4 Supplementary Problems

PROBLEM 5.27 The *factorial moment generating function* is defined as $E(\xi^x)$. Show that the moments of a density function can be obtained from $E(\xi^x)$ by differentiation with respect to x and then setting $\xi = 1$.

PROBLEM 5.28 Calculate the factorial moment generating function for the Poisson density.
Answer: $E(\xi^x) = e^{a(\xi-1)}$.

PROBLEM 5.29 Calculate the first two moments of the Poisson density from its factorial moment generating function.
Answer: $a; a^2 + a$.

PROBLEM 5.30 Show that the third cumulant γ_3 is equal to the third central moment.

PROBLEM 5.31 Determine the characteristic function for the exponential probability density function

$$p(x) = \frac{1}{a} e^{-(x/a)} \quad \text{for } x \geqslant 0$$

$$= 0 \quad \text{for } x < 0.$$

Answer: $C(\xi) = \dfrac{1}{1 - ja\xi}$.

PROBLEM 5.32 Calculate the variance of the exponential probability density function using the moment generating property of $C(\xi)$.
Answer: a^2.

PROBLEM 5.33   In the expansion

$$\ln C(\xi) = \sum_{n=0}^{\infty} \gamma_n \frac{(j\xi)^n}{n!} \,,$$

where $C(\xi)$ is the characteristic function, the quantity γ_n is the nth cumulant. Show that the cumulants of the exponential probability density function of Prob. 5.31 are given by $\gamma_1 = a$, $\gamma_n = a^n \Gamma(n)$ for $n > 1$.

PROBLEM 5.34   Find the characteristic function for the uniform probability density function

$$p(x) = \frac{1}{a} \quad \text{for } m - \frac{a}{2} \leqslant x \leqslant m + \frac{a}{2}$$

$$= 0 \quad \text{for elsewhere.}$$

Answer: $C(\xi) = \dfrac{e^{jm\xi} \sin(a\xi/2)}{a\xi/2}$.

PROBLEM 5.35   Calculate the mean and variance for the uniform distribution of Prob. 5.34 from $C(\xi)$.
Answer: Mean $= m$; Variance $= \dfrac{a^2}{12}$.

PROBLEM 5.36   The Cauchy probability density function is defined by

$$p(x) = \frac{1}{\pi b} \frac{1}{1 + [(x - a)/b]^2} \quad \text{for } -\infty < a < \infty \text{ and } 0 < b < \infty.$$

Calculate $C(\xi)$ for the case $a = 0$.
Answer: $C(\xi) = e^{-b|\xi|}$.

PROBLEM 5.37   For the Cauchy distribution of Prob. 5.36 (with $a = 0$), show that neither the mean nor the variance are defined using the characteristic function. Verify this result by direct calculation from the probability density function.

PROBLEM 5.38   A die is tossed and the six possible outcomes are represented by a random variable x which has the values 1, 2, 3, 4, 5 or 6. Find the characteristic function of the probability density function $p(x)$.

Answer: $C(\xi) = \frac{1}{6} \sum_{i=1}^{6} e^{ji\xi}, j = \sqrt{-1}$.

PROBLEM 5.39   The die of Prob. 5.38 is tossed n successive times. Find the characteristic function corresponding to the random variable which is the sum of the outcomes.

Answer: $C(\xi) = \left[\dfrac{1}{6} \sum_{i=1}^{6} e^{ji\xi} \right]^n$, $j = \sqrt{-1}$.

PROBLEM 5.40   Determine the characteristic function for the gamma distribution

$$p(x) = \frac{1}{\Gamma(n)} x^{n-1} e^{-x} \quad \text{for } 0 \leqslant x < \infty$$

$$= 0 \quad \text{for } x < 0.$$

Answer: $C(\xi) = \dfrac{1}{(1 - j\xi)^n}$.

PROBLEM 5.41 Determine the probability density function corresponding to the characteristic function

$$C(\xi) = \frac{1}{(1 - j\xi)^3} \ .$$

Answer: $p(x) = \frac{1}{2} x^2 e^{-x}$ for $0 \leqslant x < \infty$

           $= 0$ for $x < 0$.

PROBLEM 5.42 If the density function $p(x)$ has a characteristic function $C(\xi)$, determine the density function corresponding to $C(\xi)e^{j\xi a}$.

Answer: $p(x - a)$.

6 CHAPTER

SAMPLING THEORY I

6.1 Estimation of the Mean and Variance

In statistics, the term *population* is applied to any set, or collection, of objects, actual or conceptual; e.g., sets of observations or numbers. A population can be *finite* or *infinite*.

A *sample* is a part of the population.

A *random sample* of size n from a finite population of size N is a set of observations $x_1, x_2, \ldots, x_n$, with each observation having the same probability of being selected.

A *random sample* of size n from an infinite population whose density is $p(x)$ is a set of observations $x_1, x_2, \ldots, x_n$, with each x_i having the value of an independent random variable whose distribution is $p(x)$.

The *sample mean* $\bar{x}$ of a random sample of size n from a population with *(true) mean* m is

$$\bar{x} = \frac{1}{n} \sum_{i=1}^{n} x_i. \tag{6.1}$$

(See Fig. 6.1.)

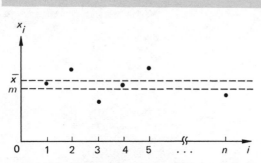

Fig. 6.1 Sample mean $\bar{x}$ of a random sample from a population with true mean m.

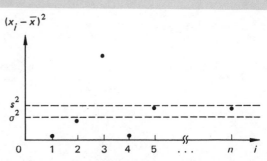

Fig. 6.2 Sample variance s^2 of a random sample from a population with true variance σ^2.

The *sample variance* s^2 of a random sample of size n from a finite population of size N with the *(true) variance* σ^2 is

$$s^2 = \frac{1}{n} \sum_{i=1}^{n} (x_i - \bar{x})^2. \tag{6.2}$$

(See Fig. 6.2.)

Note that, in general, the sample mean and variance differ from the true mean and variance because they depend on the specific n values of the sample; consequently, they are only *estimates* of the true mean and variance, and are called *estimators*. The expected value and the variance of $\bar{x}$ are

$$E[\bar{x}] = m, \tag{6.3}$$

$$\text{Var}(\bar{x}) = E[\bar{x}^2] - (E[\bar{x}])^2 = \frac{\sigma^2}{n}. \tag{6.4}$$

An estimator is *unbiased* if its expected value is equal to the true value; otherwise, it is *biased*.

The sample mean is an unbiased estimator, while the sample variance is biased since

$$E[s^2] = \frac{n-1}{n} \sigma^2. \tag{6.5}$$

Note that an unbiased estimate of the true variance σ^2 is

$$s'^2 = \frac{1}{n-1} \sum_{i=1}^{n} (x_i - \bar{x})^2. \tag{6.6}$$

Thus, $s'^2 = \frac{n}{n-1} s^2$ and $E[s'^2] = \sigma^2$.

The *central limit theorem* states that if $\bar{x}$ is the mean of a random sample of size n taken from a population having mean m and *finite* variance σ^2, then the value of a random variable whose distribution function approaches that of the normal distribution with mean zero and variance σ^2 as $n \to \infty$ is the standardized mean

$$z = \frac{\bar{x} - m}{\sigma/\sqrt{n}}. \tag{6.7}$$

PROBLEM 6.1 Show that $E[\bar{x}] = m$.

Solution: Using (6.1), the expected value of x is

$$E[\bar{x}] = E\left[\frac{1}{n} \sum_{i=1}^{n} x_i\right] = \frac{1}{n} \left(E[x_1] + E[x_2] + \cdots + E[x_n]\right) = \frac{1}{n} (nm) = m.$$

PROBLEM 6.2 Show that $E[\bar{x}^2] - (E[\bar{x}])^2 = \frac{\sigma^2}{n}$.

Solution: Using (6.1), the expected value of $\bar{x}^2$ is

$$E[\bar{x}^2] = E\left[\frac{1}{n^2} \left(\sum_{i=1}^{n} x_i\right)^2\right] = \frac{1}{n^2} E\left[\sum_{i=1}^{n} \sum_{j=1}^{n} x_i x_j\right] = \frac{1}{n^2} \sum_{i=1}^{n} \sum_{j=1}^{n} E[x_i x_j].$$

Since

$$E[x_i x_j] = m^2 \qquad \text{for } i \neq j$$
$$= \sigma^2 + m^2 \quad \text{for } i = j,$$

the expectation of $\bar{x}^2$ is

$$E[\bar{x}^2] = \frac{1}{n^2} \sum_{i=1}^{n} \sum_{j=1}^{n} m^2 + \frac{1}{n^2} \sum_{i=1}^{n} \sigma^2 = \frac{1}{n^2} (n^2 m^2) + \frac{1}{n^2} (n\sigma^2) = m^2 + \frac{\sigma^2}{n}.$$

Thus,

$$E[\bar{x}^2] - (E[\bar{x}])^2 = m^2 + \frac{\sigma^2}{n} - m^2 = \frac{\sigma^2}{n}.$$

Alternatively, since $n\bar{x}$ in (6.1) is the sum of independent random variables, the variance of $n\bar{x}$ is the sum of the variances of $x_1, x_2, \cdots, x_n$, or $n\sigma^2$. Thus,

$$\text{Var}(\bar{x}) = \frac{1}{n^2} (n\sigma^2) = \frac{1}{n} \sigma^2.$$

PROBLEM 6.3 A random variable x is sampled once, obtaining a value $\bar{x}$ that is used as an estimate of m.

Determine $E[\bar{x}]$ and $E[\bar{x}^2]$ if, as shown in Fig. 6.3, the probability density function of x is

$$p(x) = e^{-x} \quad \text{for } x \geqslant 0$$
$$= 0 \quad \text{for } x < 0.$$

Solution: From (6.3), the expectation of $\bar{x}$ is

$$E[\bar{x}] = m = \int_{-\infty}^{\infty} xp(x)dx = \int_{0}^{\infty} xe^{-x} \, dx = \Gamma(2) = 1.$$

From (6.4), the expectation of $\bar{x}^2$ is

$$E[\bar{x}^2] = \frac{\sigma^2}{n} + (E[\bar{x}])^2.$$

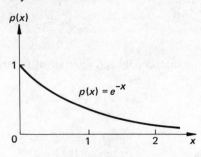

Fig. 6.3 Probability density function $p(x)$ for Prob. 6.3.

Since only one sample is used, $n = 1$; hence,

$$E[\bar{x}^2] = \sigma^2 + m^2 = m^2 + \left(\int_{-\infty}^{\infty} x^2 p(x)dx - m^2 \right) = \int_{-\infty}^{\infty} x^2 p(x)dx = \int_{0}^{\infty} x^2 e^{-x} \, dx = \Gamma(3) = 2.$$

PROBLEM 6.4 Two independent samples x_1 and x_2 of a random variable x are taken. Determine the expected value and variance of $\bar{x}$ if the probability density function is

$$p(x) = e^{-x} \quad \text{for } x \geqslant 0$$
$$= 0 \quad \text{for } x < 0.$$

Solution: Using (6.3) and the result of Prob. 6.3, the expected value is

$$E[\bar{x}] = m = 1.$$

Using (6.4), the variance of $\bar{x}$ is

$$\text{Var}(\bar{x}) = [\bar{x}^2] - (E[\bar{x}])^2 = \frac{\sigma^2}{n}.$$

The variance of $\bar{x} = \sigma^2/2$ because $n = 2$. The variance σ^2 of each sample taken individually is calculated from the results of Prob. 6.3; i.e.,

$$\sigma^2 = E[\bar{x}^2] - (E[\bar{x}])^2 = 2 - 1 = 1.$$

Thus, the variance of $\bar{x}$ is

$$\text{Var}(\bar{x}) = E[\bar{x}^2] - (E[\bar{x}])^2 = \tfrac{1}{2}\sigma^2 = \tfrac{1}{2}.$$

PROBLEM 6.5 The specific gravity of a liquid is measured n times, successively. The error ϵ in each measurement is independent of the others and is normally distributed with mean zero and standard deviation $\sigma_\epsilon = 0.1$. Find the distribution of the sample mean $\bar{x}$ when $n = 100$.

Solution: Using (6.1), the distribution of $n\bar{x}$ is the convolution of 100 normal distributions, each with mean zero and standard deviation $\sigma_\epsilon = 0.1$. The result is a normal distribution with zero mean and variance $\sigma_{n\bar{x}}^2 = 100\sigma_\epsilon^2$ since variances add for independent random variables. The distribution of $\bar{x}$ is, therefore, normal with mean zero and variance

$$\sigma_{\bar{x}}^2 = \frac{1}{n^2} \sigma_{n\bar{x}}^2 = \frac{\sigma_\epsilon^2}{100} = \frac{(0.1)^2}{100} = \frac{1}{10,000}.$$

Hence, the standard deviation is

$$\sigma_{\bar{x}} = 10^{-2}.$$

Thus, the probability density function is

$$p(\bar{x}) = \frac{1}{10^{-2}\sqrt{2\pi}} e^{-\bar{x}^2/(2 \times 10^{-4})}.$$

PROBLEM 6.6 Measurements of the reliability of a system disclose that n failures occur within a period of T_0 hr. Assume that $n \gg 1$ and the probability of failure during a time T is $1 - e^{-T/\text{MTBF}}$ for $T \geqslant 0$. Find the probability density function of the sample mean time between failures $\overline{\text{MTBF}} = T_0/n$.

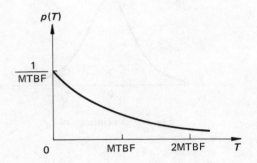

Fig. 6.4 Probability density function for mean time between failures MTBF.

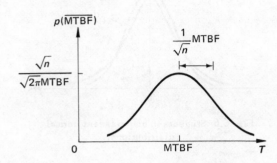

Fig. 6.5 Approximation of $\overline{\text{MTBF}}$ by a normal distribution for $n \gg 1$.

Solution: As shown in Fig. 6.4, the probability density function for the time between failures is

$$p(T) = \frac{d}{dt} \left[1 - e^{-T/(\text{MTBF})} \right] = \frac{1}{\text{MTBF}} \, e^{-T/(\text{MTBF})}.$$

The sample mean time between failures is

$$\overline{\text{MTBF}} = \frac{1}{n} (T_1 + T_2 + \cdots + T_n),$$

where $T_1, T_2, \cdots, T_n$ are a sequence of n measured times between failures. By the central limit theorem, the probability density function of $\overline{\text{MTBF}}$ can be approximated by a normal distribution if $n \gg 1$, as shown in Fig. 6.5. Note that the large sample approximation is normally not valid unless $n \gg 10$.

Since the MTBF is exponentially distributed, from (6.3),

$$E[\overline{\text{MTBF}}] = \text{MTBF},$$

and hence, using (6.4),

$$\text{Var}(\overline{\text{MTBF}}) = E[\overline{\text{MTBF}}^2] - (E[\overline{\text{MTBF}}])^2 = \frac{\sigma^2}{n} = \frac{1}{n} (\overline{\text{MTBF}})^2.$$

6.2 Sampling Distribution of the Mean: Standard Deviation Unknown

If the sample size n is *large*, the standardized mean z (6.7) is normally distributed even if the standard deviation is unknown, and the sample standard deviation s' is substituted for σ. For small n, the assumption is made that the sample comes from a *normal population*. Thus, if $\bar{x}$ is the sample mean and s'^2 is the sample variance given in (6.6) of a random sample of size n taken from a normal population with mean m and variance σ^2, then

$$t = \frac{\bar{x} - m}{s'/\sqrt{n}} \tag{6.8}$$

is the value of a random variable having *Student's t-distribution* with parameter $\nu = n - 1$. Figure 6.6 shows the Student's-t and the standard normal distributions.

The parameter ν is called the *number of degrees of freedom*, i.e., the number of independent samples.

The t-distribution is symmetrical about its mean of 0 and is very similar to the normal curve, as shown in Fig. 6.6. The variance of the t-distribution depends on ν. The variance is greater than 1 but approaches 1 as $n \longrightarrow \infty$.

Table V in the Appendix shows the values of t for selected t_q and for various degrees of freedom, where t_q is such that the area under the t-distribution to its right is equal to q. Note that if the sample size n is *greater* than 30, the t-distribution is approximated by the normal distribution. Figure 6.7 shows the tabulated values of t.

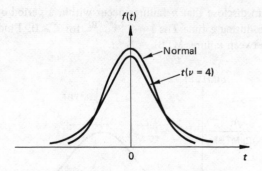

Fig. 6.6 Students-t and standard normal distributions.

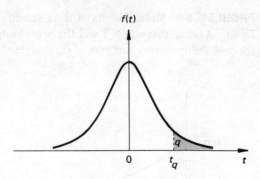

Fig. 6.7 Definition of t_q.

PROBLEM 6.7 A random sample with $n = 81$ is taken from a population having mean $m = 24.0$ and variance $\sigma^2 = 324$. Use the central limit theorem to determine the probability that the sample mean $\bar{x}$ lies between 23.9 and 24.2

Solution: Using the central limit theorem, the sample mean is approximately normally distributed with mean 24 and standard deviation $\sigma' = \sigma/\sqrt{n} = \sqrt{324}/\sqrt{81} = 2$. The probability that $\bar{x}$ lies between 23.6 and 24.2, that is, between $m - 0.2\sigma'$ and $m + 0.1\sigma'$, is 0.1191 from Table IV of the Appendix.

PROBLEM 6.8 The mean of the grades of 25 freshmen is used to estimate the true average grade of the freshman class. Find the probability that the estimate is off by 3.6 marks, if the standard deviation is known to be 20.

Solution: Since the mean is off by 3.6 marks, $| m - \bar{x} | = 3.6$. Using the central limit theorem, the sample mean is approximately normally distributed with standard deviation $\sigma' = 20/\sqrt{n} = 4$. The probability that $\bar{x}$ lies between $m - 0.9\sigma'$ and $m + 0.9\sigma'$ from Table IV of the Appendix is 0.6318.

PROBLEM 6.9 A random sample with $n = 9$ taken from a normal population has mean $\bar{x} = 24$ and standard deviation $s' = 0.25$. Determine whether it is reasonable to assume that the population mean is at least 27.

Solution: Using the t-statistic, with $m = 27$, $\bar{x} = 24$, $n = 9$, and $s' = 0.25$, the value of the random variable having the t-distribution with $\nu = 9 - 1 = 8$ degrees of freedom is

$$t = \frac{24 - 27}{0.25/\sqrt{9}} = -4.0.$$

From Table V of the Appendix, with $\nu = 8$, the probability that t will exceed 3.355 is 0.005 if $m = 27$. Since the calculated value of t is -4.0, it is *not* reasonable to assume that the mean of the population is at least 27.

PROBLEM 6.10 A system was tested for reliability over a period of four months during which it failed 4, 3, 7, and 8 times per month. Using the statistic t, determine the reasonability of assuming the maximum number of failures per month will be 17.

Solution: The mean $\bar{x}$, variance s'^2, and standard deviation s' of the sample are

$$\bar{x} = \frac{4 + 3 + 7 + 8}{4} = 5.5,$$

$$s'^2 = \frac{(4 - 5.5)^2 + (3 - 5.5)^2 + (7 - 5.5)^2 + (8 - 5.5)^2}{3} = 5.67,$$

$$s' = \sqrt{5.67} = 2.38.$$

Assuming that the failures compose a random sample from a population with mean $m = 5$, the statistic

$$t = \frac{5.5 - 17}{2.38\sqrt{4}} = 2.42$$

is a value of a random variable having the *t*-distribution with $\nu = 4 - 1 = 3$ degrees of freedom. Referring to Table V in the Appendix, when $\nu = 3$, the probability of t exceeding 2.42 is less than 0.05. Thus, it is reasonable to assume that the system will fail less than 17 times per month.

6.3 Confidence Intervals for the Mean

A *point estimate* is a single value which best estimates the population parameter.

An *interval estimate* is two numbers between which the population parameter can be expected to lie with a certain level of confidence.

A *q-percent confidence interval* is an interval which has a $q\%$ probability of containing the population parameter.

The *confidence limits*, or *fiducial limits*, are the end-points of the confidence interval.

The *confidence level* is the quantity q and the *level of significance* is the quantity $(100-q)$.

The *q-percent confidence interval for the sample mean $\bar{x}$* is

$$m - k\,\frac{\sigma}{\sqrt{n}} \leqslant \bar{x} \leqslant m + k\,\frac{\sigma}{\sqrt{n}} \,,$$

where m is the population mean, σ, the population standard deviation, n, the sample size, and k, a constant whose values for given confidence levels or levels of significance are given in Table 6.1 for the normal distribution.

The *q-percent confidence interval for the population mean m* is

$$\bar{x} - k\,\frac{\sigma}{\sqrt{n}} \leqslant m \leqslant \bar{x} + k\,\frac{\sigma}{\sqrt{n}} \,.$$

Where $p_e(x)$ is the probability density function of the estimated parameter, the confidence level is

$$q = 100\% \cdot \int_{m-k\sigma}^{m+k\sigma} p_e(x)\,dx.$$

(Cf., Fig. 6.8.)

The confidence intervals and levels are numerical measures of the precision and reliability of a statistical estimate where the smaller the confidence interval, the greater the precision and the higher the confidence level, the greater the reliability.

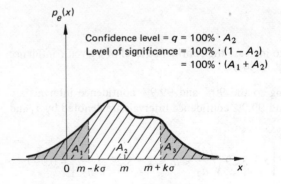

Fig. 6.8 Confidence level and level of significance for the probability density function of an estimated parameter.

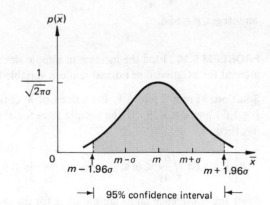

Fig. 6.9 The 95% confidence interval for the sample mean.

PROBLEM 6.11 One sample of a normally distributed random variable x with standard deviation σ is used to estimate the true mean m. Determine the 95% confidence interval for the sample mean.

Solution: The sample mean $\bar{x}$ falls 95% of the time within the interval

$$m - k\sigma \leqslant \bar{x} \leqslant m + k\sigma,$$

where k is to be determined. Since $\bar{x}$ is normally distributed, from Table 6.1, k is found corresponding to $q = 95\%$; thus, $k = 1.96$. Therefore, as shown in Fig. 6.9 the 95% confidence interval is

$$m - 1.96\sigma \leqslant \bar{x} \leqslant m + 1.96\sigma.$$

TABLE 6.1

Confidence Level $q\%$	Level of Significance $(100\text{-}q)\%$	k
90	10	1.64
95	5	1.96
99	1	2.58
99.9	0.1	3.29
99.99	0.01	3.89

PROBLEM 6.12 Using Prob. 6.11, determine the probability that the true mean lies within 2.58 of $\bar{x}$, that is, $P[\bar{x} - 2.58 \leqslant m \leqslant \bar{x} + 2.58]$. Assume that $\sigma = 1$.

Solution: Since $\sigma = 1$ and $k = 2.58$, using Table 6.1, the probability is

$$P[\bar{x} - 2.58\sigma \leqslant m \leqslant \bar{x} + 2.58\sigma] = 0.99.$$

PROBLEM 6.13 The sample mean in Prob. 6.11 is computed using (6.1). Assuming that $\sigma = 1$, determine the number of observations needed to insure that, at the 99% confidence level,

$$\bar{x} - 0.1 \leqslant m \leqslant \bar{x} + 0.1.$$

Solution: The variance of the sample mean is given by (6.4), where σ is the standard deviation of each sample. From Table 6.1, at the 99% confidence level, $k = 2.58$; thus, the probability is

$$P\left[\bar{x} - 2.58\sqrt{\frac{\sigma^2}{n}} \leqslant m \leqslant \bar{x} + 2.58\sqrt{\frac{\sigma^2}{n}}\right] = 0.99.$$

Therefore, $2.58\sqrt{\dfrac{\sigma^2}{n}} = 0.1$. Since $\sigma = 1$, the number of observations needed is $n = 665.64$, or, since n must be an integer, $n = 666$.

PROBLEM 6.14 Find the increase in sample size needed to increase the confidence level of a given confidence interval for a Gaussian or normal random variable from 90% to 99.9%.

Solution: From Table 6.1, the values of k corresponding to the 90% and 99.9% confidence intervals are $k = 1.64$ and $k = 3.29$. If the sample sizes for the 90% and 99.9% confidence intervals are denoted by n_1 and n_2, then

$$P\left[\bar{x} - 1.64\sqrt{\frac{\sigma^2}{n_1}} \leqslant m \leqslant \bar{x} + 1.64\sqrt{\frac{\sigma^2}{n_1}}\right] = 0.9, \qquad P\left[\bar{x} - 3.29\sqrt{\frac{\sigma^2}{n_2}} \leqslant m \leqslant \bar{x} + 3.29\sqrt{\frac{\sigma^2}{n_2}}\right] = 0.999.$$

Since the confidence limits are the same for the two cases,

$$1.64\sqrt{\frac{\sigma^2}{n_1}} = 3.29\sqrt{\frac{\sigma^2}{n_2}}.$$

Thus, $\dfrac{n_2}{n_1} \approx 4$. Therefore, a four-fold increase in sample size is required.

PROBLEM 6.15 A coin-tossing experiment yields y heads in n tosses. Determine if the coin appears to be biased if (a) $y = 30$ and $n = 100$, and (b) $y = 45$ and $n = 100$.

Solution: (a) Assuming that the probability of a head, p_h, and a tail, q_t, at any given toss is

$$p_h = \tfrac{1}{2}, \quad q_t = \tfrac{1}{2},$$

referring to Sec. 3.2, the parameters of the corresponding binomial distribution are

$$m = p_h \cdot n = 50,$$

where m is the expected number of heads and

$$\sigma = \sqrt{np_h q_t} = 5.$$

Since n is large, a normal distribution can be used to approximate the binomial distribution. The deviation from m is

$$m - k\sigma = y, \quad \text{or} \quad k = \frac{m - y}{\sigma} = \frac{50 - 35}{5} = 3.$$

From Table 6.1, for $y = 35$, at the 1% level of significance, the coin is biased. That is, the probability of occurrence of such a deviation from the mean (by chance) is less than 1%; thus, the coin appears to be biased.

(b) When $y = 45$ the level of significance is substantially greater than 10%; hence, no bias is suspected.

PROBLEM 6.16 A tensile strength test is made on steel cables having a nominal design strength W lb/in. Since normal manufacturing tolerances cause variations in design strength, there is a standard deviation in design strength of 50%. The value of W is to be estimated from measurements made on the strengths of n cables selected at random. Using a 99% level of confidence, determine whether the following samples appear to have an average strength of W: (a) $W_s = 0.9W$, $n = 100$ and (b) $W_s = 0.9W$, $n = 225$.

Solution: Since $n \gg 1$, Table 6.1 can be used. The deviation from m is

$$m - k\sigma = W_s, \quad \text{or} \quad k = \frac{m - W_s}{\sigma}.$$

Since $\sigma = \dfrac{(0.50)W}{\sqrt{n}}$,

$$k = \frac{m - W_s}{(0.50)W} \sqrt{n} = \frac{W - (0.9)W}{(0.50)W} \sqrt{n} = \frac{(0.1)W}{(0.50)W}\sqrt{n} = \frac{\sqrt{n}}{5} = \begin{cases} 2 \text{ if } n = 100 \\ 3 \text{ if } n = 225 \end{cases}.$$

From Table 6.1, $k = 2$ falls within the 99% confidence level, while $k = 3$ does not. Therefore, only case (a) meets the criterion.

PROBLEM 6.17 The mean time between failures of a system is measured. Find the number of failures that must be recorded before the resulting sample MTBF, i.e., $\overline{\text{MTBF}}$, lies within 20% of the true MTBF with 90% probability. Assume that the probability density function for the time between failures is

$$p(T) = \frac{1}{\text{MTBF}} \exp\left[-T/(\text{MTBF})\right].$$

(Cf., Prob. 6.6.)

Solution: For the exponential distribution, $E(T) = \text{MTBF}$ and $E(T^2) - [E(T)]^2 = (\text{MTBF})^2$. If n measurements are made,

$$E[\overline{\text{MTBF}^2}] - [E(\overline{\text{MTBF}})]^2 = \frac{1}{n}(\text{MTBF})^2.$$

(Cf., Figs. 6.4-5.) Thus, the standard deviation is

$$\sigma = \frac{1}{\sqrt{n}}(\text{MTBF}).$$

Assuming that $n \gg 1$, the density function of $\overline{\text{MTBF}}$ is

$$p(\overline{\text{MTBF}}) = \frac{1}{\sqrt{2\pi}\,\sigma} \exp\left[-(\overline{\text{MTBF}} - \text{MTBF})^2/2\sigma^2\right].$$

From Table 6.1, $(MTBF - 1.64\sigma) \leqslant \overline{MTBF} \leqslant (MTBF + 1.64\sigma)$ with 90% probability. In order that $\overline{MTBF}$ lies within 20% of MTBF,

$$1.64\sigma = 0.2\,MTBF, \quad \text{or} \quad 1.64\,\frac{MTBF}{\sqrt{n}} = 0.2\,MTBF.$$

Hence, $n = 68$.

6.4 Confidence Intervals for the True Mean: Standard Deviation Unknown

If the standard deviation of the sampled random variable is unknown and can only be estimated, the confidence interval in estimating the mean at a given confidence level is increased.

If the true mean value m of a normal variate is to be estimated by the sample mean $\overline{x}$ (6.1), and the variance is estimated by s'^2 (6.6), the confidence levels can be found using *Student's t-distribution*. The distribution is shown in Fig. 6.10, where the probability of exceeding a value t or of not exceeding a value $-t$ (t positive) is given for various values of t. For a given probability, t is a function of the number of *independent* samples used, i.e., the number of *degrees of freedom*. The confidence levels are found from

$$\overline{x} - \frac{s'}{\sqrt{n}}\,t_q(n-1) \leqslant m \leqslant \overline{x} + \frac{s'}{\sqrt{n}}\,t_q(n-1),$$

$$(6.9)$$

where $t_q(n-1)$ is the value of t corresponding to the confidence level q that is evaluated for $(n-1)$ degrees of freedom.

If $n > 30$, the resulting confidence intervals are almost identical with those obtained using the true variance.

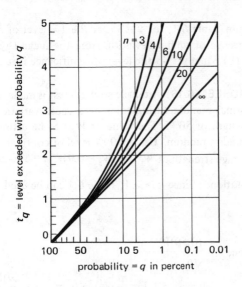

Fig. 6.10 Student's *t*-distribution.

PROBLEM 6.18 Determine $t_q(n-1)$ for the 90% confidence level with 7 samples.

Solution: From Fig. 6.10, with $n - 1 = 6$ degrees of freedom and a 10% probability of exceeding $t_q(n-1)$ (in either direction),

$$t_q(n-1) = 2.$$

PROBLEM 6.19 The sample mean of a normally distributed random variable with unknown standard deviation is calculated. Find the number of samples needed to insure that, at the 90% confidence level,

$$\overline{x} - \frac{3s'}{\sqrt{n}} \leqslant m \leqslant \overline{x} + \frac{3s'}{\sqrt{n}}.$$

Solution: Comparison with (6.9) shows that

$$t_q(n-1) = 3.$$

Using Fig. 6.10, with $q = 10\%$, 4 samples are needed.

PROBLEM 6.20 Determine the confidence interval for the true mean that corresponds to a sample size of 11 and a confidence level of 99%.

Solution: Since $t_q(n-1) = t_q(10) = 3.2$, from Fig. 6.10, the confidence interval is

$$\overline{x} - \frac{s'}{\sqrt{n}}\,t_q(n-1) \leqslant m \leqslant \overline{x} + \frac{s'}{\sqrt{n}}\,t_q(n-1),$$

that is,

$$\bar{x} - \frac{3.2}{\sqrt{11}} s' \leqslant m \leqslant \bar{x} + \frac{3.2}{\sqrt{11}} s'.$$

PROBLEM 6.21 A chemical analysis of a substance is made to determine its percentage of iron. Ten measurements are made using different samples of the substance from which $\bar{x} = 30\%$, $s' = 0.5\%$. Find the limits of the true mean for the 99% confidence interval. Assume that the concentration of iron is normally distributed in the samples.

Solution: In this case, $n = 10$. From Fig. 6.10, the 99% confidence interval, corresponding to the value of $|t|$ exceeded 1% of the time for 9 degrees of freedom, gives

$$t_q(n - 1) = 3.3;$$

thus, from (6.9), the confidence interval is

$$\bar{x} - \frac{s'}{\sqrt{n}} t_q(n - 1) \leqslant m \leqslant \bar{x} + \frac{s'}{\sqrt{n}} t_q(n - 1), \quad \text{or} \quad 30\% - \frac{0.5\%(3.3)}{\sqrt{10}} \leqslant m \leqslant 30\% + \frac{0.5\%(3.3)}{\sqrt{10}}.$$

Hence, $29.48\% \leqslant m \leqslant 30.52\%$.

Therefore, the true mean m lies in the above interval with probability 0.99.

PROBLEM 6.22 A chemical analysis of a substance is made to determine its percentage of iron content. Ten measurements are made using different samples of the substance from which $\bar{x} = 30\%$. Find the limits of the true mean for the 99% confidence interval. Assume that the concentration of iron is normally distributed in the samples and that $\sigma = 0.5\%$.

Solution: From Table 6.1, for the 99% confidence level, the confidence interval is

$$\bar{x} - 2.58 \frac{\sigma}{\sqrt{n}} \leqslant m \leqslant \bar{x} + 2.58 \frac{\sigma}{\sqrt{n}}, \quad \text{or} \quad 30\% - \frac{2.58(0.5\%)}{\sqrt{10}} \leqslant m \leqslant 30\% + \frac{2.58(0.5\%)}{\sqrt{10}}.$$

Hence, $29.6\% \leqslant m \leqslant 30.4\%$.

Thus, for the same confidence level, the confidence interval is smaller than that in Prob. 6.21. As expected, this results in a more precise estimate since prior knowledge of σ improves the accuracy of the estimate.

6.5 Sampling Distribution of the Variance

The theoretical sampling distribution of the variance s^2 of random samples from normal populations is *not* a normal curve because s *cannot* be negative; in fact, it is related to the *gamma distribution* with $\alpha = n/2 - 1$ and $\beta = 2$. The probability density function

$$p_n(x) = \frac{x^{n/2-1}}{2^{n/2}\Gamma\left(\frac{n}{2}\right)} e^{-x/2} \quad \text{for } x \geqslant 0$$

$$= 0 \qquad \qquad \text{for } x < 0,$$

(6.10)

where $E[x] = n$ and $\text{Var}[x] = E[x^2] - (E[x])^2 = 2n$.

The *chi-square* distribution where the probability $p(x) = \chi_p^2$ that a value is exceeded is given by

$$p = \int_{\chi_p^2}^{\infty} p_n(x)\,dx = \int_{\chi_p^2}^{\infty} \frac{x^{n/2-1}}{2^{n/2}\Gamma\left(\frac{n}{2}\right)} e^{-x/2}\,dx.$$

(6.11)

Figure 6.11 shows the graph of χ_p^2 versus p (in %).

The chi-square distribution with ν degrees of freedom has the following properties:

(1) It is a continuous curve extending from $\chi^2 = 0$ to ∞.

(2) It has a single maximum which occurs at $\chi^2 = \nu - 2$ for $\nu \geq 2$.

(3) The mean of the χ^2 distribution is ν and the standard deviation is equal to $\sqrt{2\nu}$.

(4) It is not symmetric.

(5) If x is a normal variate with zero mean and unit standard deviation, the sum of the squares of n random variables of x, i.e.,

$$x_1^2 + x_2^2 + \cdots + x_n^2,$$

is a value of a random variable having the χ^2 distribution with $\nu = n$ degrees of freedom.

(6) If s^2 is the variance of a random variable of size n taken from a normal population having the variance σ^2,

$$\chi^2 = \frac{(n-1)s'^2}{\sigma^2} = \frac{ns^2}{\sigma^2} \tag{6.12}$$

is a value of a random variable having the chi-square distribution with $\nu = n - 1$ degrees of freedom.

(7) If χ_1^2 and χ_2^2 are independent chi-square distributions with n_1 and n_2 degrees of freedom, $\chi_1^2 + \chi_2^2$ has a chi-square distribution with $n_1 + n_2$ degrees of freedom.

Table VIII of the Appendix contains values of χ_p^2 for various values of ν and p. (Cf., Fig. 6.11.)

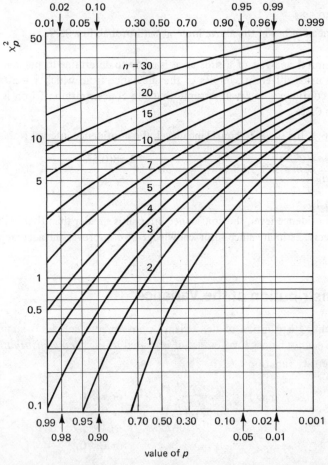

Fig. 6.11 Chi-squared distribution χ_p^2 for n degrees of freedom.

(8) If s_1^2 and s_2^2 are the variances of independent random samples of sizes n_1 and n_2, respectively, taken from two normal populations of equal variance, then the ratio

$$F = \frac{s_1'^2}{s_2'^2} = \frac{(n_1/n_1 - 1)}{(n_2/n_2 - 1)} \frac{s_1^2}{s_2^2} \tag{6.13}$$

defines a random variable having the *F-distribution* with $\nu_1 = n_1 - 1$ degrees of freedom for the numerator and $\nu_2 = n_2 - 1$ degrees of freedom for the denominator.

Table VI of the Appendix gives values of F_p corresponding to $p = 0.01$ and Table VII gives values of F_p corresponding to $p = 0.05$ for various values of ν_1 and ν_2. (Cf., Fig. 6.11.)

PROBLEM 6.23 A random sample with $n = 17$ is taken from a normal population having a variance $\sigma^2 = 34$. Find the probability that the standard deviation s' of the sample exceeds 8.

Solution: Since the standard deviation of the sample $s' = 8$, the variance $s'^2 = 64$. From (6.12),

$$\chi^2 = \frac{ns'^2}{\sigma^2} = \frac{17 \times 64}{34} = 32.$$

From Table VIII of the Appendix for $\nu = 16$, the probability $p = 0.01$ for $\chi^2 = 32$. Thus, the probability that the standard deviation of the sample exceeds 8 is equal to 0.01.

PROBLEM 6.24 A random sample with $n = 20$ is taken from a normal population. Is the sample variance s^2 more likely to be greater than the true variance?

Solution: Setting $s^2 = \sigma^2$,

$$\chi^2 = \frac{ns^2}{\sigma^2} = n = 20.$$

From Table VIII of the Appendix with $\nu = n - 1 = 19$ degrees of freedom, the probability of obtaining a value of $\chi^2 > 20$, that is, a value of $s^2 > \sigma^2$, is less than 0.50. Therefore, it is more likely that s^2 will be less than σ^2.

PROBLEM 6.25 Approximate the probability that the variance of a sample with $n_1 = 31$ is at least 2 times that of a sample with $n_2 = 25$. Assume that both samples are independently taken from the same normal population.

Solution: If s_1^2 is the variance of the first sample and s_2^2 is the variance of the second sample, then the quantities $n_1 s_1^2 / \sigma^2$ and $n_2 s_2^2 / \sigma^2$ possess independent χ^2 distributions with $n_1 - 1$ and $n_2 - 1$ degrees of freedom, respectively, where σ^2 is the true variance of the population. Using the F-test,

$$F = \frac{(n_1 s_1^2 / \sigma^2)/(n_1 - 1)}{(n_2 s_2^2 / \sigma^2)/(n_2 - 1)} = \frac{n_1 (n_2 - 1)}{n_2 (n_1 - 1)} \frac{s_1^2}{s_2^2} = \frac{31 \times 24 \times 2}{25 \times 30} = 1.98.$$

From Tables VI–VII of the Appendix, with $\nu_1 = 31 - 1 = 30$ and $\nu_2 = 25 - 1 = 24$, the value $F = 2.58$ is exceeded 1% of the time while the value $F = 1.94$ is exceeded 5% of the time. Thus, the probability that the variance of the first sample is at least two times the variance of the second is slightly less than 0.05.

6.6 Confidence Intervals for the Variance

The confidence intervals for the true variance of a normal variate can be found using the *chi-square distribution*. For n samples,

$$\frac{ns^2}{\chi_{p_1}^2 (n - 1)} \leqslant \sigma^2 \leqslant \frac{ns^2}{\chi_{p_2}^2 (n - 1)}, \tag{6.14}$$

where σ^2 is the true variance and s^2 is the sample variance (6.2). The quantities $\chi_{p_1}^2 (n - 1)$ and $\chi_{p_2}^2 (n - 1)$ vs. p are found from Fig. 6.11; $\chi_{p_1}^2 (n - 1)$ is the value of χ^2 for $(n - 1)$ degrees of freedom evaluated at $p = p_1$, where

$$100\% \cdot p_1 = \tfrac{1}{2} (100\% - \text{confidence level}). \tag{6.15}$$

Similarly, $\chi_{p_2}^2 (n - 1)$ is evaluated for $(n - 1)$ degrees of freedom for $p = p_2$, where

$$100\% \cdot p_2 = \tfrac{1}{2} (100\% + \text{confidence level}). \tag{6.16}$$

PROBLEM 6.26 Determine the value of χ^2 that corresponds to a sample with $n = 7$ for $p = 30\%$.

Solution: Since $n = 7$, $p = 30\%$, from Fig. 6.11, $\chi^2 = 8.6$.

PROBLEM 6.27 Three samples having the values 3, 4, and 5 are taken at random from a normal variate. Determine the confidence interval for σ^2 for a confidence level of 90%.

Solution: From (6.14), the confidence interval for σ^2 is

$$\frac{ns^2}{\chi^2_{p_1}(n-1)} \leqslant \sigma^2 \leqslant \frac{ns^2}{\chi^2_{p_2}(n-1)} .$$

Since there are three samples, $n = 3$; hence,

$$\frac{3s^2}{\chi^2_{p_1}(2)} \leqslant \sigma^2 \leqslant \frac{3s^2}{\chi^2_{p_2}(2)} .$$

From (6.1-2),

$$\bar{x} = \frac{1}{n}\sum_{i=1}^{n} x_i = \tfrac{1}{3}(3+4+5) = 4, \qquad s^2 = \frac{1}{n}\sum_{i=1}^{n}(x_i - \bar{x})^2 = \tfrac{1}{3}[(3-4)^2 + (4-4)^2 + (5-4)^2] = \tfrac{2}{3}.$$

Thus,

$$\frac{2}{\chi^2_{p_1}(2)} \leqslant \sigma^2 \leqslant \frac{2}{\chi^2_{p_2}(2)} .$$

From (6.14-15),

$$100\% \cdot p_1 = \tfrac{1}{2}(100\% - 90\%), \text{ or } p_1 = 0.05, \qquad 100\% \cdot p_2 = \tfrac{1}{2}(100\% + 90\%), \text{ or } p_2 = 0.95.$$

Using Fig. 6.11, with $\nu = 2$,

$$\chi^2_{p_1}(2) = \chi^2_{0.05}(2) = 5.99, \qquad \chi^2_{p_2}(2) = \chi^2_{0.95}(2) = 0.10.$$

Therefore, the confidence interval for σ^2 is, with 90% probability,

$$\frac{2}{5.99} \leqslant \sigma^2 \leqslant \frac{2}{0.10}, \qquad \text{or} \qquad 0.334 \leqslant \sigma^2 \leqslant 20.$$

PROBLEM 6.28 Find the confidence interval for the true variance for 20 samples at the 90% confidence level. Assume that $s'^2 = 1$ and is a normal variate.

Solution: Using (6.2) and (6.6),

$$s^2 = \frac{n-1}{n}s'^2 = \frac{19}{20} .$$

From (6.14), the confidence interval for the variance is

$$\frac{20\left(\frac{19}{20}\right)}{\chi^2_{p_1}(n-1)} \leqslant \sigma^2 \leqslant \frac{20\left(\frac{19}{20}\right)}{\chi^2_{p_2}(n-1)}, \qquad \text{or} \qquad \frac{19}{\chi^2_{p_1}(n-1)} \leqslant \sigma^2 \leqslant \frac{19}{\chi^2_{p_2}(n-1)} .$$

With $n = 20$, the values of the chi-square distribution are

$$\chi^2_{p_1}(n-1) = \chi^2_p(n-1)\Big|_{p=\frac{1}{2}\left(\frac{100\% - 90\%}{100\%}\right)} = \chi^2_p(19)\Big|_{p=.05} \approx 30,$$

$$\chi^2_{p_2}(n-1) = \chi^2_p(n-1)\Big|_{p=\frac{1}{2}\left(\frac{100\% + 90\%}{100\%}\right)} = \chi^2_p(19)\Big|_{p=0.95} \approx 10.$$

Thus, σ^2, with a probability of 0.9, lies in the interval,

$$\frac{19}{30} \leqslant \sigma^2 \leqslant \frac{19}{10} .$$

PROBLEM 6.29 Two sets of data are obtained from sampling two independent normal variates. The values obtained are denoted by $x_1^{(1)}, x_2^{(1)}, \cdots, x_{n_1}^{(1)}$ and $x_1^{(2)}, x_2^{(2)}, \cdots, x_{n_2}^{(2)}$ where superscripts (1) and (2) refer to samples of the first and second variable. Determine the confidence limits for σ^2 if the two random variables have the same variance and means.

Solution: Since the two normal random variables have the same means and variances, the data can be considered to be from a single variate. Therefore, from (6.14), the confidence limits for σ^2 are

$$\frac{ns^2}{\chi_{p_1}^2(n-1)} \leqslant \sigma^2 \leqslant \frac{ns^2}{\chi_{p_2}^2(n-1)},$$

where

$$n = n_1 + n_2, \qquad s^2 = \frac{1}{n}\left[\sum_{i=1}^{n_1}\left(x_i^{(1)} - \overline{x}\right)^2 + \sum_{i=1}^{n_2}\left(x_i^{(2)} - \overline{x}\right)^2\right], \qquad \overline{x} = \frac{1}{n}\left[\sum_{i=1}^{n_1} x_i^{(1)} + \sum_{i=1}^{n_2} x_i^{(2)}\right].$$

PROBLEM 6.30 Show that the confidence intervals (6.12) for the true variance of a normal variate (6.14) follow from property 6 of the χ^2 distribution.

Solution: From property 6, ns^2/σ^2 has a χ^2 distribution with $n-1$ degrees of freedom. Thus, for a $q\%$ confidence level,

$$P\left[\chi_2^2 < \frac{ns^2}{\sigma^2} < \chi_1^2\right] = \frac{1}{100}q,$$

where χ_1^2 and χ_2^2 are chosen so that

$$P\left[\frac{ns^2}{\sigma^2} < \chi_2^2\right] = \frac{1}{2}\left(1 - \frac{1}{100}q\right), \qquad P\left[\frac{ns^2}{\sigma^2} > \chi_1^2\right] = \frac{1}{2}\left(1 - \frac{1}{100}q\right).$$

Rearranging terms in the inequality,

$$P\left[\frac{ns^2}{\chi_1^2} < \sigma^2 < \frac{ns^2}{\chi_2^2}\right] = \frac{1}{100}q.$$

Thus, χ_1^2 is evaluated for $p = \frac{1}{2}\left(1 - \frac{1}{100}q\right)$ with $n-1$ degrees of freedom. Similarly, χ_2^2 is evaluated for $p = 1 - \frac{1}{2}\left(1 - \frac{1}{100}q\right) = \frac{1}{2}\left(1 + \frac{1}{100}q\right)$ with $n-1$ degrees of freedom.

PROBLEM 6.31 Two sets of data are obtained from sampling two independent normal variates. The values obtained are denoted by $x_1^{(1)}, x_2^{(1)}, \cdots, x_{n_1}^{(1)}$ and $x_1^{(2)}, x_2^{(2)}, \cdots, x_{n_2}^{(2)}$, where superscripts (1) and (2) refer to samples of the first and second variable. Determine the confidence limits for σ^2 if the two random variables have the same variance but different mean values.

Solution: The sample variances of the two sets of data are

$$s_1^2 = \frac{1}{n_1}\sum_{i=1}^{n_1}\left(x_i^{(1)} - \overline{x}_1\right)^2 \quad \text{and} \quad s_2^2 = \frac{1}{n_2}\sum_{i=1}^{n_2}\left(x_i^{(2)} - \overline{x}_2\right)^2,$$

where

$$\overline{x}_1 = \frac{1}{n_1}\sum_{i=1}^{n_1} x_i^{(1)}, \qquad \overline{x}_2 = \frac{1}{n_2}\sum_{i=1}^{n_2} x_i^{(2)}.$$

From property 2, $n_1 s_1^2/\sigma^2$ and $n_2 s_2^2/\sigma^2$ have χ^2 distributions with $n_1 - 1$ and $n_2 - 1$ degrees of freedom. Accordingly, from property 7, $n_1 s_1^2/\sigma^2 + n_2 s_2^2/\sigma^2$ has a χ^2 distribution with $n_1 + n_2 - 2$ degrees of freedom. Thus, the confidence limits for σ^2 are

$$\frac{n_1 s_1^2 + n_2 s_2}{\chi_{p_1}^2(n_1 + n_2 - 2)} \leqslant \sigma^2 \leqslant \frac{n_1 s_1^2 + n_2 s_2^2}{\chi_{p_2}^2(n_1 + n_2 - 2)}.$$

6.7 Comparison of Means

Either the normal distribution test or Student's t-test can determine if a set of observations appears to be drawn from a distribution with a given mean. The former test is used if each observation is normally distributed (or nearly so) and if the standard deviation of the distribution is known or can be accurately estimated (from 30 or more samples). The t-test is applied to a set of normal or nearly normal samples (fewer than 30). Both tests can be used to compare the means of two independent sets of observations to determine whether they appear to be drawn from the same distribution.

Frequently it is of interest to determine the confidence intervals for the difference between two means or to test the hypothesis that two independent sets of samples with equal variances have the same mean.

Consider samples taken from two independent normally distributed variables x and y of size n_x and n_y. The true mean values of x and y are denoted by m_x and m_y. The quantity

$$t = \frac{(\overline{x} - \overline{y}) - (m_x - m_y)}{\sqrt{n_x s_x^2 + n_y s_y^2}} \sqrt{\frac{n_x n_y (n_x + n_y - 2)}{n_x + n_y}} \qquad (6.17)$$

has a Student's t-distribution with $(n_x + n_y - 2)$ degrees of freedom, where $\overline{x}$ is the sample mean of x, $\overline{y}$ is the sample mean of y, s_x^2 is the sample variance of x, and s_y^2 is the sample variance of y. The cumulative distribution is given in Fig. 6.10, and in tabular form, in Table V of the Appendix.

In general, Student's t-distribution arises if two independent variates u and v^2 are considered, where u is normally distributed with zero mean and unit variance and v^2 has a χ^2 distribution with v degrees of freedom. Then,

$$t = \frac{u\sqrt{v}}{v} \qquad (6.18)$$

has Student's t-distribution with v degrees of freedom. The t-distribution has slightly more dispersion than the normal distribution, as shown in Fig. 6.6 for four degrees of freedom.

The probability density function of Student's t-distribution for v degrees of freedom is

$$p(t) = c \left(1 + \frac{t^2}{v}\right)^{-\frac{v+1}{2}},$$

where c is constant $\left(\text{chosen so that } \int_{-\infty}^{\infty} p(t)dt = 1\right)$.

PROBLEM 6.32 Determine whether one hundred normally distributed observations of unit standard deviation with mean $\overline{x} = 10$ appear to be drawn from a normal distribution whose mean value is 10.3.

Solution: The normal distribution test consists of calculating the quantity $k = |z|$; that is,

$$k = \frac{|m - \overline{x}|}{\sigma/\sqrt{n}},$$

where m is the true mean, $\overline{x}$ is the sample mean, σ is the standard deviation of each observation (true or estimated from 30 or more samples), and n is the number of samples. Thus,

$$k = \frac{|10.3 - 10|}{\sqrt{\frac{1}{100}}} = 3.$$

From Table 6.1, the probability of obtaining a value of k less than 3 is less than 1%. Accordingly, the observations do not appear to fit the assumed distribution.

PROBLEM 6.33 Determine whether one hundred normally distributed observations of unknown standard deviation with $m = 10$ and $s = 1$ appear to be drawn from a normal distribution whose mean value is 10.3.

Solution: Since $n \geqslant 30$, the estimated standard deviation can be used in the test. Therefore, the test is identical to that of Prob. 6.32.

PROBLEM 6.34 A set of 100 normally distributed observations x_1 is compared with an independent set of 50 normally distributed observations x_2. The sample means and standard deviations of the two sets are

$$\overline{x}_1 = 5, \quad s_1 = 1, \quad \overline{x}_2 = 5.2, \quad s_2 = 1.23.$$

Determine whether the samples of the observations appear to be drawn from the same distribution.

Solution: Since

$$\sigma_d^2 = \frac{s_1^2}{n_1} + \frac{s_2^2}{n_2} = \frac{1^2}{100} + \frac{1.23^2}{50} = 0.01 + 0.03 = 0.04,$$

$\sigma_d = 0.2$; hence, to compare the means,

$$k = \frac{|\overline{x}_1 - \overline{x}_2|}{\sigma_d} = \frac{|5 - 5.2|}{0.2} = 1.$$

From Table 6.1, the level of significance is greater than 30%; hence, the observations appear to be drawn from the same distribution.

PROBLEM 6.35 Six samples are taken from each of two independent normal variables with equal mean values. Determine the value of t if the sample means are $\overline{x} = 2$, $\overline{y} = 1$ and the sample variances are $s_x^2 = 2$, $s_y^2 = \frac{2}{3}$.

Solution: Substituting into (6.17), with $m_x = m_y$ and $n_x = n_y = 6$,

$$t = \frac{(2-1)}{\sqrt{6(2) + 6\left(\frac{2}{3}\right)}} \sqrt{\frac{(6)(6)(6+6-2)}{6+6}} = \frac{\sqrt{30}}{4}.$$

PROBLEM 6.36 Determine the probability that the value of t, calculated in Prob. 6.35, is exceeded by chance, i.e., the probability that the absolute value of t will exceed $\sqrt{30}/4$.

Solution: From Fig. 6.10, with $\nu = n_x + n_y - 2 = 10$ degrees of freedom, the probability of $|t|$ exceeding $\sqrt{30}/4 = 1.37$ is about 20%.

PROBLEM 6.37 Determine the conclusions that can be drawn if in Probs. 6.35-6 the mean values of x and y are unknown but hypothesized to be equal.

Solution: The mean values are equal at the 20% level of significance. Thus, the hypothesis is a reasonable one.

PROBLEM 6.38 Using Prob. 6.37, determine the 95% confidence interval for $m_x - m_y$.

Solution: Substituting into (6.17), with $n_x = n_y = 6$, $\overline{x} = 2$, $\overline{y} = 1$, $s_x^2 = 2$, and $s_y^2 = \frac{2}{3}$,

$$t = \frac{2 - 1 - (m_x - m_y)}{\sqrt{6(2) + 6\left(\frac{2}{3}\right)}} \sqrt{\frac{(6)(6)(6+6-2)}{6+6}} = \frac{1 - (m_x - m_y)}{4}\sqrt{30} = 1.37[1 - (m_x - m_y)].$$

From Table V of the Appendix, at the 95% confidence level, or when the probability of exceeding $|t|$ is 0.05, with $n_x + n_y - 2 = 10$ degrees of freedom, $t = 2.228$. Thus, the 95% confidence limits are

$$\left| 1.37[1 - (m_x - m_y)] \right| < 2.228, \quad \text{or} \quad \left| 1 - (m_x - m_y) \right| < 1.6.$$

Thus,

$$-1.6 < 1 - (m_x - m_y) < 1.6.$$

Rearranging terms in the inequality, the 95% confidence limits for $(m_x - m_y)$ are

$$-0.6 < m_x - m_y < 2.6;$$

that is, $m_x - m_y$ lies in the above interval with a probability of 0.95.

PROBLEM 6.39 A set x_1 of 10 observations is compared with an independent set x_2 of 10 observations, where $\overline{x}_1 = 10,630$, $s_1 = 400$, $\overline{x}_2 = 10,000$, and $s_2 = 400$. Determine whether there is a significant difference between $\overline{x}_1$ and $\overline{x}_2$.

Solution: Since $n < 30$, Student's t-test is used. In this test, the quantity t is calculated using (6.17), with

$$m_x = m_y, \quad n_x = n_y = 10.$$

The number of degrees of freedom is $(n_x - 1) + (n_y - 1) = 18$, and $t = 3.34$. Table V of the Appendix gives $t = 3.34$ at less than the 1% level of significance (for $\nu = 18$). Hence, a significant difference does exist.

PROBLEM 6.40 Using (6.18), show that the quantity

$$t = \frac{(\overline{x} - \overline{y}) - (m_x - m_y)}{\sqrt{n_x s_x^2 + n_y s_y^2}} \sqrt{\frac{n_x n_y (n_x + n_y - 2)}{n_x + n_y}}$$

has Student's t-distribution.

Solution: If u is normally distributed with zero mean and unit variance, $\dfrac{u\sqrt{\nu}}{\nu}$ has Student's t-distribution and ν^2 has a χ^2 distribution with ν degrees of freedom. Defining

$$u = \frac{(\overline{x} - \overline{y}) - (m_x - m_y)}{\sqrt{\sigma^2/n_x + \sigma^2/n_y}},$$

u possesses the desired characteristics since $E[\overline{x} - \overline{y}] = m_x - m_y$, and, hence,

$$E[u] = 0,$$

$$\text{Var}(u) = \frac{\text{Var}(\overline{x} - m_x) + \text{Var}(\overline{y} - m_y)}{\sigma^2/n_x + \sigma^2/n_y} = \frac{\sigma^2/n_x + \sigma^2/n_y}{\sigma^2/n_x + \sigma^2/n_y} = 1.$$

Defining

$$\nu^2 = \frac{n_x s_x^2 + n_y s_y^2}{\sigma^2}$$

from properties 6 and 7 of the χ^2 distribution, ν^2 has a χ^2 distribution with $n_x + n_y - 2$ degrees of freedom. Hence,

$$t = u\sqrt{n_x + n_y - 2}/\nu$$

$$= \left[\frac{(\overline{x} - \overline{y}) - (m_x - m_y)}{\sqrt{\sigma^2/n_x + \sigma^2/n_y}} \sqrt{n_x + n_y - 2}\right] \bigg/ \sqrt{\frac{n_x s_x^2 + n_y s_y^2}{\sigma^2}}$$

$$= \frac{(\overline{x} - \overline{y}) - (m_x - m_y)}{\sqrt{n_x s_x^2 + n_y s_y^2}} \sqrt{\frac{n_x n_y (n_x + n_y - 2)}{n_x + n_y}}$$

has the Student t-distribution.

6.8 Supplementary Problems

PROBLEM 6.41 Ten independent samples of the random variable x are taken. Determine the expected value of the sample mean if

$$p(x) = \frac{1}{\sqrt{2\pi}} e^{-\frac{1}{2}(x-3)^2}.$$

Answer: $E[\overline{x}] = 3$.

PROBLEM 6.42 Calculate the variance of the sample mean for the conditions of Prob. 6.41.
Answer: $\text{Var}(\overline{x}) = 0.1$.

PROBLEM 6.43 For the conditions of Prob. 6.41, calculate the expected value of the sample variance.
Answer: $E[s^2] = 0.9$.

PROBLEM 6.44 Four hundred samples of a random variable are taken and the sample mean is calculated. Determine the probability density function (approximately) of the sample mean if the random variable has a gamma distribution with unit mean and variance.

Answer: $p(\bar{x}) = \dfrac{20}{\sqrt{2\pi}} e^{-200(\bar{x}-1)^2}$.

PROBLEM 6.45 A coin is tossed n times where $n \gg 1$. How many heads should appear in order for the coin not to appear biased at the 0.1% level of significance?

Answer: $\frac{1}{2}n - 1.65\sqrt{n} \leqslant$ number of heads $\leqslant \frac{1}{2}n + 1.65\sqrt{n}$.

PROBLEM 6.46 A die is tossed 144 times and it is noted that a three appears 36 times. Does the die appear to be honest? Use the 1% level of significance.

Answer: No.

PROBLEM 6.47 A card is drawn at random from a deck of 52 cards and replaced. The procedure is repeated 27 times and it is noted that a total of two spades are drawn. Does the deck appear to be honest? Use the 1% level of significance.

Answer: Yes.

PROBLEM 6.48 The probability density function for Student's t-distribution is

$$p(t) = \frac{[(\nu - 1)/2]!}{\sqrt{\nu\pi}\,[(\nu - 2)/2]!} \; \frac{1}{(1 + t^2/\nu)^{(\nu+1)/2}} \qquad \text{for } -\infty < t < \infty,$$

where ν is the number of degrees of freedom. Show that Student's t-distribution approaches the normal distribution as the number of degrees of freedom approaches infinity.

PROBLEM 6.49 Show that

$$z = \sum_{i=1}^{n} \chi_i^2$$

has a chi-square distribution with $\displaystyle\sum_i^n n_i$ degrees of freedom if $\chi_1^2, \chi_2^2, \cdots, \chi_n^2$ are independent chi-square variates with $n_1, n_2, \cdots, n_n$ degrees of freedom, respectively.

PROBLEM 6.50 Show that if x is normally distributed with mean m and variance σ^2, then the variate

$$z = \frac{[x - m]^2}{\sigma^2}$$

has a chi-square distribution with one degree of freedom.

PROBLEM 6.51 The probability density function of a random variable, which has an F-distribution with m and n degrees of freedom, is given by

$$p(F) = \frac{\left(\dfrac{m+n-2}{2}\right)!}{\left(\dfrac{m-2}{2}\right)!\left(\dfrac{n-2}{2}\right)!} \left(\frac{m}{n}\right)^{m/2} \frac{F^{(m-2)/2}}{\left(1 + \dfrac{mF}{n}\right)^{(m+n)/2}} \qquad \text{for } F > 0.$$

Show that the variable

$$z = \frac{mF/n}{1 + mF/n}$$

has a beta-distribution with $\alpha = \frac{1}{2}(m - 2)$ and $\beta = \frac{1}{2}(n - 2)$.

PROBLEM 6.52 The characteristic function corresponding to the chi-square distribution with one degree of freedom is given by

$$C(\xi) = \frac{1}{\sqrt{1 - 2j\xi}} \ .$$

Find the characteristic function corresponding to the chi-square distribution with n degrees of freedom. *Answer:* $(1 - 2j\xi)^{-(n/2)}$.

PROBLEM 6.53 Using the characteristic function for the chi-square distribution with n degrees of freedom (cf., Prob. 6.52), show that the moments of the distribution are given by

$$m_i = n(n + 2) \cdots (n + 2i - 2) \quad \text{for } i = 1, 2, \cdots.$$

PROBLEM 6.54 Determine the probability density function of the variable $\sum_{i=1}^{n} x_i^2$ where the independent variables $x_1, x_2, \cdots, x_n$ are normally distributed with mean zero and variance σ^2.

Answer: $p(x) = \dfrac{1}{2^{n/2} \sigma^n \Gamma(n/2)} \, x^{(n/2)-1} e^{-(x/2\sigma^2)} \quad$ for $x \geqslant 0$

$$\qquad\qquad = 0 \qquad\qquad\qquad\qquad\qquad \text{for } x < 0.$$

PROBLEM 6.55 Determine the probability density function of the variable $\sqrt{\sum_{i=1}^{n} x_i^2}$, where the independent variables $x_1, x_2, \cdots, x_n$ are normally distributed with mean zero and variance σ^2.

Answer: $p(x) = \dfrac{2}{2^{n/2} \sigma^n \Gamma(n/2)} \, x^{n-1} e^{-(x^2/2\sigma^2)} \quad$ for $x \geqslant 0$

$$\qquad\qquad = 0 \qquad\qquad\qquad\qquad\qquad \text{for } x < 0.$$

SAMPLING THEORY II

7.1 Sample Range

The *range* of a given set of samples is defined as the difference between the largest and smallest sample values. Thus, if n samples are taken and written in order of increasing value (not necessarily the order in which they occurred), $x_1, x_2, \cdots, x_n$, then the range is

$$R = x_n - x_1. \tag{7.1}$$

The range is a random variable whose probability density function $p_R(R)$ is given by

$$p_R(R) = n(n-1) \int_a^{b-R} p(x)p(x+R) \left[\int_x^{x+R} p(y)dy \right]^{n-2} dx, \tag{7.2}$$

where n is the sample size, and the continuous density function $p(x)$ vanishes outside the interval $a \leqslant x \leqslant b$.

The standard deviation of a set of normally distributed samples can be efficiently estimated from R. The standard deviation is estimated by the ratio

$$\sigma_e = \frac{R}{C_n}, \tag{7.3}$$

where C_n is a function of the sample size n and is given in Table 7.1.

TABLE 7.1   Values of C_n for samples of size n.

n	2	3	4	5	10	20	30	50	100	1000
C_n	1.13	1.69	2.06	2.33	3.08	3.73	4.09	4.50	5.02	6.48

For small values of $n (n \leqslant 10)$, the estimate obtained is almost as precise as the one which is obtained from calculating s from (6.2).

The *joint probability density function* of x_1 and x_n is given by

$$g(x_1, x_n) = n(n-1)p(x_1)p(x_n)\left[\int_{x_1}^{x_n} p(x)dx \right]^{n-2}. \tag{7.4}$$

The *expected value* $\bar{R}$ of R is

$$\bar{R} = \int_{-\infty}^{\infty} \{1 - [p(x)]^n - [1 - p(x)]^n \}dx. \tag{7.5}$$

Values of $\bar{R}$ have been calculated by Tippett and are given in *Biometrika Tables for Statisticians*.

PROBLEM 7.1   Samples taken at random from a normally distributed random variable are found to have the measurements

$$-3.0, -3.3, -1.8, -1.6, -3.1, -2.6, -2.8, -2.0, -2.3, -2.5.$$

Determine the range.

Solution: Since the smallest and largest sample measurements are -3.3 and -1.6, respectively, the range is

$$R = (\text{Largest sample value} - \text{Smallest sample value}) = -1.6 - (-3.3) = 1.7.$$

PROBLEM 7.2 Establish (7.4).

Solution: To establish (7.4), consider a sample of size n taken from a continuous population whose probability density function is $p(x)$. Next, divide the x-axis into the five intervals $I_1: (-\infty, x_1), I_2: (x_1, x_1 + \Delta x_1),$ $I_3: (x_1 + \Delta x_1, x_n), I_4: (x_n, x_n + \Delta x_n),$ and $I_5: (x_n + \Delta x_n, \infty),$ where $x_1 < x_n$ are any two values of x. The probabilities $P_1, \cdots, P_5$ that x will fall in any particular $I_i, i = 1, \cdots, 5,$ are

$$P_1 = \int_{-\infty}^{x_1} p(x)dx, \qquad P_2 = \int_{x_1}^{x_1+\Delta x_1} p(x)dx, \qquad P_3 = \int_{x_1+\Delta x_1}^{x_n} p(x)dx,$$

$$P_4 = \int_{x_n}^{x_n+\Delta x_n} p(x)dx, \qquad P_5 = \int_{x_n+\Delta x_n}^{\infty} p(x)dx.$$

The probability that the smallest value in the sample falls between x_1 and $x_1 + \Delta x_1$ while the largest value falls between x_n and $x_n + \Delta x_n$ is found by calculating the probability that no samples fall in I_1 or I_5, one falls in each of I_2 and I_4, and $(n-2)$ samples fall in I_3. Since there are $n(n-1)$ ways in which these two extreme values can be obtained [that is, the smallest value can be obtained in n ways and the largest value in I_4 in $(n-1)$ ways], the desired probability is

$$n(n-1)P_1^0 P_2^1 P_3^{n-2} P_4^1 P_5^0 = n(n-1)P_2^1 P_3^{n-2} P_4^1$$

$$= n(n-1)\int_{x_1}^{x_1+\Delta x_1} p(x)dx \left[\int_{x_1+\Delta x_1}^{x_n} p(x)dx\right]^{n-2} \int_{x_n}^{x_n+\Delta x_n} p(x)dx. \quad (7.6)$$

The right-hand side of the above equation can be simplified by using the mean-value theorem since $p(x)$ is continuous. Thus,

$$P_2 = \int_{x_1}^{x_1+\Delta x_1} p(x)dx = \Delta x_1 p(x_1 + \theta_1 \Delta x_1), \quad 0 \leqslant \theta_1 \leqslant 1.$$

In the limit as $\Delta x_1 \to 0$ and $\Delta x_n \to 0$, the right-hand side of (7.6) approaches

$$n(n-1)p(x_1)\Delta x_1 p(x_n)\Delta x_n \left[\int_{x_1}^{x_n} p(x)dx\right]^{n-2},$$

from which it follows that the joint density function $g(x_1, x_n)$ is given by

$$g(x_1, x_n) = n(n-1)p(x_1)p(x_n)\left[\int_{x_1}^{x_n} p(x)dx\right]^{n-2}.$$

PROBLEM 7.3 Establish (7.2).

Solution: Using (7.4), a change of variable $R = x_n - x_1$ is made. The joint distribution $g_0(x_1, R)$ of x_1 and R is then

$$g(x_1, x_n) = g_0(x_1, R) = n(n-1)p(x_1)p(x_1 + R)\left[\int_{x_1}^{x_1+R} p(x)dx\right]^{n-2}.$$

The density function $p_R(R)$ of R is obtained by integrating $g_0(x_1, R)$ with respect to x_1 over the range of x_1 with R fixed. If the density function $p(x)$ vanishes outside the interval $a \leqslant x \leqslant b$, the range of variation of x_1 is $a \leqslant x_1 \leqslant b - R$. Thus,

$$p_R(R) = n(n-1)\int_a^{b-R} p(x_1)p(x_1 + R)\left[\int_{x_1}^{x_1+R} p(x)dx\right]^{n-2} dx_1.$$

PROBLEM 7.4 Estimate the standard deviation σ_e for the samples of Prob. 7.1.

Solution: Since the range $R = 1.7$ and the number of samples is 10, the constant C_n, from Table 7.1, is 3.08

and, hence, the estimated standard deviation is

$$\sigma_e = \frac{R}{C_n} = \frac{1.70}{3.08} = 0.55.$$

PROBLEM 7.5 Calculate the actual standard deviation of the samples of Prob. 7.1 and compare the result to that obtained in Prob. 7.4. Also show the relation between the range and the standard deviation.

Solution: Since $n = 10$, the mean of the sample is

$$\bar{x} = \frac{1}{10}(-1.6 - 1.8 - 2.0 - 2.3 - 2.5 - 2.6 - 2.8 - 3.0 - 3.1 - 3.3)$$

$$= -2.5.$$

Table 7.2 shows the tabulations to calculate the standard deviation. Hence, the standard deviation is, from (6.2),

$$s = \sqrt{\frac{1}{n}\sum_{i=1}^{n}(x_i - \bar{x})^2} = \sqrt{\frac{2.94}{10}} = \sqrt{0.29} = 0.54.$$

Thus, for these samples, the error in the estimated value of the sample standard deviation is $0.55 - 0.54 = 0.01$, or about 2%.

The ratio of the range to the standard deviation is

$$\frac{R}{s} = \frac{1.7}{0.54} \approx 3.1.$$

TABLE 7.2

x	$x - \bar{x}$	$(x - \bar{x})^2$
−1.6	0.9	0.81
−1.8	0.7	0.49
−2.0	0.5	0.25
−2.3	0.2	0.04
−2.5	0.0	0.00
−2.6	−0.1	0.01
−2.8	−0.3	0.09
−3.0	−0.5	0.25
−3.1	−0.6	0.36
−3.3	−0.8	0.64
Total		2.94

PROBLEM 7.6 Determine the probability density function for the range R for samples uniformly distributed according to

$$p(x) = \frac{1}{a} \quad \text{for } 0 \leqslant x \leqslant a$$

$$= 0 \quad \text{elsewhere.}$$

Solution: From (7.2), the probability density function of R is

$$p_R(R) = n(n-1)\int_a^{b-R} p(x)p(x+R)\left[\int_x^{x+R} p(y)dy\right]^{n-2} dx.$$

Since $p(x) = 0$ for $x < 0$ and for $x > a$, and since $p(x + R) = 0$ for $x < -R$ and for $x > a - R$, $p(R) = 0$ for $x < 0$ and $x > a - R$. For $0 \leqslant x \leqslant a$,

$$p_R(R) = n(n-1)\int_0^{a-R}\left(\frac{1}{a}\right)\left(\frac{1}{a}\right)\left(\int_x^{x+R}\frac{1}{a}dy\right)^{n-2} dx$$

$$= \frac{n(n-1)}{a^n}\int_0^{a-R} R^{n-2}\,dx$$

$$= \frac{n(n-1)}{a^n} R^{n-2}(a-R).$$

Hence, the probability density function of R is

$$p_R(R) = \frac{n(n-1)}{a^n} R^{n-2}(a-R) \quad \text{for } 0 < R < a$$

$$= 0 \quad \text{elsewhere.}$$

Figure 7.1 shows $p_R(R)$ for $n = 2$ and $n = 3$.

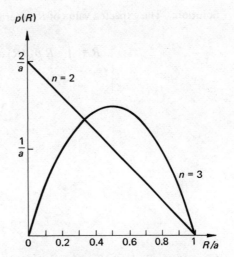

Fig. 7.1 Probability density function $p_R(R)$ vs. R/a for $n = 2$ and $n = 3$.

PROBLEM 7.7 Find the probability density function for the range R for samples distributed according to

$$p(x) = e^{-x} \quad \text{for } x \geqslant 0$$
$$= 0 \quad \text{elsewhere.}$$

Solution: From (7.2), the probability density function of R is

$$p_R(R) = n(n-1) \int_a^{b-R} p(x)p(x+R) \left[\int_x^{x+R} p(y)dy \right]^{n-2} dx.$$

Here the limits of integration are $a = 0$ and $b = \infty$. Substituting in (7.2) yields

$$p_R(R) = n(n-1) \int_0^\infty e^{-x} e^{-(x+R)} \left[\int_x^{x+R} e^{-y} dy \right]^{n-2} dx$$

$$= n(n-1) \int_0^\infty e^{-2x} e^{-R} \left(-e^{-y} \Big|_x^{x+R} \right)^{n-2} dx$$

$$= n(n-1)e^{-R} \int_0^\infty e^{-2x} [-(e^{-x-R} - e^{-x})]^{n-2} dx$$

$$= n(n-1)e^{-R} \int_0^\infty e^{-2x} (-e^{-x} e^{-R} + e^{-x})^{n-2} dx$$

$$= n(n-1)e^{-R} \int_0^\infty e^{-2x} e^{-(n-2)x} (e^{-R} - 1)^{n-2} dx$$

$$= n(n-1)e^{-R} (e^{-R} - 1)^{n-2} \int_0^\infty e^{-nx} dx$$

$$= n(n-1)e^{-R} (e^{-R} - 1)^{n-2} \frac{e^{-nx}}{n} \Big|_0^\infty$$

$$= (n-1)e^{-R} (1 - e^{-R})^{n-2}.$$

PROBLEM 7.8 Determine the relationship between the expected value of the range R of Prob. 7.6 and the standard deviation.

Solution: The expected value of R in terms of $p_R(R)$ is

$$\bar{R} = \int_0^\infty R\, p_R(R)\, dR = \int_0^a \frac{n(n-1)}{a^n} R^{n-1}(a-R)dR$$

$$= \frac{n(n-1)}{a^n} \left(a \int_0^a R^{n-1}\, dR - \int_0^a R^n\, dR \right)$$

$$= \frac{n(n-1)}{a^n} \left(a \frac{R^n}{n} \Big|_0^a - \frac{R^{n+1}}{n+1} \Big|_0^a \right)$$

$$= \frac{n(n-1)}{a^n} \left(\frac{a^{n+1}}{n} - \frac{a^{n+1}}{n+1} \right)$$

$$= \left(\frac{n-1}{n+1} \right) a.$$

Since, from Prob. 3.18, the standard deviation for the uniform distribution is $\sigma = (\sqrt{3}/6)a$, $a = (6/\sqrt{3})\sigma = 2\sqrt{3}\sigma$. Hence,

$$\bar{R} = 2\sqrt{3} \left(\frac{n-1}{n+1} \right) \sigma.$$

Problem 7.8 shows that the standard deviation may be estimated from

$$\sigma_e = \frac{n+1}{2\sqrt{3}(n-1)}\,\bar{R},$$

where R is the range of a set of n uniformly distributed samples.

PROBLEM 7.9 Five uniformly distributed samples are drawn at random. Calculate the expected value of the range R. Assume that the samples are drawn from a distribution whose standard deviation is equal to one.

Solution: From Prob. 7.8 for the uniform distribution,

$$\bar{R} = 2\sqrt{3}\left(\frac{n-1}{n+1}\right)\sigma.$$

For $n = 5$ and $\sigma = 1$,

$$\bar{R} = 2\sqrt{3}\left(\frac{5-1}{5+1}\right) = \left(\frac{4}{3}\right)\sqrt{3}.$$

7.2 Comparison of Variance: *F*-Test

To determine if two sets of normally distributed observations appear to be drawn from the same normal distribution, the sample variances of the two sets can be tested by the *F-test*. In this test the quantity F is calculated as the variance ratio

$$F = \frac{s_1'^2}{s_2'^2}, \tag{7.7}$$

where $s_1'^2$ and $s_2'^2$ are the unbiased sample variances of the two sets of data and it is assumed that $s_1'^2 \geqslant s_2'^2$. [Cf., (6.13).] The quantity F is tabulated in Table VI of the Appendix for the 1% level of significance and in Table VII of the Appendix for the 5% level of significance. If the calculated value of F [using (7.7)] exceeds the tabulated value at the appropriate level of significance it is concluded that a statistically significant difference does exist between the two sets. The number of degrees of freedom are $(n_1 - 1)$ and $(n_2 - 1)$ where n_1 and n_2 are the sample sizes of the two sets.

In general, the *F-distribution* arises when the ratio

$$F = \frac{x/v_x}{y/v_y} \tag{7.8}$$

is formed, where x and y have independent χ^2 distributions with v_x and v_y degrees of freedom, respectively. The ratio possesses the *F-distribution* with v_x and v_y degrees of freedom. The probability density function is of the form

$$p(F) = \frac{kF^{\frac{v_x-2}{2}}}{(v_y + v_xF)^{\frac{v_x+v_y}{2}}}, \quad F \geqslant 0$$

$$= 0, \qquad\qquad F < 0, \tag{7.9}$$

where k is a constant [chosen so that $\int_0^\infty p(F)dF = 1$]. A typical form for $p(F)$ is shown in Fig. 7.2.

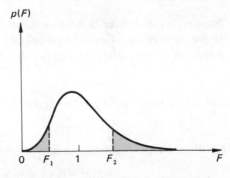

Fig. 7.2 Probability density function $p(F)$ for the *F*-distribution.

PROBLEM 7.10 Show that the ratio $s_1'^2/s_2'^2$ for two independent sets of normally distributed samples of equal variance possesses the F-distribution. Use the properties of s_1^2 and s_2^2 given in Chap. 6.

Solution: From Sec. 6.5, $n_1 s_1^2/\sigma^2$ and $n_2 s_2^2/\sigma^2$ possess χ^2 distributions with $(n_1 - 1)$ and $(n_2 - 1)$ degrees of freedom, respectively, where n_1 and n_2 are the sample sizes associated with the (independent) sample variances s_1^2 and s_2^2. Accordingly, from (7.8), with $x = n_1 s_1^2/\sigma^2$, $\nu_x = n_1 - 1$, and $y = n_2 s_2^2/\sigma^2$, $\nu_y = n_2 - 1$,

$$F = \frac{(n_1 s_1^2/\sigma^2)[1/(n_1 - 1)]}{(n_2 s_2^2/\sigma^2)[1/(n_2 - 1)]} = \frac{[n_1/(n_1 - 1)] s_1^2}{[n_2/(n_2 - 1)] s_2^2}.$$

From (6.2) and (6.6),

$$s_1'^2 = \frac{n_1}{n_1 - 1} s_1^2, \qquad s_2'^2 = \frac{n_2}{n_2 - 1} s_2^2.$$

Hence,

$$F = \frac{s_1'^2}{s_2'^2}. \qquad\qquad [7.7]$$

PROBLEM 7.11 Explain the use of Tables VI-VII of the Appendix.

Solution: Tables VI-VII tabulate the values of F which are exceeded with probability 1% and 5%, respectively, for specified values of ν_1 and ν_2. (The 1% and 5% values are commonly used levels of significance.)
Figure 7.2 is the graph of $p(F)$ showing a typical pair of values of F.
The requirement that $s_1'^2$ and $s_2'^2$ in (7.7) be ordered such that $s_1'^2 \geqslant s_2'^2$ insures that the calculated value of F exceeds 1. Accordingly, only the right-hand tail of the distribution need be considered in making the F-test using Tables VI-VII.
It is noted, however, that since

$$P(F > F_2) = P\left(\frac{1}{F} < \frac{1}{F_2}\right), \qquad\qquad (7.10)$$

from Table VII of the Appendix for $\nu_1 = 12$ and $\nu_2 = 40$, $F_2 = 2.00$; i.e.,

$$P(F > 2.00) = 0.05.$$

Therefore, from (7.10),

$$P(F < 0.5) = 0.05 \quad \text{for } \nu_2 = 12 \text{ and } \nu_1 = 40$$

since $1/F$ is F-distributed with ν_2 and ν_1 degrees of freedom.

PROBLEM 7.12 Determine the value of F which is exceeded with probability 0.05 for 8 and 10 degrees of freedom.

Solution: The degrees of freedom stated first, $\nu_1 = 8$, refers to the numerator while the second, $\nu_2 = 10$, refers to the denominator. Since the probability of exceeding F is 0.05 (5% level of significance), Table VII of the Appendix is used with $\nu_1 = 8$ and $\nu_2 = 10$. Thus,

$$F = 3.07.$$

Therefore, the value $F = 3.07$ is exceeded 5% of the time for 8 and 10 degrees of freedom.

PROBLEM 7.13 It is found from two sets of data that

$$s_x^2 = 0.5 \quad \text{with } n_x = 11, \qquad s_y^2 = 1.0 \quad \text{with } n_y = 11.$$

Do these sample variances appear to differ significantly; that is, do they appear *not* to be drawn from the same normal distribution? Use the 5% level of significance.

Solution: According to the F-test, to test the equality of two variances, the quantity $F = s_1'^2/s_2'^2$ is first calculated ($s_1'^2 \geqslant s_2'^2$). Thus,

$$s_1'^2 = \frac{n_y}{n_y - 1} s_y^2 = \frac{11}{10},$$

$$s_2'^2 = \frac{n_x}{n_x - 1} s_x^2 = \frac{11}{10}(0.5) = \frac{11}{20}.$$

Hence,

$$F = \frac{11/10}{11/20} = 2.$$

The number of degrees of freedom are

$$\nu_1 = n_y - 1 = 10, \qquad \nu_2 = n_x - 1 = 10.$$

From Table VII of the Appendix, for $\nu_1 = 10$ and $\nu_2 = 10$, $F = 2.98$. Since the value calculated is less than 2.98, it is concluded that there is no significant difference between the sample variances calculated from the two sets of samples. Thus, according to the criterion selected (5% level of significance) the actual differences between s_x^2 and s_y^2 are presumably due to chance; that is, due to the particular values of the samples selected.

PROBLEM 7.14 In Prob. 7.13, determine the number of samples that are required before the difference between s_x^2 and s_y^2 becomes statistically significant. Assume $n_x = n_y$.

Solution: Since $n_x = n_y$,

$$F = \frac{s_1'^2}{s_2'^2} = \frac{s_y^2}{s_x^2} = \frac{1.0}{0.5} = 2.$$

From Table VII of the Appendix, the calculated value of F is significant over $F = 1.98$ with $\nu_1 = \nu_2 = 24$. Since $n_y = \nu_1 + 1$ and $n_x = \nu_2 + 1$, a sample size of 25 is needed to detect a significant difference between the given values of the variances. Thus, with larger sample sizes, true differences are more easily distinguishable from differences due to chance.

PROBLEM 7.15 Determine if there is a significant difference between the following sample variances calculated from normally distributed samples:

$$s_1^2 = 5, \quad n_1 = 16; \qquad s_2^2 = 2, \quad n_2 = 9.$$

Solution: The value of F is

$$F = \frac{[n_1/(n_1 - 1)]s_1^2}{[n_2/(n_2 - 1)]s_2^2} = \frac{\frac{16}{15}(5)}{\frac{9}{8}(2)} = \frac{64}{27} = 2.37.$$

From Table VII of the Appendix (5% level of significance) with

$$\nu_1 = n_1 - 1 = 15, \qquad \nu_2 = n_2 - 1 = 8,$$

$F = 3.22$, which exceeds the calculated value. Therefore, it is concluded that the difference is not significant.

PROBLEM 7.16 Twenty-five samples are used to calculate the sample variance from normally distributed samples. If $s_1^2 = 10$, does this sample appear to be drawn from the same normal distribution as a second set of 100,000 samples for which $s_2^2 = 6$?

Solution: The F-test can be applied by taking $s_1^2 = 10, n_1 = 25$, and $s_2^2 = 6, n_2 = \infty$. In other words, the given variance against which the sample variance is to be tested is considered to arise from an infinite number of samples, since it can be observed from Tables VI-VII in the Appendix, for ν_2 (or ν_1) $\gg$ 120 the appropriate value of F is very nearly the value corresponding to ν_2 (or ν_1) $= \infty$. Thus,

$$F = \frac{[n_1/(n_1 - 1)]s_1^2}{[n_2/(n_2 - 1)]s_2^2} = \frac{\frac{25}{24}(10)}{(1)(6)} = 1.74.$$

From Table VII of the Appendix with

$$\nu_1 = n_1 - 1 = 24, \qquad \nu_2 = n_2 - 1 = \infty,$$

$F = 1.52$. Since the calculated value of 1.74 exceeds this value, the difference is significant at the 5% level so that the sample does not appear to be drawn from the stated distribution.

PROBLEM 7.17 Determine the value of F_0 such that $P(F < F_0) = 0.05$. Assume $\nu_1 = 12$ and $\nu_2 = 6$.

Solution: Since $P(F < F_0) = 1 - P(F > F_0)$, $P(F > F_0) = 1 - P(F < F_0) = 1 - 0.05 = 0.95$. But the F-distribution is not tabulated at the 95% level of significance. However,

$$P(F < F_0) = P\left(\frac{1}{F_0} < \frac{1}{F}\right)$$

or defining $F' = 1/F$,

$$P\left(F' > \frac{1}{F_0}\right) = 0.05.$$

From Table VII of the Appendix with $\nu_1 = 12$ and $\nu_2 = 6$, $\frac{1}{F_0} = 4$, so that $F_0 = 0.25$.

PROBLEM 7.18 Show that the probability distribution function of the variance ratio $F = s_1'^2/s_2'^2$ with $\nu_1 - 1$ and $\nu_2 - 1$ degrees of freedom is

$$p_F(F) = \frac{(\nu_1/\nu_2)^{\nu_1/2}}{B(\frac{1}{2}\nu_1, \frac{1}{2}\nu_2)} \cdot \frac{F^{\frac{1}{2}\nu_1 - 1}}{(1 + \nu_1 F/\nu_2)^{\frac{1}{2}(\nu_1 + \nu_2)}}, \qquad 0 \leqslant F \leqslant \infty, \tag{7.11}$$

where $B(\cdot, \cdot)$ is the beta function.

Solution: Since both the numerator and denominator of F are χ^2 variates with ν_1 and ν_2 degrees of freedom, the ratio $F = s_1'^2/s_2'^2$ is a beta-prime variate with parameters $\alpha = \frac{1}{2}\nu_1$ and $\beta = \frac{1}{2}\nu_2$, and its density function is

$$p(x) = \frac{x^{\frac{1}{2}\nu_1 - 1}(1 + x)^{-\frac{1}{2}(\nu_1 + \nu_2)}}{B(\frac{1}{2}\nu_1, \frac{1}{2}\nu_2)},$$

where $x = \nu_1 F/\nu_2$. The density function of F is obtained from

$$p_F(F)dF = p_F(F)\frac{\nu_2}{\nu_1}\ dx = p(x)dx;$$

that is,

$$p_F(F) = \frac{(\nu_1/\nu_2)^{\nu_1/2}}{B(\frac{1}{2}\nu_1, \frac{1}{2}\nu_2)} \frac{F^{\frac{1}{2}\nu_1 - 1}}{(1 + \nu_1 F/\nu_2)^{\frac{1}{2}(\nu_1 + \nu_2)}}, \qquad 0 \leqslant F < \infty.$$

Note that the F-distribution is positively skew.

The variable $z = \frac{1}{2} \ln F$ is said to possess Fisher's z-distribution.

PROBLEM 7.19 Show that the probability distribution function of Fisher's z-distribution is

$$p_z(z) = \frac{2\nu_1^{\nu_1/2}\nu_2^{\nu_2/2}}{B(\frac{1}{2}\nu_1, \frac{1}{2}\nu_2)} \cdot \frac{e^{\nu_1 z}}{(\nu_1 e^{2z} + \nu_2)^{(\nu_1+\nu_2)/2}}.$$ (7.12)

Solution: Substitute $F = e^{2z}$ and, hence, $dF = 2e^{2z}\,dz = 2F\,dz$ in (7.11).

7.3 Goodness of Fit Test

The chi-square test can be used to determine whether observed frequencies of occurrence in a set of samples drawn at random appear to be drawn from an assumed distribution. In this way, one can judge whether any differences between the observed and expected frequencies are real or due to chance.

To perform the test, we calculate the quantity

$$\chi^2 = \sum_{i=1}^{n} \frac{(o_i - e_i)^2}{e_i},$$ (7.13)

where o = observed frequency and e = expected frequency. The distribution of χ^2 is frequently closely approximated by the χ^2 distribution function with $(n-1)$ degrees of freedom discussed in Chap. 6. In fact, as the number of samples approaches infinity, the distribution of the sum in (7.13) approaches that of a χ^2 function with $(n-1)$ degrees of freedom. Figure 7.3 shows the distribution of χ^2 for various degrees of freedom. If the assumed distribution is not completely known, the unknown parameters are replaced by their maximum likelihood estimates and the number of degrees of freedom is reduced by the number of unknown parameters in the distribution. The quantity calculated according to (7.13) is then compared with the value of χ^2 in Fig. 7.3 or Table VIII in the Appendix for the appropriate level of significance and number of degrees of freedom. If the calculated value exceeds the tabulated value it is concluded that the samples are not drawn from the assumed distribution.

The chi-square test is normally satisfactory only if $n \geqslant 5$ and $e_i \geqslant 5$, although when $e_i > 5$, then $n < 5$ can give satisfactory results.

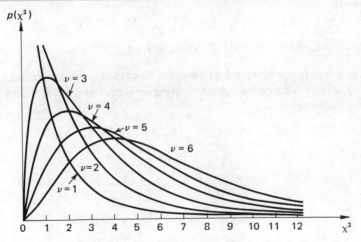

Fig. 7.3 Distribution of χ^2 for various degrees of freedom.

PROBLEM 7.20 Determine the value of χ^2 which is exceeded with probability 0.05 for six degrees of freedom.

Solution: From Table VIII of the Appendix with $\nu = 5$, $\chi^2 = 12.592$.

PROBLEM 7.21 Cards are drawn at random 20 times, each time from a full deck. The result is 8 clubs, 3 diamonds, 5 hearts, and 4 spades. Does the deck appear to be honest?

Solution: In this case, it is to be determined whether the cards appear to be drawn from a deck in which the probability density function according to suits is as shown in Fig. 7.4 (clubs = 1, diamonds = 2, hearts = 3, spades = 4).

Since the probability of drawing a card of one suit on any given selection is $\frac{1}{4}$, in 20 drawings the expected number of cards drawn in each of the four suits is 5. Therefore, $e_1 = e_2 = e_3 = e_4 = 5$. But the observed frequencies are $o_1 = 8, o_2 = 3, o_3 = 5, o_4 = 4$. Calculating χ^2 from (7.13),

$$\chi^2 = \frac{(o_1 - e_1)^2}{e_1} + \frac{(o_2 - e_2)^2}{e_2} + \frac{(o_3 - e_3)^2}{e_3} + \frac{(o_4 - e_4)^2}{e_4} = \frac{(8-5)^2}{5} + \frac{(3-5)^2}{5} + \frac{(5-5)^2}{5} + \frac{(4-5)^2}{5}$$

$$= \frac{9}{5} + \frac{4}{5} + 0 + \frac{1}{5}$$

$$= 2.8.$$

Since $n = 4$, the number of degrees of freedom is $n - 1 = 4 - 1 = 3$. This is so, since with the number of cards drawn specified, only the values for three suits can be assigned arbitrarily. From Table VIII in the Appendix, for $\nu = 3$ and $\chi^2 = 2.8$, the level of significance is greater than 30% so that the deck appears honest. Ordinarily, the 1% or 5% level of significance would be used to accept or reject a hypothesis.

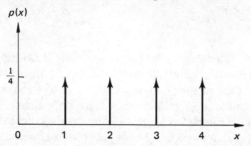

Fig. 7.4 Probability density function
for Prob. 7.21.

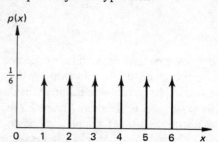

Fig. 7.5 Probability density function
for an ideal die.

PROBLEM 7.22   A die is rolled 48 times with the following results:

Result	one	two	three	four	five	six	Total
Observed Frequency	12	4	8	15	1	8	48

Does the die appear honest? Use the 1% level of significance.

Solution: In this problem, it is determined whether the observations appear to come from an "ideal" die in which the probability density function for rolling numbers between 1 and 6 is as shown in Fig. 7.5.

The expected frequencies are

$$e_1 = e_2 = \cdots = e_6 = \tfrac{1}{6}(48) = 8.$$

The observed frequencies are

$$o_1 = 12, \quad o_2 = 4, \quad o_3 = 8, \quad o_4 = 15, \quad o_5 = 1, \quad o_6 = 8.$$

Using (7.13),

$$\chi^2 = \sum_{i=1}^{6} \frac{(o_i - e_i)^2}{e_i} = \tfrac{1}{8}[(12-8)^2 + (4-8)^2 + (8-8)^2 + (15-8)^2 + (1-8)^2 + (8-8)^2]$$

$$= \tfrac{1}{8}(16 + 16 + 0 + 49 + 49 + 0)$$

$$= 16.25.$$

The number of degrees of freedom $(n - 1)$ is 5, since for a fixed number of rolls (48), only 5 of the 6 frequencies can be assigned arbitrarily. From Table VIII of the Appendix, with $\nu = 5$, the probability of χ^2 exceeding 15.08 by chance is 0.01. Accordingly, at the 1% level of significance, the die appears biased.

PROBLEM 7.23 Three machines are used to produce a certain product. If the number produced by each machine and the corresponding number of rejections are as indicated below, does there appear to be a difference in the rejection rates of the machines? Use the 5% level of significance.

Machine	A	B	C
Number Produced	24	21	30
Number Rejected	5	10	10

Solution: Assuming that the machines are identical,

$$\text{Expected Rejection Rate} = \frac{\text{Total number rejected}}{\text{Total number produced}} = \frac{5 + 10 + 10}{24 + 21 + 30} = \frac{1}{3}.$$

Therefore, the expected number of rejects for each machine is

$$e_A = \tfrac{1}{3} \times 24 = 8, \qquad e_B = \tfrac{1}{3} \times 21 = 7, \qquad e_C = \tfrac{1}{3} \times 30 = 10.$$

The observed number of rejects for each machine is

$$o_A = 5, \qquad o_B = 10, \qquad o_C = 10,$$

so that

$$\chi^2 = \frac{(5-8)^2}{8} + \frac{(7-10)^2}{7} + \frac{(10-10)^2}{10} = \frac{9}{8} + \frac{9}{7} + 0 = 2.41.$$

The number of degrees of freedom is two and from Table VIII of the Appendix, at the 5% level of significance, $\chi^2 = 5.99$. Since the tabulated value exceeds the calculated value, it is concluded that there is no apparent difference between the machines.

PROBLEM 7.24 The number of cars entering a tunnel is assumed to be Poisson distributed in time. If in five successive 1-hr periods the number of cars observed were 250, 245, 225, 205, and 225, is the Poisson assumption reasonable? Use the 5% level of significance.

Solution: In the Poisson distribution (see Chap. 3), the probability of an event occurring in any interval Δt is $\nu \Delta t$, where ν is the average number of events per unit time. In this case ν corresponds to the average number of cars passing per hour. Since ν is not specified, it can be estimated from

$$\nu_e = \tfrac{1}{5}(250 + 245 + 225 + 205 + 225) = 230 \text{ cars/hr}.$$

In applying the χ^2 test with $n = 5$, the number of degrees of freedom is $(n - 2)$ rather than $(n - 1)$ since it was necessary to determine one unknown parameter (ν) of the assumed distribution. Using (7.13), with $e_1 = e_2 = \cdots = e_5 = 230$, $o_1 = 250$, $o_2 = 245$, $o_3 = 225$, $o_4 = 205$, $o_5 = 225$,

$$\chi^2 = \sum_{i=1}^{5} \frac{(o_1 - e_1)^2}{e_i} = \tfrac{1}{230}[(250 - 230)^2 + (245 - 230)^2 + (225 - 230)^2 + (205 - 230)^2 + (225 - 230)^2]$$

$$= \tfrac{1}{230}(400 + 225 + 25 + 625 + 25)$$

$$= \tfrac{1,300}{230}$$

$$= 5.65.$$

From Table VIII of the Appendix with $n - 2 = 3$ degrees of freedom, at the 5% level of significance, $\chi^2 = 7.8$. Since the calculated value does not exceed 7.8, the Poisson assumption appears to be a reasonable one.

PROBLEM 7.25 The number of cars entering a tunnel are assumed to be Poisson distributed. If observations are taken during varying time intervals with the following observed frequencies, is it reasonable to assume that the data is Poisson distributed at the 5% level of significance?

Time	9:00–9:30	9:30–10:30	10:30–11:00	11:00–12:00	12:00–1:30
Frequency	50	60	40	75	90

Solution: Since the average frequency is not specified, it is necessary to estimate ν, the average number of cars passing per hour. Thus, since the elapsed interval is 4.5 hr,

$$\nu_e = \frac{1}{4.5}(50 + 60 + 40 + 75 + 90) = 70.$$

The expected frequencies in each of the five intervals are

$$e_1 = 70(\tfrac{1}{2}) = 35, \quad e_2 = 70(1) = 70, \quad e_3 = 70(\tfrac{1}{2}) = 35, \quad e_4 = 70(1) = 70, \quad e_5 = 70(\tfrac{3}{2}) = 105.$$

Applying the χ^2 test using (7.13),

$$\chi^2 = \frac{(50-35)^2}{35} + \frac{(60-70)^2}{70} + \frac{(40-35)^2}{35} + \frac{(75-70)^2}{70} + \frac{(90-105)^2}{105}$$

$$= \frac{225}{35} + \frac{100}{70} + \frac{25}{35} + \frac{25}{70} + \frac{225}{105}$$

$$= 11.1.$$

From Table VIII of the Appendix with $n - 2 = 3$ degrees of freedom, at the 5% level of significance, $\chi^2 = 7.8$. Since the calculated value exceeds 7.8, the result is significant. It is concluded that the observed data do not appear to be drawn from a Poisson distribution.

PROBLEM 7.26 According to the theory of Mendelian inheritance, the offspring of a certain species should be colored brown, black, or white in the ratios 5:2:4. If an experiment gives 40, 35, and 35 in those categories, does the observed data fit the Mendelian theory? Use the 1% level of significance.

Solution: The total number of offspring is 110. Since the ratio is 5:2:4, the theoretical frequencies are

$$e_1 = 110(\tfrac{5}{11}) = 50, \quad e_2 = 110(\tfrac{2}{11}) = 20, \quad e_3 = 110(\tfrac{4}{11}) = 40.$$

Since the observed frequencies are $o_1 = 40, o_2 = 35$, and $o_3 = 35$,

$$\chi^2 = \frac{(50-40)^2}{50} + \frac{(20-35)^2}{20} + \frac{(40-35)^2}{40} = 13.875$$

Since the degrees of freedom are 2, $\chi^2 = 9.21$ with a probability 0.01. Hence, the calculated value is significant, and Mendelian theory does not appear to be confirmed by the observed data.

PROBLEM 7.27 Hardy-Weinberg's formula states that the number of flies resulting from certain crossings should be in the ratio $p^2 : 2pq : q^2$, where $p + q = 1$. If $q = 0.4$, is this formula compatible with observed frequencies of 12, 32, and 26?

Solution: With $q = 0.4$, the ratio is 0.36:0.48:0.16. Since the total number of flies observed is 70, the theoretical frequencies should be

$$e_1 = 70(0.36) = 25.2, \quad e_2 = 70(0.48) = 33.6, \quad e_3 = 70(0.16) = 11.2.$$

Since the observed frequencies are $o_1 = 12, o_2 = 32$, and $o_3 = 26$,

$$\chi^2 = \frac{(25.2-12)^2}{25.2} + \frac{(33.6-32)^2}{33.6} + \frac{(11.2-26)^2}{11.2} = 26.55.$$

Since $\chi^2 = 9.21$ for 2 degrees of freedom at the 1% level of significance, the above result is significant and, hence, the observed data is not compatible with the Hardy-Weinberg formula.

7.4   Contingency Tables

A *contingency table* is a two-way table designed to test the compatibility of observed and expected frequencies. It is generally constructed to study the relationship between two variables in which the χ^2 test is used to test the hypothesis that the two variables are independent. Table 7.3 shows a contingency table with m rows and n columns.

TABLE 7.3

variable B / variable A	1	2	$\cdots$	j	$\cdots$	$n-1$	n	Totals
1	x_{11}	x_{12}	$\cdots$	x_{1j}	$\cdots$	$x_{1(n-1)}$	x_{1n}	r_1
2	x_{21}	x_{22}	$\cdots$	x_{2j}	$\cdots$	$x_{2(n-1)}$	x_{2n}	r_2
.	.	.		.		.	.	.
.	.	.		.		.	.	.
.	.	.		.		.	.	.
i	x_{i1}	x_{i2}	$\cdots$	x_{ij}	$\cdots$	$x_{i(n-1)}$	x_{in}	r_i
.	.	.		.		.	.	.
.	.	.		.		.	.	.
.	.	.		.		.	.	.
m	x_{m1}	x_{m2}	$\cdots$	x_{mj}	$\cdots$	$x_{m(n-1)}$	x_{mn}	r_m
Totals	c_1	c_2	$\cdots$	c_j	$\cdots$	c_{n-1}	c_n	$N = nm$

The probability corresponding to the cell in the ith row and jth column is denoted by p_{ij}. The probability corresponding to the ith row is denoted by p_i. The probability corresponding to the jth column is denoted by $\bar{p}_j$.

The hypothesis that the two variables A and B are independent can be written as $H:p_{ij} = p_i\bar{p}_j$ ($i = 1, \cdots, m$, and $j = 1, \cdots, n$). The number of degrees of freedom for testing independence in a contingency table with m rows and n columns is

$$\text{d.f.} = (m-1)(n-1). \tag{7.14}$$

The maximum likelihood estimates of p_i and p_j are

$$\hat{p}_i = \frac{r_i}{N} \quad \text{and} \quad \hat{p}_j = \frac{c_j}{N}, \tag{7.15}$$

where r_i and c_j are the sums of the frequencies in the ith row and in the jth column, respectively; i.e.,

$$r_i = \sum_{j=1}^{n} x_{ij}, \tag{7.16}$$

$$c_j = \sum_{i=1}^{n} x_{ij}, \tag{7.17}$$

$$N = \sum_{i=1}^{m} \sum_{j=1}^{n} x_{ij}. \tag{7.18}$$

The measure of compatibility of observed and expected frequencies is

$$\chi^2 = \sum_{i=1}^{m} \sum_{j=1}^{n} \frac{[x_{ij} - (r_i c_j/N)]^2}{r_i c_j/N} \tag{7.19}$$

$$= N\left(\sum_{i=1}^{m} \sum_{j=1}^{n} \frac{x_{ij}^2}{r_i c_j} - 1\right), \tag{7.20}$$

where N is the number of samples taken. Equation (7.19) possesses a χ^2 distribution with $(m-1)(n-1)$ degrees of freedom, provided that N is sufficiently large and H is true.

PROBLEM 7.28 Establish (7.14).

Solution: If m and n are the numbers of rows and columns in the contingency table, then mn is the number of cells in the table. Hence, $mn - 1$ is the number of degrees of freedom for testing independence in the table. But, in general, since $\sum_1^m p_i = 1$ and $\sum_1^n \bar{p}_j = 1$, there are $(m-1) + (n-1) = m + n - 2$ parameters that must be estimated; hence, the *proper* number of degrees of freedom to test independence in a contingency table is

$$\text{d.f.} = (\text{No. of cells}) - 1 - (\text{No. of estimated parameters})$$
$$= mn - 1 - (m + n - 2)$$
$$= (m-1)(n-1).$$

PROBLEM 7.29 Establish (7.15).

Solution: Consider the contingency table described above. To determine the maximum likelihood estimates of p_i and $\bar{p}_j$, let x_i and x_j be the sums of the frequencies of the ith row and jth column, respectively. The likelihood of the sample is the probability of obtaining the sample in the order in which it occurred. Thus, since the selections are discrete and independent, the likehihood of the sample is

$$L = \prod_{i=1}^m \prod_{j=1}^n p_{ij}{}^{x_{ij}}.$$

But, because of H, this reduces to

$$L = \prod_{i=1}^m \prod_{j=1}^n (p_i \bar{p}_j)^{x_{ij}} = \prod_{i=1}^m \prod_{j=1}^n (p_i)^{x_{ij}} \prod_{i=1}^m \prod_{j=1}^n (\bar{p}_j)^{x_{ij}} = \prod_{i=1}^m p_i^{\sum_{j=1}^n x_{ij}} \bar{p}_j^{\sum_{i=1}^m x_{ij}} = \prod_{i=1}^m p_i^{r_i} \prod_{j=1}^n \bar{p}_j^{c_j}.$$

For convenience, one of the $\bar{p}_j$'s, say $\bar{p}_r$, is expressed in terms of the remaining ones by using the relation $\sum_{j=1}^n \bar{p}_j = 1$; that is,

$$\sum_{\substack{j=1 \\ j \neq r}}^{n-1} \bar{p}_j + \bar{p}_r = 1, \quad \text{or} \quad \bar{p}_r = 1 - \sum_{\substack{j=1 \\ j \neq r}}^{n-1} \bar{p}_j.$$

Hence,

$$L = \left(1 - \sum_{\substack{j=1 \\ j \neq r}}^{n-1} \bar{p}_j\right)^{c_n} \prod_{i=1}^m p_i^{r_i} \prod_{\substack{j=1 \\ j \neq r}}^{n-1} \bar{p}_j{}^{c_j}.$$

Taking logarithms,

$$\log L = c_n \log\left(1 - \sum_{\substack{j=1 \\ j \neq r}}^{n-1} \bar{p}_j\right) + \sum_{i=1}^m r_i \log p_i + \sum_{\substack{j=1 \\ j \neq r}}^{n-1} c_j \log \bar{p}_j.$$

Now, differentiating with respect to p and setting the derivative equal to zero for a maximum,

$$\frac{\partial \log L}{\partial p_j} = \frac{-c_n}{1 - \sum_{\substack{j=1 \\ j \neq n}}^{n-1} p_j} + \frac{c_j}{p_j} = 0.$$

But $1 - \sum_{j=1}^{n-1} \bar{p}_j = \bar{p}_n$; thus,

$$\bar{p}_j = \frac{p_r}{x_n} c_j = \lambda c_j,$$

where λ is independent of the index i. Since this must be true for all $j = 1, \cdots, n$,

$$1 = \sum_{j=1}^{n} \bar{p}_j = \lambda \sum_{1}^{n} c_j = \lambda N.$$

Thus, $\lambda = 1/N$ and the maximum likelihood estimate of $\bar{p}_j$ is

$$\hat{p}_j = \frac{c_j}{N}.$$

Similarly, the maximum likelihood estimate of p_i is

$$\hat{p}_i = \frac{r_i}{N}.$$

PROBLEM 7.30   Establish (7.19–20).

Solution: Consider the contingency table described for the two variables A and B. Let N samples be drawn at random. Then the hypothesis that A and B are independent can be written as $H : p_{ij} = p_i \bar{p}_j$ ($i = 1, \cdots, m$, and $j = 1, \cdots, n$).

If N selections are made and if x_{ij} are observed to be in the cell in the ith row and jth column, then, since the expected number should be $N p_{ij}$, from (7.13),

$$\chi^2 = \sum_{i=1}^{m} \sum_{j=1}^{n} \frac{(x_{ij} - N p_{ij})^2}{N p_{ij}}. \tag{7.21}$$

But, $p_{ij} = p_i \bar{p}_j$; hence,

$$\chi^2 = \sum_{i=1}^{m} \sum_{j=1}^{n} \frac{(x_{ij} - N p_i \bar{p}_j)^2}{N p_i \bar{p}_j} \tag{7.21}$$

with $(m-1)(n-1)$ degrees of freedom. (Cf., Prob. 7.28.) The maximum likelihood estimates of p_i and $\bar{p}_j$ must be obtained (since they are unknown) for the χ^2 test to be applicable. But, from (7.15), the maximum likelihood estimates of p_i and p_j are

$$\hat{p}_i = \frac{r_i}{N} \quad \text{and} \quad \hat{p}_j = \frac{c_j}{N},$$

where r_i and c_j are the sums of the frequencies in the ith row and jth column, respectively. Substituting p_i and $\bar{p}_j$ with $\hat{p}_i$ and $\hat{p}_j$ in (7.21) yields

$$\chi^2 = \sum_{i=1}^{m} \sum_{j=1}^{n} \frac{[x_{ij} - (r_i c_j/N)]^2}{r_i c_j/N}.$$

Now, let $\phi_{ij} = r_i c_j/N$. Then,

$$\chi^2 = \sum_{i=1}^{m} \sum_{j=1}^{n} \frac{(x_{ij} - \phi_{ij})^2}{\phi_{ij}} = \sum_{i=1}^{m} \sum_{j=1}^{n} \frac{x_{ij}^2 - 2\phi_{ij} x_{ij} + \phi_{ij}^2}{\phi_{ij}} = \sum_{i=1}^{m} \sum_{j=1}^{n} \frac{x_{ij}^2}{\phi_{ij}} - 2 \sum_{i=1}^{m} \sum_{j=1}^{n} x_{ij} + \sum_{i=1}^{m} \sum_{j=1}^{n} \phi_{ij}.$$

Since $\sum_{i=1}^{m} \sum_{j=1}^{n} x_{ij} = \sum_{i=1}^{m} \sum_{j=1}^{n} r_i c_j / N = N,$

$$\chi^2 = \sum_{i=1}^{m} \sum_{j=1}^{n} \frac{x_{ij}^2}{\phi_{ij}} - N = N\left(\sum_{i=1}^{m} \sum_{j=1}^{n} \frac{x_{ij}^2}{r_i c_j} - 1\right).$$

PROBLEM 7.31 Show that for the contingency table given below,

$$\chi^2 = \frac{(\alpha + \beta + \gamma + \sigma)(\alpha\sigma - \beta\gamma)^2}{(\alpha + \beta)(\gamma + \sigma)(\beta + \sigma)(\alpha + \gamma)}.$$

		Totals
α	β	$\alpha + \beta$
γ	δ	$\gamma + \delta$
Totals $\alpha + \gamma$	$\beta + \delta$	$\alpha + \beta + \gamma + \delta$

Solution: Let $\alpha + \beta + \gamma + \delta = N$. Using (7.20),

$$\chi^2 = N\left[\frac{\alpha^2}{(\alpha + \beta)(\alpha + \gamma)} + \frac{\beta^2}{(\alpha + \beta)(\beta + \delta)} + \frac{\gamma^2}{(\alpha + \gamma)(\gamma + \delta)} + \frac{\sigma^2}{(\gamma + \delta)(\beta + \delta)} - 1\right]$$

$$= N\left[\frac{\alpha^2(\gamma + \delta)(\beta + \delta) + \beta^2(\gamma + \delta)(\alpha + \delta) + \gamma^2(\alpha + \beta)(\beta + \delta) + \delta^2(\alpha + \beta)(\alpha + \gamma)}{(\alpha + \beta)(\gamma + \delta)(\beta + \delta)(\alpha + \gamma)}\right.$$

$$\left. - \frac{(\alpha + \beta)(\gamma + \delta)(\beta + \delta)(\alpha + \gamma)}{(\alpha + \beta)(\gamma + \delta)(\beta + \delta)(\alpha + \gamma)}\right].$$

The numerator on the right-hand side is

$$\alpha^2(\beta\gamma + \beta\delta + \gamma\delta + \delta^2) + \beta^2(\alpha\gamma + \alpha\delta + \gamma^2 + \gamma\delta) + \gamma^2(\alpha\beta + \beta^2 + \alpha\delta + \beta\delta) + \delta^2(\alpha^2 + \alpha\beta + \alpha\gamma + \beta\gamma)$$

$$- (\alpha\gamma + \beta\gamma + \alpha\delta + \beta\delta)(\alpha\beta + \alpha\delta + \beta\gamma + \gamma\delta)$$

$$= \alpha^2\beta\alpha + \alpha^2\beta\delta + \alpha^2\gamma\delta + \alpha^2\delta^2 + \alpha\beta^2\gamma + \alpha\beta^2\delta + \beta^2\gamma^2 + \beta^2\gamma\delta + \alpha\beta\gamma^2 + \beta^2\gamma^2 + \alpha\gamma^2\delta + \beta\gamma^2\delta + \alpha^2\delta^2$$

$$+ \alpha\beta\delta^2 + \alpha\gamma\delta^2 + \beta\gamma\delta^2 - \alpha^2\beta\gamma - \alpha\beta^2\gamma - \alpha^2\beta\delta - \alpha\beta^2\delta - \alpha^2\gamma\delta - \alpha\beta\gamma\delta - \alpha^2\delta^2 - \alpha\beta\delta^2 - \alpha\beta\gamma^2$$

$$- \beta^2\gamma^2 - \alpha\beta\gamma\delta - \beta^2\gamma\delta - \alpha\gamma^2\sigma - \beta\gamma^2\delta - \alpha\gamma\delta^2 - \beta\gamma\delta^2$$

$$= \alpha^2\delta^2 = 2\alpha\beta\gamma\delta + \beta^2\gamma^2 = (\alpha\delta - \beta\gamma)^2.$$

Hence,

$$\chi^2 = \frac{(\alpha + \beta + \gamma + \delta)(\alpha\delta - \beta\gamma)^2}{(\alpha + \beta)(\gamma + \delta)(\beta + \delta)(\alpha + \gamma)}.$$

PROBLEM 7.32   A lubricant said to reduce failures of a machine was tested as follows: 30 machines were lubricated and 30 others were not. The 60 machines were run simultaneously and the number of failures for each machine was noted. The results were as follows:

	Failed	Not failed	Totals
With lubricant	10	20	30
Without lubricant	19	11	30
Totals	29	31	60

Does this show an association between the use of the lubricant and immunity from failure?

Solution: Using the result of Prob. 7.31,

$$\chi^2 = \frac{(\alpha + \beta + \gamma + \delta)(\alpha\delta - \beta\gamma)^2}{(\alpha + \beta)(\gamma + \delta)(\beta + \delta)(\alpha + \gamma)} = \frac{60(10 \times 11 - 19 \times 20)^2}{(10 + 20)(19 + 11)(20 + 11)(10 + 19)} = \frac{60 \times 72,900}{30 \times 30 \times 31 \times 29} = 5.4.$$

From Table VIII of the Appendix the probability of obtaining a value as high as 5.4 by chance with 1 degree of freedom is less than 0.05, so that an association between the use of the lubricant and greater immunity from failure is indicated.

PROBLEM 7.33 The question "Do you believe in unquestioning patriotism (your country right or wrong)?" was asked of 100 people in different income brackets. The results were as indicated:

	Under $5000	$5-10000	$10-15000	Over $15000	Totals
Questioning	8	10	7	4	29
Unquestioning	10	17	7	3	37
No opinion	15	15	3	1	34
Totals	33	42	17	8	100

Is there an association between income level and unquestioning patriotism?

Solution: Using (7.20),

$$\chi^2 = 100\left(\frac{8^2}{29 \times 33} + \frac{10^2}{37 \times 33} + \frac{15^2}{34 \times 33} + \frac{10^2}{29 \times 42} + \frac{17^2}{37 \times 42} + \frac{15^2}{34 \times 42} + \frac{7^2}{29 \times 17}\right.$$

$$+ \frac{7^2}{37 \times 17} + \frac{3^2}{34 \times 17} + \frac{4^2}{29 \times 8} + \frac{3^2}{37 \times 8} + \frac{1^2}{34 \times 8} - 1\bigg)$$

$$= 100\left(\frac{64}{957} + \frac{100}{1221} + \frac{225}{1122} + \frac{100}{1218} + \frac{289}{1554} + \frac{225}{1428} + \frac{49}{493} + \frac{49}{629}\right.$$

$$+ \frac{9}{578} + \frac{16}{232} + \frac{9}{296} + \frac{1}{272} - 1\bigg)$$

$$= 7.1.$$

The number of degrees of freedom is

$$\text{d.f.} = (m - 1)(n - 1) = (3 - 1)(4 - 1) = 6.$$

From Table VIII of the Appendix, $\chi^2 = 16.812$ for 6 degrees of freedom and the 0.01 level of significance. Thus the above result is not significant and the hypothesis of independence may be accepted. Apparently, there is no statistical basis for concluding that people in different income brackets think differently about "questioning patriotism."

The calculations of χ^2 for a contingency table with two rows and n columns (or n rows and two columns) are simpler. (See Table 7.4.)

TABLE 7.4

	y_1	y_2	y_3		y_n	Totals
x_1	a_1	a_2	a_3	$\cdots$	a_n	r_1
x_2	b_1	b_2	b_3	$\cdots$	b_n	r_2
Totals	c_1	c_2	c_3	$\cdots$	c_n	N

Sometimes a table which looks like a contingency table may actually reflect a completely different situation. Each row represents a different set of observations and the samples in the set are classified according to different attributes y. The number of observations is arbitrary and does not depend on the population. The test is designed to find out if each sample (represented by a row of the table) comes from the same population in which the probability of attribute y_j is p_j.

Brandt-Snedecor's formula, with frequencies as given by Table 7.4, is

$$\chi^2 = \frac{N^2}{r_1 r_2}\left(\sum_j \frac{a_j^2}{c_j} - \frac{r_1^2}{N}\right),\tag{7.22}$$

where $c_j = a_j + b_j$, with $(n-1)$ degrees of freedom. This formula is used in the situation described above.

PROBLEM 7.34 Prove Brandt-Snedecor's formula.

Solution: From (7.20), on substituting the values in Table 7.4,

$$\chi^2 = N\left(\sum_i^m \sum_j^n \frac{x_{ij}^2}{r_i c_j} - 1\right)$$

$$= N\left(\sum_j \frac{a_j^2}{r_1 c_j} + \sum_j \frac{b_j^2}{r_2 c_j} - 1\right)$$

$$= \frac{N}{r_1 r_2}\left(r_2 \sum_j \frac{a_j^2}{c_j} + r_1 \sum_j \frac{(c_j - a_j)^2}{c_j} - r_1 r_2\right)$$

$$= \frac{N}{r_1 r_2}\left(r_2 \sum_j \frac{a_j^2}{c_j} + r_1 \sum_j \frac{c_j^2 - 2c_j a_j + a_j^2}{c_j} - r_1 r_2\right)$$

$$= \frac{N}{r_1 r_2}\left(r_2 \sum_j \frac{a_j^2}{c_j} + r_1 \sum_j c_j - 2r_1 \sum_j a_j + r_1 \sum_j \frac{a_j^2}{c_j} - r_1 r_2\right)$$

$$= \frac{N}{r_1 r_2}\left[(r_1 + r_2)\sum_j \frac{a_j^2}{c_j} + Nr_1 - 2r_1^2 - r_1(N - r_1)\right]$$

$$= \frac{N}{r_1 r_2}\left(N\sum_j \frac{a_j^2}{c_j} - r_1^2\right)$$

$$= \frac{N^2}{r_1 r_2}\left(\sum_j \frac{a_j^2}{c_j} - \frac{r^2}{N}\right)$$

PROBLEM 7.35 A random sample of 50 men and 50 women was surveyed as to drinking habits, and classified as alcoholics, heavy drinkers, light drinkers, and teetotalers. The results were

	Alcoholics	Heavy Drinkers	Light Drinkers	Teetotalers	Totals
Male	1	10	30	9	50
Female	2	8	25	15	50
Totals	3	18	55	24	100

Is there any significant difference between the alcohol consumption of men and women?

Solution: In this situation, Brandt-Snedecor's formula is used. Thus,

$$\chi^2 = \frac{(100)^2}{(50)(50)}\left(\frac{1^2}{3} + \frac{(10)^2}{18} + \frac{(30)^2}{55} + \frac{9^2}{24} - \frac{(50)^2}{100}\right) = 2.52.$$

With 3 degrees of freedom, $\chi^2 = 7.815$ at the 5% level of significance; consequently, the result is not significant and the hypothesis of independence may be accepted.

If a set of data is believed to come from either a binomial or Poisson population but there are so few values that it is useless to fit a binomial or Poisson distribution to the observed distribution, then the hypothesis that the data came from the population is tested by determining the compatibility of the sample variance with the theoretical variance.

Samples are drawn from a binomial population from which there are x_1 "successes" and $(n - x_1)$ "failures" in n trials. The experiment is repeated k times, that is, k groups of n samples are taken, resulting in $x_1, x_2, \cdots,$ x_k successes and $(n - x_1), (n - x_2), \cdots, (n - x_k)$ failures. These two sets of numbers can be arranged in a 2-way table as shown in Table 7.5.

TABLE 7.5

Successes	x_1	x_2	$\cdots$	x_k
Failures	$n - x_1$	$n - x_2$	$\cdots$	$n - x_k$

The test for the compatibility of the sample variance with the theoretical variance for the data of Table 7.5, is called *the binomial index of dispersion*, namely,

$$\chi^2 = \frac{\sum_{i=1}^{k} (x_i - \bar{x})^2}{\bar{x}(1 - \bar{x}/n)}, \tag{7.23}$$

where $\bar{x}$ is the maximum likelihood estimates for the theoretical frequencies.

If the probability p of success is very small and n is very large, the binomial index of dispersion reduces to *the Poisson index of dispersion*, namely,

$$\chi^2 = \sum_{i=1}^{k} \frac{(x_i - \bar{x})^2}{\bar{x}}. \tag{7.24}$$

PROBLEM 7.36   What is the difference between Table 7.5 and an ordinary contingency table?

Solution: In an ordinary contingency table, successive observations are free to fall in any cell of the table, whereas in Table 7.5, the first n trials *must* fall in one of the two cells of the first column only, the second n trials *must* fall in one of the two cells of the second column, and so on. Note that (7.19-20) are also applicable to this modified contingency table.

PROBLEM 7.37   Derive (7.23).

Solution: Treating Table 7.5 as an ordinary contingency table, and using the technique used to find the maximum likelihood estimates for the theoretical frequencies e_i in (7.15), the maximum likelihood estimates for the first row are

$$\hat{e}_i = \frac{\sum_{i=1}^{k} x_i}{nk} \, n = \bar{x}, \quad i = 1, \cdots, k.$$

Hence, for the second row, they are $n - \bar{x}$. Substituting these in (7.22),

$$\chi^2 = \sum_{i=1}^{k} \frac{(x_i - \bar{x})^2}{\bar{x}} + \frac{\sum_{i=1}^{k}(x_i - \bar{x})^2}{n - \bar{x}} = \left(\frac{1}{\bar{x}} + \frac{1}{n - \bar{x}}\right)\sum_{i=1}^{k}(x_i - \bar{x})^2 = \frac{\sum_{i=1}^{k}(x_i - \bar{x})^2}{\bar{x}(1 - \bar{x}/n)} \ . \qquad [7.23]$$

Hence, (7.23) also possesses the χ^2 distribution with $(k-1)$ degrees of freedom.

PROBLEM 7.38 Six boxes of different brands of $\frac{5}{8}$-in. screws containing 12 screws each are inspected for specifications. The number of screws below specifications are 2, 4, 1, 6, 0, 5, respectively. Are the six brands of comparable quality? Use the 5% level of significance.

Solution: The maximum likelihood estimate is

$$\bar{x} = \frac{\sum_{i=1}^{k} x_k}{k} = \frac{2 + 4 + 1 + 6 + 0 + 5}{6} = 3.$$

Then,

$$\sum_{i=1}^{6}(x_i - \bar{x})^2 = (2 - 3)^2 + (4 - 3)^2 + (1 - 3)^2 + (6 - 3)^2 + (0 - 3)^2 + (5 - 3)^2 = 28,$$

$$\bar{x}(1 - \bar{x}/n) = 3(1 - \tfrac{3}{12}) = 2.25.$$

Hence,

$$\chi^2 = \frac{\sum_{i=1}^{6}(x_i - \bar{x})^2}{\bar{x}(1 - \bar{x}/n)} = \frac{28}{2.25} = 12.3$$

with 5 degrees of freedom. From Table VIII of the Appendix, $\chi^2 = 11.07$ at the 5% level of significance. Since the calculated value $\chi^2 = 12.3$ exceeds the tabulated value, the six brands do not appear to be of comparable quality.

PROBLEM 7.39 A housing project consists of 10 buildings, each having 45 apartments. Each building is inspected, and the number of apartments violating the fire laws are 15, 10, 8, 7, 15, 7, 4, 2, 5, 14. Is it reasonable to assume that the number of violations are comparable in all 10 buildings?

Solution: The maximum likelihood estimate is

$$\bar{x} = \frac{\sum_{i=1}^{k} x_i}{k} = \frac{15 + 10 + 8 + 7 + 15 + 7 + 4 + 2 + 5 + 14}{10} = 8.7.$$

Then,

$$\sum_{i=1}^{10}(x_i - \bar{x})^2 = (15 - 8.7)^2 + (10 - 8.7)^2 + (8 - 8.7)^2 + (7 - 8.7)^2 + (15 - 8.7)^2$$

$$+ (7 - 8.7)^2 + (4 - 8.7)^2 + (2 - 8.7)^2 + (5 - 8.7)^2 + (14 - 8.7)^2$$

$$= 196.10,$$

$$\bar{x}(1 - \bar{x}/n) = 8.7(1 - 8.7/45)$$

$$= 7.00.$$

Hence,

$$\chi^2 = \frac{\sum_{i=1}^{10} (x_i - \bar{x})^2}{\bar{x}(1 - \bar{x}/n)} = \frac{196.10}{7.00} = 28.01.$$

From Table VIII of the Appendix for 9 degrees of freedom, $p(\chi^2 \geq 28) < 0.001$ so that it is not reasonable to assume that all 10 buildings are comparable.

PROBLEM 7.40 Derive (7.24).

Solution: Since the sample estimate of p is $\bar{x}/n$, $1 - \bar{x}/n$ will be approximately equal to 1 because $\bar{x}/n$ is very close to zero when p is very small. Hence, from (7.23) with $1 - \bar{x}/n \approx 1$,

$$\chi^2 = \frac{\sum_{i=1}^{k} (x_i - \bar{x})^2}{\bar{x}}.$$

PROBLEM 7.41 The number of accidents per month in a certain locality for the year 1969 were as follows: 5, 8, 10, 15, 4, 2, 6, 7, 9, 1, 20, 33. Assume that accidents follow a Poisson distribution. Test the homogeneity of the above frequencies.

Solution: Since the accidents are assumed to be Poisson distributed, the Poisson index of dispersion is used to test the homogeneity of the data. Hence,

$$\bar{x} = \frac{5 + 8 + 10 + 15 + 4 + 2 + 6 + 7 + 9 + 1 + 20 + 33}{12} = 10,$$

$$\sum_{i=1}^{12} (x_i - \bar{x})^2 = (5 - 10)^2 + (8 - 10)^2 + (10 - 10)^2 + (15 - 10)^2 + (4 - 10)^2 + (2 - 10)^2$$

$$+ (6 - 10)^2 + (7 - 10)^2 + (9 - 10)^2 + (1 - 10)^2 + (20 - 10)^2 + (33 - 10)^2$$

$$= 890.$$

Therefore,

$$\chi^2 = \frac{890}{10} = 89.$$

For 11 degrees of freedom, $\chi^2 = 24.7$ at the 1% level of significance. Since the calculated value exceeds the tabulated value, this test *does* give reason to question the assumption that the data comes from a Poisson population.

PROBLEM 7.42 Consider the frequencies 8, 4, 6, 5, 9, 12, 10, 2. (a) Determine if they appear to be Poisson distributed. (b) Determine if it might be more appropriate to say they appear to be binomially distributed.

Solution: (a) The Poisson index of dispersion is used to determine if the given frequencies are Poisson distributed. Hence,

$$\bar{x} = \frac{8 + 4 + 6 + 5 + 9 + 12 + 10 + 2}{8} = \frac{56}{8} = 7,$$

$$\sum_{i=1}^{8} (x_i - \bar{x})^2 = (3 - 7)^2 + (4 - 7)^2 + (6 - 7)^2 + (5 - 7)^2 + (9 - 7)^2$$

$$+ (12 - 7)^2 + (10 - 7)^2 + (2 - 7)^2$$

$$= 78.$$

Therefore,

$$\chi^2 = \frac{\displaystyle\sum_{i=1}^{8} (x_i - \bar{x})^2}{\bar{x}} = \frac{78}{7} = 11.1.$$

For 7 degrees of freedom, $\chi^2 = 14.1$ at the 5% level of significance; consequently, the result is not significant. Thus, the given frequencies *can* be said to be Poisson distributed.

(b) The binomial index of dispersion is used to determine if the given frequencies are binomially distributed. From part (a), $\bar{x} = 7$ and $\sum_{i=1}^{8} (x_i - \bar{x})^2 = 78$. Hence,

$$\chi^2 = \frac{\displaystyle\sum_{i=1}^{8} (x_i - \bar{x})^2}{\bar{x}(1 - \bar{x}/n)} = \frac{78}{7(1 - \frac{7}{8})} = 89.1.$$

For 7 degrees of freedom, $p(\chi^2 \geqslant 24.3) < 0.001$; consequently, the result is highly significant. Thus, the given frequencies do not appear to be binomially distributed.

7.5   Analysis of Variance: Comparison of a Set of Means

Analysis of variance is a technique used to trace the different sources that bring about the variation between the observed and true mean of a sample. This splitting of the variation helps to eliminate the effects of interfering variables and, thereby increases the sensitivity of the experiment. All common analysis of variance tests make the following assumptions:

(1) The samples are *normally* and *independently* distributed.
(2) The samples have the *same* variance.
(3) Each sample has been "treated" differently and these treatments have had an additive effect on the samples.

Table 7.6 shows m sets of n independently and normally distributed (with the same variance) samples, displayed in a rectangular array.

TABLE 7.6.   A Rectangular Array of m Sets of n Independently and Normally Distributed Samples of Equal Variance.

Sets	Samples 1	2	$\cdots$	j	$\cdots$	n	Row Means[a]
1	x_{11}	x_{12}	$\cdots$	x_{1j}	$\cdots$	x_{1n}	$\bar{r}_1$
2	x_{21}	x_{22}	$\cdots$	x_{2j}	$\cdots$	x_{2n}	$\bar{r}_2$
3	.	.		.		.	.
.	.	.		.		.	.
.	.	.		.		.	.
i	x_{i1}	x_{i2}	$\cdots$	x_{ij}	$\cdots$	x_{in}	$\bar{r}_i$
.	.	.		.		.	.
.	.	.		.		.	.
.	.	.		.		.	.
m	x_{m1}	x_{m2}	$\cdots$	x_{mj}	$\cdots$	x_{mn}	$\bar{r}_m$
Column Means[b]	$\bar{c}_1$	$\bar{c}_2$	$\cdots$	$\bar{c}_j$	$\cdots$	$\bar{c}_n$	Sample Mean[c] $= \bar{x}$

[a]Row mean $\bar{r}_i = \dfrac{1}{n} \displaystyle\sum_{j=1}^{n} x_{ij}$.   [b]Column mean $\bar{c}_j = \dfrac{1}{m} \displaystyle\sum_{i=1}^{m} x_{ij}$.   [c]Sample mean $\bar{x} = \dfrac{1}{nm} \displaystyle\sum_{i=1}^{m}\sum_{j=1}^{n} x_{ij}$.

Then the analysis of variance technique can be used to test if the true column means of Table 7.6 are equal.

Let μ_{ij} be the mean of the sample x_{ij} in Table 7.6, which is the outcome of a single random experiment of mn random variables. To perform the analysis, it is assumed that μ_{ij} can be written as

$$\mu_{ij} = m_i + n_j + p, \tag{7.25}$$

where m_i, n_j, and p denote the expected values $E[\bar{r}_i - \bar{x}]$, $E[\bar{c}_j - \bar{x}]$, and $E[\bar{x}]$, respectively.

The hypothesis that the *theoretical column means* of the random variables x_{ij} of Table 7.6 are *equal*, that is,

$$H: n_j = 0, \quad j = 1, 2, \cdots, n, \tag{7.26}$$

can be tested by using the right-hand tail of the F-distribution as the critical region, where

$$F = \frac{(m-1) \sum\limits_{i=1}^{m} \sum\limits_{j=1}^{n} (\bar{c}_j - \bar{x})^2}{\sum\limits_{i=1}^{m} \sum\limits_{j=1}^{n} (x_{ij} - \bar{r}_i - \bar{c}_j + \bar{x})^2} \tag{7.27}$$

and where $\nu_1 = n - 1$ and $\nu_2 = (m-1)(n-1)$ are the degrees of freedom.

Alternatively, when row classifications are not available, (7.27) can be written as

$$F = \frac{n(m-1) \sum\limits_{i=1}^{m} \sum\limits_{j=1}^{n} (\bar{c}_j - \bar{x})^2}{(n-1) \sum\limits_{i=1}^{m} \sum\limits_{j=1}^{n} (x_{ij} - \bar{c}_j)^2}, \quad \nu_1 = n-1, \nu_2 = n(m-1), \tag{7.28}$$

or

$$F = \frac{nm(m-1) \sum\limits_{j=1}^{n} (\bar{c}_j - \bar{x})^2}{(n-1) \sum\limits_{i=1}^{m} \sum\limits_{j=1}^{n} (x_{ij} - \bar{c}_j)^2}, \quad \nu_1 = n-1, \nu_2 = n(m-1). \tag{7.29}$$

Tables VI and VII of the Appendix give values of F for the 1% and 5% levels of significance. The value of F calculated using (7.27-9) is compared against the tabulated values in Tables VI-VII of the Appendix for the appropriate number of degrees of freedom and level of significance. If the calculated value exceeds the tabulated value, it is concluded that the variation of the sample column means $\bar{c}_j$, $j = 1, \cdots, n$, exceeds what one would normally expect from a random sampling of a normal variate.

The value of F can be calculated directly in terms of the array elements using

$$\sum_{j=1}^{n} (\bar{c}_j - \bar{x})^2 = \frac{1}{m^2} \sum_{j=1}^{n} \left(\sum_{i=1}^{m} x_{ij} \right)^2 - \frac{1}{m^2 n} \left(\sum_{i=1}^{m} \sum_{j=1}^{n} x_{ij} \right)^2, \tag{7.30}$$

$$\sum_{i=1}^{m} \sum_{j=1}^{n} (x_{ij} - \bar{c}_j)^2 = \sum_{i=1}^{m} \sum_{j=1}^{n} x_{ij}^2 - \frac{1}{m} \sum_{j=1}^{n} \left(\sum_{i=1}^{m} x_{ij} \right)^2. \tag{7.31}$$

PROBLEM 7.43 Explain the meaning of the hypothesis (7.25). Use an example.

Solution: Hypothesis (7.25) states that the mean of the variable is the sum of the row and column effects m_i and n_j, and the general mean p.

Consider an archery contest in which five men participate. If the ith archer was superior to the others, then his mean score would exceed the mean score for all five archers by a positive amount m_i, whereas if he was inferior, m_i would be negative. Similarly, if the contest was to test the superiority (inferiority) of the brands of bows and arrows, n_j would be used to determine this (as with m_i above).

PROBLEM 7.44   What are the restrictions of hypothesis (7.25)?

Solution: In many practical problems it is not possible to assume that the effects of the two variables of classification are additive in the simple fashion suggested by (7.25).

For example, if the columns of Table 7.6 represent the different amount of oil of Type I added to a machine, and the rows correspond to different amounts of oil of Type II added to the same machine, one would not expect that the effects of these two oils on the operation of the machine would act independently in the simple manner suggested by (7.25).

PROBLEM 7.45   Show that

$$\sum_{i=1}^{m} m_i = \sum_{j=1}^{n} n_j = 0 \tag{7.32}$$

under the hypothesis (7.25).

Solution: Since $\bar{x}$ is the sample mean of both $\bar{r}_i$ and $\bar{c}_j$,

$$\sum_{i=1}^{m} (\bar{r}_i - \bar{x}) = 0 \quad \text{and} \quad \sum_{j=1}^{n} (\bar{c}_j - \bar{x}) = 0.$$

Hence, taking the expected value of these sums, $\displaystyle\sum_{i=1}^{m} m_i = \sum_{j=1}^{n} n_j = 0.$

PROBLEM 7.46   (a) Prove that the expected values of $\bar{r}_i$ and $\bar{c}_j$ are given by, respectively,

$$E(\bar{r}_i) = p \quad \text{and} \quad E(\bar{c}_j) = p, \tag{7.33}$$

where p is the expected value of $\bar{x}$, under the hypothesis (7.25). (b) If σ^2 is the variance of x_{ij}, show that the variances of $\bar{r}_i$ and $\bar{c}_j$ are σ^2/n and σ^2/m, respectively.

Solution: (a) The mean of $\bar{r}_i$ is

$$E(\bar{r}_i) = E\left(\frac{1}{n} \sum_{j=1}^{n} x_{ij}\right) = \frac{1}{n}\sum_{j=1}^{n} E(x_{ij}) = \frac{1}{n}\sum_{j=1}^{n} p = p.$$

The second equation can be proved in a similar manner.

(b) Since $\bar{r}_i = \dfrac{1}{n} \displaystyle\sum_{j=1}^{n} x_{ij}$, the variance of $n\bar{r}_i$ is the sum of the variances of $x_{i1}, x_{i2}, \cdots, x_{in}$. Thus,

$$\mathrm{Var}\,(\bar{r}_i) = \frac{1}{n^2}\,(n\sigma^2) = \frac{1}{n}\sigma^2.$$

In a similar manner,

$$\mathrm{Var}\,(\bar{c}_j) = \frac{1}{m^2}(m\sigma^2) = \frac{1}{m}\,\sigma^2.$$

PROBLEM 7.47   Establish (7.27).

Solution: All assumptions stated for (7.27) are assumed and the samples are as given in Table 7.6. The total variation is separated into components that are of experimental interest and which can be used in the significance test using the F-distribution in Chap. 6. Then the total sum of the square of deviations of the samples x_{ij} from their sample mean $\bar{x}$ is

$$\sum_{i=1}^{m} \sum_{j=1}^{n} (x_{ij} - \bar{x})^2 = \sum_{i=1}^{m} \sum_{j=1}^{n} [(\bar{r}_i - \bar{x}) + (\bar{c}_j - \bar{x}) + (x_{ij} - \bar{r}_i - \bar{c}_j + \bar{x})]^2$$

$$= \sum_{i=1}^{m} \sum_{j=1}^{n} [(\bar{r}_i - \bar{x})^2 + (\bar{c}_j - \bar{x})^2 + (x_{ij} - \bar{r}_i - \bar{c}_j + \bar{x})^2]$$

$$+ 2 \sum_{i=1}^{m} \sum_{j=1}^{n} [(\bar{r}_i - \bar{x})(\bar{c}_j - \bar{x}) + (\bar{r}_i - \bar{x})(x_{ij} - \bar{r}_i + \bar{c}_j + \bar{x})$$

$$+ (\bar{c}_j - \bar{x})(x_{ij} - \bar{r}_i - \bar{c}_j + \bar{x})] . \tag{7.34}$$

But all the cross-product terms of the second part of the right-hand side are zero since from (7.32) and Table 7.6, $\sum_{i=1}^{m} m_i = \sum_{j=1}^{n} n_i = 0$; thus,

$$\sum_{i=1}^{m} \sum_{j=1}^{n} (\bar{r}_i - \bar{x})(\bar{c}_j - \bar{x}) = \sum_{i=1}^{m} (\bar{r}_i - \bar{x}) \sum_{j=1}^{n} (\bar{c}_j - \bar{x})$$

$$= \sum_{i=1}^{n} m_i \sum_{j=1}^{n} n_j$$

$$= 0,$$

$$\sum_{i=1}^{m} \sum_{j=1}^{n} (\bar{r}_i - \bar{x})(x_{ij} - \bar{r}_i - \bar{c}_j + \bar{x}) = \sum_{i=1}^{m} (\bar{r}_i - \bar{x}) \sum_{j=1}^{n} (x_{ij} - \bar{r}_i - \bar{c}_j + \bar{x})$$

$$= \sum_{i=1}^{n} (\bar{r}_i - \bar{x})(n\bar{r}_i - m\bar{r}_i - m\bar{x} + n\bar{x})$$

$$= 0,$$

$$\sum_{i=1}^{m} \sum_{j=1}^{n} (\bar{c}_j - \bar{x})(\bar{x}_{ij} - \bar{r}_i - \bar{c}_j + \bar{x}) = \sum_{j=1}^{n} (\bar{c}_j - \bar{x}) \sum_{i=1}^{m} (x_{ij} - \bar{r}_i - \bar{c}_j + \bar{x})$$

$$= \sum_{j=1}^{n} (\bar{c}_j - \bar{x})(m\bar{c}_j - m\bar{c}_j - m\bar{x} + m\bar{x})$$

$$= 0.$$

Hence, (7.34) becomes

$$\sum_{i=1}^{m} \sum_{j=1}^{n} (x_{ij} - \bar{x})^2 = \sum_{i=1}^{m} \sum_{j=1}^{n} [(\bar{r}_i - \bar{x})^2 + (\bar{c}_j - \bar{x})^2 + (x_{ij} - \bar{r}_i - \bar{c}_j + \bar{x})^2] . \tag{7.35}$$

Only two of the quantities of the right-hand side of (7.35) represent the components of variation that are of experimental interest and that can be used in a significance test using the F-distribution. Since the experiment is to test the equality of theoretical column means, the first term on the right-hand side of (7.35) is of no interest because it gives variations between the row means, with which the experimenter is not concerned; but, the second term is of interest because it measures the variation of column means and this variation will be determined by the validity of the hypothesis (7.26). The last term is a measure of the x_{ij}'s after the variation due to both row and column differences has been eliminated. Hence, the last term is of interest because it presents a basis for comparison for the second term. Since these are the only two terms of interest, they are converted into χ^2 variables so that the F-distribution can be applied.

Since $\bar{c}_j$ is a linear combination of the normal and independent variables x_{ij}, it is normally and independently distributed with mean p and variance σ^2/m when (7.26) is true. (Cf., Prob. 7.46.) Now, dividing the second term by the variance,

$$\sum_{j=1}^{n} \frac{\bar{c}_j - \bar{x}}{\sigma^2/m} = \sum_{i=1}^{m} \sum_{j=1}^{n} \frac{(\bar{c}_j - \bar{x})^2}{\sigma^2}, \tag{7.36}$$

which possesses a χ^2 distribution with $(n-1)$ degrees of freedom. Hence, the second term on the right-hand side of (7.35) possesses a χ^2 distribution with $(n-1)$ degrees of freedom when (7.26) is true.

The third term on the right-hand side of (7.35) divided by σ^2, that is,

$$\frac{1}{\sigma^2} \sum_{i=1}^{m} \sum_{j=1}^{n} (x_{ij} - \bar{r}_i - \bar{c}_j + \bar{x}), \tag{7.37}$$

also possesses a χ^2 distribution, but it is beyond the scope of this book to demonstrate its proof. The degrees of freedom are determined as follows: the left-hand side of (7.35) possesses a χ^2 distribution with $(mn-1)$ degrees of freedom. Since μ_{ij} are equal by hypothesis and the second sum has $(m-1)$ degrees of freedom, it follows by subtraction that the last sum on the right must have

$$mn - 1 - [(m-1) + (n-1)] = (m-1)(n-1)$$

degrees of freedom.

Once again, it is beyond the scope of this book to show that the χ^2 distribution of both the second and third terms of the right-hand side of (7.35) is independently distributed; hence, this independence is accepted without proof.

Thus, dividing (7.36) by $(n-1)$ and (7.37) by $(m-1)(n-1)$, the ratio will possess an F-distribution; that is, (7.27) is established.

PROBLEM 7.48 Establish (7.28).

Solution: Since the row classification is not available, the identity (7.35) becomes

$$\sum_{i=1}^{m} \sum_{j=1}^{n} (x_{ij} - \bar{x})^2 = \sum_{i=1}^{m} \sum_{j=1}^{n} (\bar{c}_j - \bar{x})^2 + \sum_{i=1}^{m} \sum_{j=1}^{n} (x_{ij} - \bar{c}_j)^2 \tag{7.38}$$

since $\bar{r}_i = \bar{x}$ when row classifications are not available.

The second term of the right-hand side of (7.38), when divided by σ^2, has a χ^2 distribution with $n(m-1)$ degrees of freedom. (Cf., Prob. 7.47.) Then, assuming that this χ^2 variable and the χ^2 variable given by (7.36) are independently distributed,

$$F = \frac{n(m-1) \sum_{i=1}^{m} \sum_{j=1}^{n} (\bar{c}_j - \bar{x})^2}{(n-1) \sum_{i=1}^{m} \sum_{j=1}^{n} (x_{ij} - \bar{c}_j)^2}, \quad \nu_1 = (n-1), \nu_2 = n(m-1).$$

PROBLEM 7.49 Two independent sets of normally distributed samples are obtained. Test the hypothesis that the two sets given below were obtained from the same normal distribution. Use the 5% level of significance.

Sets \ Samples	1	2	3
1	3	2	2
2	5	4	2

Solution: Since there are two sets of samples, $m = 2$. Also, since each set contains three samples, $n = 3$. Hence,

$$x_{11} = 3, \quad x_{12} = 2, \quad x_{13} = 2, \quad x_{21} = 5, \quad x_{22} = 4, \quad x_{23} = 2.$$

From the data table, the column means are

$$\bar{c}_1 = \tfrac{1}{2}(3 + 5) = 4, \quad \bar{c}_2 = \tfrac{1}{2}(2 + 4) = 3, \quad \bar{c}_3 = \tfrac{1}{2}(2 + 2) = 2.$$

The sample mean is

$$\bar{x} = \frac{1}{(2)(3)}(3 + 5 + 2 + 4 + 2 + 2) = 3.$$

Substitution into (7.29) then gives

$$F = \frac{(3)(2)(1)[(4 - 3)^2 + (3 - 3)^2 + (2 - 3)^2]}{(2) \displaystyle\sum_{i=1}^{2} [(x_{i1} - \bar{x}_1)^2 + (x_{i2} - \bar{x}_2)^2 + (x_{i3} - \bar{x}_3)^2]}$$

$$= \frac{3(1 + 0 + 1)}{(x_{11} - \bar{x}_1)^2 + (x_{21} - \bar{x}_1)^2 + (x_{12} - \bar{x}_2)^2 + (x_{22} - \bar{x}_2)^2 + (x_{13} - \bar{x}_3)^2 + (x_{23} - \bar{x}_3)^2}$$

$$= \frac{6}{(3 - 4)^2 + (5 - 4)^2 + (2 - 3)^2 + (4 - 3)^2 + (2 - 2)^2 + (2 - 2)^2}$$

$$= 1.5.$$

To determine whether $F = 1.5$ exceeds the tabulated value of F at the 5% level of significance, Table VII of the Appendix, with $\nu_1 = n - 1 = 2$ and $\nu_2 = n(m - 1) = 3$, shows that $F = 9.55$. Hence, the difference between sample means is not significant.

PROBLEM 7.50 Calculate F in Prob. 7.49 using (7.30–31).

Solution: From (7.30–31),

$$\sum_{j=1}^{3} (\bar{c}_j - \bar{x})^2 = \frac{1}{2^2} \sum_{j=1}^{3} \left(\sum_{i=1}^{2} x_{ij} \right)^2 - \frac{1}{2^2 \cdot 3} \left(\sum_{i=1}^{2} \sum_{j=1}^{3} x_{ij} \right)^2$$

$$= \tfrac{1}{4}[(x_{11} + x_{21})^2 + (x_{12} + x_{22})^2 + (x_{13} + x_{23})^2] - \tfrac{1}{12}(x_{11} + x_{21} + x_{12} + x_{22} + x_{13} + x_{23})^2$$

$$= \tfrac{1}{4}(8^2 + 6^2 + 4^2) - \tfrac{1}{12}(3 + 5 + 2 + 4 + 2 + 2)^2$$

$$= 29 - 27$$

$$= 2,$$

$$\sum_{i=1}^{2} \sum_{j=1}^{3} (x_{ij} - \bar{c}_j)^2 = \sum_{i=1}^{2} \sum_{j=1}^{3} x_{ij}^2 - \frac{1}{2} \sum_{j=1}^{3} \left(\sum_{i=1}^{2} x_{ij} \right)^2.$$

Since the second term on the right-hand side of (7.30) is just $-m$ times the first term on the right-hand side of (7.29), previously found equal to 29, it follows that

$$\sum_{i=1}^{2} \sum_{j=1}^{3} (x_{ij} - \bar{c}_j)^2 = x_{11}^2 + x_{21}^2 + x_{12}^2 + x_{22}^2 + x_{13}^2 + x_{23}^2 - 2(29) = 9 + 25 + 4 + 16 + 4 + 4 - 58 = 4.$$

Therefore, from (7.8),

$$F = \frac{(2)(3)(1)(2)}{(2)(4)} = 1.5.$$

PROBLEM 7.51 A certain engine is made by two assembly lines. A sample of four engines are drawn at random from the outputs of each assembly line and the efficiencies measured. For the values given below, is there a significant difference between the engines produced by the two lines?

Engine Efficiency	1	2	3	4
Line A	30	26	26	26
Line B	32	24	36	40

Solution: The data above is arranged in the form of the array of Table 7.6. Since the variability of the columns is to be tested, (7.27) is used. Since $m = 4$ and $n = 2$, from (7.27),

$$F = \frac{(4)(3) \sum_{j=1}^{2} (\bar{c}_j - \bar{x})^2}{\sum_{i=1}^{4} \sum_{j=1}^{2} (x_{ij} - \bar{r}_i - \bar{c}_j - \bar{x})^2}.$$

The sample mean is

$$\bar{x} = \frac{1}{4.2} (30 + 26 + 26 + 26 + 32 + 24 + 36 + 40) = 30.$$

The column means are given by

$$\bar{c}_A = \tfrac{1}{4}(30 + 26 + 26 + 26) = 27, \qquad \bar{c}_B = \tfrac{1}{4}(32 + 24 + 36 + 40) = 33.$$

Similarly, the means of the rows are

$$\bar{r}_1 = \tfrac{1}{2}(30 + 32) = 31, \qquad \bar{r}_2 = \tfrac{1}{2}(26 + 24) = 25, \qquad \bar{r}_3 = \tfrac{1}{2}(26 + 36) = 31, \qquad \bar{r}_4 = \tfrac{1}{2}(26 + 40) = 33.$$

Therefore,

$$F = \frac{12[(27 - 30)^2 + (33 - 30)^2]}{\sum_{i=1}^{4} (x_{i1} - \bar{c}_A - \bar{r}_i + \bar{x})^2 + (x_{i2} - \bar{c}_B - \bar{r}_i + \bar{x})^2]}$$

$$= \frac{216}{\sum_{i=1}^{4} [(x_{i1} - \bar{r}_i + 3)^2 + (x_{i2} - \bar{r}_i - 3)^2]}.$$

The denominator can be expanded to give

$$(30 - 31 + 3)^2 + (26 - 25 + 3)^2 + (26 - 31 + 3)^2 + (26 - 33 + 3)^2 + (32 - 31 - 3)^2$$
$$+ (24 - 25 - 3)^2 + (36 - 31 - 3)^2 + (40 - 33 - 3)^2 = 80.$$

Thus,

$$F = \frac{216}{80} = 2.7.$$

The number of degrees of freedom are

$$\nu_1 = n - 1 = 1, \qquad \nu_2 = (n - 1)(m - 1) = 3.$$

From Table VII of the Appendix, at the 5% level of significance with $v_1 = 1$ and $v_2 = 3$, $F = 10.13$. Since the calculated value is smaller than 10.13, it is concluded that on the basis of the available data no significant difference exists between the two outputs.

7.6 Components of Variances

Analysis of variance is also used to determine whether "treatments" on a set of samples have had any additive effects. The n samples in each of the m sets examined are assumed to be a random selection from a large population x of possible samples. A linearity assumption is made about the variable x_{ij} rather than its mean μ_{ij}. To perform the necessary analysis, it is assumed that the x_{ij} are normally distributed and each can be expressed as

$$x_{ij} = \alpha_i + \beta_j + \gamma_{ij}, \tag{7.39}$$

where α_i, β_j, and γ_{ij} are normal and independent variates. If the means of α_i, β_j, and γ_{ij} are μ_r, μ_s, and μ_t, and if their variances are σ_r^2, σ_s^2, and σ_t^2, respectively, then the expected value and the variance of x_{ij} are

$$E[x_{ij}] = \mu_r + \mu_s + \mu_t, \qquad \sigma_{x_{ij}}^2 = \sigma_r^2 + \sigma_s^2 + \sigma_t^2. \tag{7.40}$$

The hypothesis that there are no column effects, that is

$$H: \sigma_s^2 = 0, \tag{7.41}$$

can be tested by using the right-hand tail of the F-distribution as the critical region, where

$$F = \frac{(m-1)\sum_{i=1}^{m}\sum_{j=1}^{n}(\bar{c}_j - \bar{x})^2}{\sum_{i=1}^{m}\sum_{j=1}^{n}(x_{ij} - \bar{r}_i - \bar{c}_j + \bar{x})^2}, \tag{7.42}$$

and where $v_1 = n - 1$ and $v_2 = (m - 1)(n - 1)$ are the degrees of freedom. (Cf., Table 7.6.)

PROBLEM 7.52 Show that the variables x_{ij} above are not independent.

Solution: This result follows immediately from (7.39–40) and can be seen by comparing the two variables $x_{11} = \alpha_1 + \beta_1 + \gamma_{11}$ and $x_{21} = \gamma_2 + \beta_1 + \gamma_{21}$. Since x_{11} and x_{21} contain the common variable β_1, with the remaining variables being independent, if follows that x_{11} and x_{21} are not independent.

PROBLEM 7.53 Interpret (7.42) and explain the difference between it and (7.27).

Solution: Even though (7.27) and (7.42) are the same, their mathematical formulations are quite different. Consider the example of Prob. 7.43. Under the hypothesis (7.41), the bows or arrows used in the archery contest are assumed to be essentially of the same quality because $\sigma_s^2 = 0$. In the components of variance model, the F-test yields conclusions about the population of the marksmen and the population of the bows or arrows.

Note that neither of the two tests (7.27) and (7.42) apply to this example since the test needed would have to yield conclusions about all the populations involved. Thus, a mixture of the two tests would appear to be more realistic in this example. These two tests can be extended to cover mixed cases also. It is beyond the scope of this book to discuss these extensions.

PROBLEM 7.54 Establish (7.42).

Solution: To show that

$$\sum_{j=1}^{n}\frac{\bar{c}_j - \bar{x}}{\sigma^2/m} = \sum_{i=1}^{m}\sum_{j=1}^{n}\frac{(\bar{c}_j - \bar{x})^2}{\sigma^2} \tag{7.36}$$

possesses a χ^2 distribution in this case also, use the hypothesis (7.39) to obtain

$$\bar{c}_j - \bar{x} = \frac{1}{m} \sum_{i=1}^{m} x_{ij} - \frac{1}{mn} \sum_{i=1}^{m} \sum_{j=1}^{n} x_{ij}$$

$$= \frac{1}{m} \sum_{i=1}^{m} (\gamma_i + \beta_j + \gamma_{ij}) - \frac{1}{mn} \sum_{i=1}^{m} \sum_{j=1}^{n} (\alpha_i + \beta_j + \gamma_{ij})$$

$$= \bar{\alpha} + \beta_j + \frac{1}{m} \sum_{i=1}^{m} \gamma_{ij} - (\bar{\alpha} - \bar{\beta} + \bar{\gamma})$$

$$= \beta_j + \frac{1}{m} \sum_{i=1}^{m} \gamma_{ij} - (\bar{\beta} + \bar{\gamma})$$

$$= z_j - \bar{z}, \tag{7.43}$$

where $z_j = \beta_j + \dfrac{1}{m} \sum_{i=1}^{m} \gamma_{ij}$, and

$$\bar{z} = \frac{1}{n} \sum_{j=1}^{n} \beta_j + \frac{1}{mn} \sum_{i=1}^{m} \sum_{j=1}^{n} \gamma_{ij} = \bar{\beta} + \bar{\gamma} .$$

Since z_j $(j = 1, 2, \cdots, n)$ is a linear combination of the independent normal variates β_j and γ_{ij}, $i = 1, 2, \cdots, m$, z_j is also an independent normal variable, whose mean and variance are

$$\bar{z} = E[\beta_j] + E\left[\frac{1}{m} \sum \gamma_{ij}\right] = \mu_r + \mu_t , \qquad \sigma_{z_j}^2 = \sigma_{\beta_j}^2 + \frac{\sigma_{\gamma_{ij}}^2}{m} = \sigma_s^2 + \frac{\sigma_t^2}{m} .$$

Since the sum of squares of independently distributed normal variates possesses a χ^2 distribution, the quantity

$$\frac{\sum_{j=1}^{n} (z_j - \bar{z})}{\sigma_s^2 + \sigma_t^2/m} = \frac{\sum_{j=1}^{n} (\bar{c}_j - \bar{x})}{\sigma_s^2 + \sigma_t^2/m} = \frac{\sum_{i=1}^{m} \sum_{j=1}^{n} (\bar{c}_j - \bar{x})}{m\sigma_s^2 + \sigma_t^2} \tag{7.44}$$

also possesses a χ^2 distribution with $n - 1$ degrees of freedom. Now,

$$\sum_{i=1}^{m} \sum_{j=1}^{n} (\bar{c}_j - \bar{x}) = \sum_{i=1}^{m} \sum_{j=1}^{n} (\bar{r}_i - \bar{x})^2 + \sum_{i=1}^{m} \sum_{j=1}^{n} (\bar{c}_j - \bar{x})^2 + \sum_{i=1}^{m} \sum_{j=1}^{n} (x_{ij} - \bar{r}_i - \bar{c}_j + \bar{x})^2. \tag{7.35}$$

Using the arguments of Prob. 7.47, concerning (7.35), only the second and third terms on the right-hand side of (7.35) represent components of variation that are of experimental interest and can be used in a significance test using the F-distribution. They both possess the χ^2 distribution with $(n - 1)$ and $(m - 1)(n - 1)$ degrees of freedom. Hence, applying the F-distribution,

$$F = \frac{\sigma_t^2(m - 1) \sum_{i=1}^{m} \sum_{j=1}^{n} (\bar{c}_j - \bar{x})^2}{(m\sigma_s^2 + \sigma_t^2) \sum_{i=1}^{m} \sum_{j=1}^{n} (x_{ij} - \bar{r}_i - \bar{c}_j + \bar{x})^2} . \tag{7.45}$$

with $\nu_1 = n - 1$ and $\nu_2 = (m - 1)(n - 1)$.

Note that F can never be evaluated in a particular problem if σ_s^2 and σ_t^2 are not known. But when the hypothesis (7.41) is true, (7.45) becomes zero; thus, the value of F in (7.45) can be calculated from the given data.

PROBLEM 7.55 Test the homogeneity of the means of the rows of the array of Prob. 7.51.

Solution: To test the row means, (7.14) is used. Thus,

$$F = \frac{(2)(1) \sum_{i=1}^{4} (\bar{x}_{ir} - \bar{x})^2}{\sum_{i=1}^{4} \sum_{j=1}^{2} (x_{ij} - \bar{x}_j - \bar{x}_{ir} + \bar{x})^2}.$$

The denominator has been previously calculated in Prob. 7.51 and is equal to 80. Using the results of calculations made in Prob. 7.51,

$$\sum_{i=1}^{4} (\bar{x}_{ir} - \bar{x})^2 = (31 - 30)^2 + (25 - 30)^2 + (31 - 30)^2 + (33 - 30)^2 = 36.$$

Thus,

$$F = \frac{2(36)}{80} = 0.9.$$

From Table VII of the Appendix, at the 5% level of significance, with $\nu_1 = n - 1 = 3$ and $\nu_2 = (n - 1)(m - 1) = 3$, $F = 9.28$, so that no significant difference exists between the row means. Were a significant difference found to exist, the row variability would be presumed to be caused by an effect other than random sampling.

7.7 Supplementary Problems

PROBLEM 7.56 Determine the range of samples taken at random from a normally distributed random variable whose measurements are −6.4, −5.0, −5.2, −6.8, −3.3, −6.0, −5.9, −6.2, −6.4, and −3.8.
Answer: 3.5.

PROBLEM 7.57 Establish (7.5).

PROBLEM 7.58 Estimate the standard deviation σ_e for the samples of Prob. 7.56.
Answer: 1.14.

PROBLEM 7.59 Determine the probability density function for the range R for samples uniformly distributed according to $p(x) = 1$ for $0 \leqslant x \leqslant 1$.
Answer: $p_R(R) = n(n - 1)R^{n-2}(1 - R)$, where n is the sample size.

PROBLEM 7.60 The expected value of the range of ten uniformly distributed samples is 2.4. Determine the standard deviation of the distribution from which the samples are drawn.
Answer: $\frac{4.4}{9}\sqrt{3}$.

PROBLEM 7.61 Calculate the expected value of the range of five samples drawn at random from a distribution whose standard deviation is 3.9.
Answer: $5.2\sqrt{3}$.

PROBLEM 7.62 Determine the value of F which is exceeded with probability 0.01 for 8 and 10 degrees of freedom.
Answer: 5.06.

PROBLEM 7.63 Determine if there is a significant difference between the following sample variances calculated from normally distributed samples:

$$s_1^2 = 1, \quad n_1 = 15; \quad s_2^2 = 4, \quad n_2 = 5.$$

Answer: No at both 5% and 1% levels of significance.

PROBLEM 7.64 Determine the expected value $E(F)$ of the F-distribution if the sample sizes are n_1 and n_2.
Answer: $E(F) = (n_2 - 1)/(n_2 - 3)$.

PROBLEM 7.65 Is there a relationship between the t- and F-distributions?
Answer: Yes. The variable t^2 with ν degrees of freedom is a special case of the variable F with $\nu_1 = 1$ and $\nu_2 = \nu$.

PROBLEM 7.66 Two independent random samples of size $n_1 = 21$ and $n_2 = 20$ are taken from a normal population. Find the probability that either sample variance will be 3 times as large as the other.
Answer: 0.02.

PROBLEM 7.67 A certain radioactive material is tested to determine if the number of gamma rays emitted per second possess a Poisson distribution with $\lambda = 5.3$. Test this hypothesis at the 0.01 level if the result observed for 96 one-second intervals is as follows:

Number of gamma rays per second	0	1	2	3	4	5 or more
Frequency	4	14	21	6	31	20

Answer: The rays do appear to be Poisson distributed.

PROBLEM 7.68 A hospital claims that the 4 major blood types are distributed in the proportion 2:3:3:2. Given the observed data 50, 75, 85, 14, test for the validity of the claim.
Answer: The claim does not appear to be valid.

PROBLEM 7.69 In an epidemic of smallpox, 100 individuals contracted the disease. Of the 62 who received medical treatment, 18 suffered aftereffects. Of the remainder who received no medical care, 13 suffered aftereffects. Test the hypothesis that the medical treatment was not effective and comment on the conclusion.
Answer: $\chi^2 = 0.3$ with 1 degree of freedom; hence, accept the hypothesis. It appears that the treatment did not have a harmful effect on the patients.

PROBLEM 7.70 Samples of three brands A, B, and C of a certain material are subjected to a treatment of sulphuric acid for an equal amount of time. The results are shown in the following table.

Result \ Brand	A	B	C
Remained perfect	51	40	64
Slight defects	20	25	34
Destroyed completely	9	14	18

Test at the 5% level of significance whether the proportions of samples falling into the three categories are the same for all three brands of the material.
Answer: $\chi^2 = 2.58$ with 4 degrees of freedom; cannot reject null hypothesis.

PROBLEM 7.71 A random sample of 250 individuals is taken to determine if there is a relationship between an individual's educational level and his marital adjustment level. The results were

Education \ Marriage Adjustment Score	Very Low	Low	High	Very High	Totals
College	15	26	52	62	155
High School	13	25	23	34	95
Totals	28	51	75	96	250

Use Brandt-Snedecor's formula (7.22) to test the hypothesis that there is no association between marital adjustment and educational level. Explain the conclusion.

Answer: $\chi^2 = 5.41$ at 3 degrees of freedom. Hence, the hypothesis of no association is rejected and there appears to be an association between educational level and marital compatibility.

PROBLEM 7.72 The number of divorces per month in a certain locality for the year 1969 were as follows: 20, 15, 18, 8, 6, 2, 3, 6, 15, 19, 7, 1. Assume that divorces follow a Poisson distribution. Test the homogeneity of divorces with the Poisson index of dispersion.

Answer: $\chi^2 = 53.4$. Hence, it is questionable that divorces are Poisson-distributed.

PROBLEM 7.73 Could the divorce frequencies of Prob. 7.72 be binomially distributed?

Answer: No.

PROBLEM 7.74 Derive (7.38) from (7.35).

PROBLEM 7.75 Six machines produce steel wire. The following table gives the diameter at ten positions along the wire for each machine. Examine whether the machine means can be regarded as constant at the 1% level of significance. Also interpret the result.

Machine	Diameters in thousandths of an inch									
A	12	13	13	16	16	14	15	15	16	17
B	12	14	14	16	16	18	17	19	20	18
C	14	21	17	14	19	18	17	17	16	15
D	23	27	25	21	26	24	27	24	20	21
E	12	14	13	16	13	17	16	15	15	14
F	13	18	13	16	17	15	15	16	16	17

Answer: $F = 28.6$; hence, difference in the means is significant and the hypothesis is rejected. That is, there is a significant variation of the diameters of the wires produced from machine to machine.

PROBLEM 7.76 Five doctors test five treatments for a certain disease and observe the number of days each patient takes to recover. The results are as follows:

Doctor \ Treatment	1	2	3	4	5
A	10	14	23	19	20
B	11	15	24	17	21
C	9	12	20	16	19
D	8	13	17	17	20
E	12	15	19	15	22

Discuss the difference between (a) doctors and (b) treatments at both the 5 and 1% levels of significance.

Answer: (a) $F = 2.99$; difference is significant at the 5% level while not significant at the 1% level. (b) $F = 47.06$; difference is significant at both 5% and 1% levels.

8 CHAPTER

LEAST-SQUARES AND CORRELATION

8.1 Scatter Diagrams

A *scatter diagram* is a graph of sample values plotted on the xy-plane. From such a diagram it can be seen whether the values fall in a *linear* or a *nonlinear* pattern. If the points lie close to a straight line, the variables are assumed to have a linear relationship as in Fig. 8.1 (a), where n samples of the variable $x(t)$ versus t are plotted. If, as in Fig. 8.1 (b), the points cannot be approximated by a straight line, the variables are assumed to have a nonlinear relationship. A linear relationship between two sample values is represented by a polynomial of degree one, whereas a nonlinear relationship is represented by a polynomial of higher degree; i.e.,

$$x(t) = a_0 + a_1 t,$$

$$x(t) = a_0 + a_1 t + a_2 t^2,$$

$$.$$
$$.$$
$$.$$

$$x(t) = a_0 + a_1 t + \cdots + a_n t^n.$$

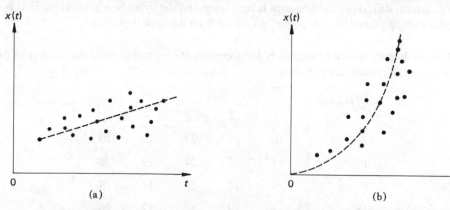

Fig. 8.1 Scatter diagram of (a) a linear and (b) a nonlinear relationship.

The straight line which represents the relationship between two variables is called the *regression line*. The general equation of a straight line is

$$x(t) = a + bt \tag{8.1}$$

or

$$x(t) - x(t_1) = \frac{x(t_2) - x(t_1)}{t_2 - t_1}(t - t_1), \tag{8.2}$$

where $x(t_1)$ and $x(t_2)$ are points on the line.

The *slope m* of (8.1) is b and the slope of (8.2) is $\dfrac{x(t_2) - x(t_1)}{t_2 - t_1}$.

PROBLEM 8.1 Show that the equation of a straight line passing through the points $[t_1, x(t_1)]$ and $[t_2, x(t_2)]$ is

$$x(t) - x(t_1) = \frac{x(t_2) - x(t_1)}{t_2 - t_1}(t - t_1).$$

Solution: The general equation of a straight line is

$$x(t) = a + bt.$$

Since the line passes through the points $[t_1, x(t_1)]$ and $[t_2, x(t_2)]$,

$$x(t_1) = a + bt_1, \qquad x(t_2) = a + bt_2.$$

Hence, $x(t_2) - x(t_1) = b(t_2 - t_1)$. Solving for b,

$$b = \frac{x(t_2) - x(t_1)}{t_2 - t_1}.$$

Since $x(t) - x(t_1) = b(t - t_1)$, substituting the value of b yields

$$x(t) - x(t_1) = \frac{x(t_2) - x(t_1)}{t_2 - t_1}(t - t_1).$$

PROBLEM 8.2 Table 8.1 shows the data obtained from testing 12 specimens of a metallic alloy for hardness (Rockwell units) and tensile strength (tons/in.^{2}). (a) Draw the scatter diagram of this data. (b) Draw the line which approximates the data. (c) Find the equation of this line.

TABLE 8.1

Hardness	70	65	80	70	45	65	75	73	80	69	72	59
Tensile strength	1.7	1.6	1.8	1.6	1.5	1.6	1.6	1.4	1.7	1.5	1.7	1.5

Solution: (a) The scatter diagram is shown in Fig. 8.2 where x is hardness and t is tensile strength.

(b) Although several straight lines approximating this data can be drawn, the line shown in Fig. 8.2 contains an equal number of points above and below it.

(c) Since this approximating line passes through the points $(1.5, 59)$ and $(1.8, 80)$,

$$t_1 = 1.5, \qquad t_2 = 1.8,$$

$$x(t_1) = 59, \qquad x(t_2) = 80.$$

Hence, from (8.2), the equation of the line is

$$x(t) - 59 = \frac{80 - 59}{1.8 - 1.5}(t - 1.5),$$

which on simplification becomes

$$x(t) = 70t - 46.$$

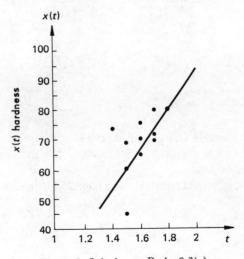

Fig. 8.2 Solution to Prob. 8.2(a).

8.2 Least-Mean-Squares Smoothing

If $x(t)$ for n pairs $[t_i, x(t_i)]$ of data is estimated by

$$x_e(t) = a + bt, \tag{8.3}$$

where a and b are constants and the t_i's are equally spaced, the error e_i in estimating $x(t)$ for a given t_i is

$$x(t_i) - x_e(t_i) = e_i.$$

(Cf., Fig. 8.3.) Note that the *actual* error ϵ_i in predicting $x(t)$ is estimated by e_i. To provide the "best" fit, the constants a and b are determined so that the estimated errors are minimized according to some criterion.

As shown in Fig. 8.3, the e_i's cannot be minimized individually. The sum $\Sigma_{i=1}^n$ can be made equal to zero by several choices of unsuitable straight lines for which the positive and negative errors cancel. Using a more useful criterion, $\Sigma_{i=1}^n e_i^2$ is minimized, that is, the sum of the squares of the vertical distances from the points to the line is minimized. In other words, the constants a and b are chosen so that

$$\sum_{i=1}^{n} [x(t_i) - x_e(t_i)]^2 = \min \qquad (8.4)$$

or

$$\sum_{i=1}^{n} [x(t_i) - (a + bt_i)]^2 = \min. \qquad (8.5)$$

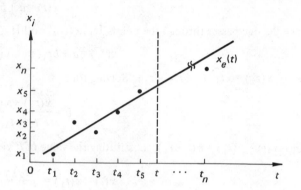

Fig. 8.3   Error in least-mean-squares smoothing.

This criterion is called the *criterion of least squares* and yields values of a and b.

Since a necessary condition for a relative minimum is the vanishing of the partial derivatives with respect to a and b,

$$2\sum_{i=1}^{n} [x(t_i) - (a + bt_i)]\,(-1) = 0, \qquad 2\sum_{i=1}^{n} [x(t_i) - (a + bt_i)]\,(-t_i) = 0.$$

In a simpler form,

$$\sum_{i=1}^{n} x(t_i) = an + b \sum_{i=1}^{n} t_i, \qquad (8.6)$$

$$\sum_{i=1}^{n} t_i x(t_i) = a \sum_{i=1}^{n} t_i + b \sum_{i=1}^{n} t_i^2. \qquad (8.7)$$

Equations (8.6-7) are called *normal equations*, and their simultaneous solutions give the values of a and b for the line that provides the best fit to the given data according to the least-mean-squares method, i.e., the regression line.

The normal equations are simplified if the t-origin is selected so that the data are symmetrical in t_i, i.e., if

$$t_1 = -t_n, \; t_2 = -t_{n-1}, \cdots, t_k = -t_{n-(k-1)}, \cdots.$$

Hence,

$$\sum_{i=1}^{n} t_i = t_1 + t_2 + \cdots + t_{n-1} = (t_1 + t_n) + (t_2 + t_{n-1}) + \cdots = 0.$$

Substituting $\Sigma_{i=1}^n t_i = 0$ in (8.6-7) and solving for a and b,

$$a = \frac{1}{n} \sum_{i=1}^{n} x(t_i), \qquad (8.8)$$

$$b = \frac{\sum\limits_{i=1}^{n} t_i x(t_i)}{\sum\limits_{i=1}^{n} t_i^2}.$$ (8.9)

Thus, the least-mean-squares estimate is

$$x_e(t) = \frac{1}{n} \sum_{i=1}^{n} x(t_i) + \frac{\sum\limits_{i=1}^{n} t_i x(t_i)}{\sum\limits_{i=1}^{n} t_i^2} t.$$ (8.10)

If the t_i's are *not* equally spaced, (8.6-7) are simplified by taking the t-origin at the mean value of t, that is,

$\bar{t} = \frac{1}{n} \sum\limits_{i=1}^{n} t_i.$ Hence, in general, the least-squares estimate is

$$x_e(t) = \frac{1}{n} \sum_{i=1}^{n} x(t_i) + \frac{\sum\limits_{i=1}^{n} (t_i - \bar{t}) x(t_i)}{\sum\limits_{i=1}^{n} (t_i - \bar{t})} (t - \bar{t}).$$ (8.11)

If the relationship between the variates is *nonlinear*, a polynomial of the form

$$x_e(t) = a_0 + a_1 t + \cdots + a_n t^n$$

is chosen of degree indicated from inspection of the scatter diagram. Thus, a set of data consisting of the n points $[t_i, x(t_i)]$ is fitted to an nth degree polynomial by minimizing

$$\sum_{i=1}^{n} [x(t_i) - (a_0 + a_1 t + \cdots + a_n t^n)]^2.$$

That is, the least-squares criterion is applied by minimizing the sum of the squares of the distances from the points to the curve. Equating the partial derivatives with respect to $a_0, a_1, \cdots, a_n$ equal to zero and rearranging terms yields

$$\sum_{i=1}^{n} x(t_i) = na_0 + a_1 \sum_{i=1}^{n} t_i + \cdots + a_n \sum_{i=1}^{n} t^n,$$

$$\sum_{i=1}^{n} t_i x(t_i) = a_0 \sum_{i=1}^{n} t_i + a_1 \sum_{i=1}^{n} t_i^2 + \cdots + a_n \sum_{i=1}^{n} t^{n+1},$$

$$\cdot$$
$$\cdot$$
$$\cdot$$

$$\sum_{i=1}^{n} t^n x(t_i) = a_0 \sum_{i=1}^{n} t_i^n + a_1 \sum_{i=1}^{n} t_i^{n+1} + \cdots + a_n \sum_{i=1}^{n} t^{2n}.$$

Note that this is a system of $n + 1$ *linear* equations in $n + 1$ unknowns and has a *unique* solution.

PROBLEM 8.3 Find the estimate W_e of the true weight W_0 of an object by minimizing the sum of the squared errors if the measured weights are W_1 and W_2.

Solution: The error at data point 1 between the estimated weight W_e and the measured weight W_1 is

$$e_1 = W_e - W_1.$$

Similarly, at data point 2, the error is

$$e_2 = W_e - W_2.$$

The sum of the squared errors is

$$e^2 = e_1^2 + e_2^2 = (W_e - W_1)^2 + (W_e - W_2)^2.$$

In least-squares smoothing, W_e is chosen to minimize e^2; thus,

$$\frac{\partial e^2}{\partial W_e} = 0.$$

Differentiating e^2 with respect to W_e,

$$\frac{\partial e^2}{\partial W_e} = 2(W_e - W_1) + 2(W_e - W_2) = 0.$$

Hence,

$$W_e = \tfrac{1}{2}(W_1 + W_2);$$

that is, W_e should be taken as the average value of the two measurements in order to minimize e^2.

PROBLEM 8.4   Find the estimate W_e of the true weight W_0 of an object by minimizing the sum of the squared errors if there are n measurements. (See Fig. 8.4.)

Solution: The sum of the squared errors is

$$e^2 = \sum_{i=1}^{n} (W_e - W_i)^2.$$

Since $\dfrac{\partial e^2}{\partial W_e} = 0$ for W_e to be a minimum,

$$\frac{\partial e^2}{\partial W_e} = 2\sum_{i=1}^{n} (W_e - W_i) = 0.$$

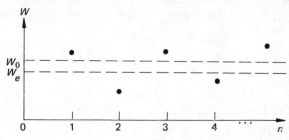

Fig. 8.4   Estimate W_e of the true weight W_0 of an object.

Hence,

$$\sum_{i=1}^{n} (W_e - W_i) = 0 \qquad \text{or} \qquad \sum_{i=1}^{n} W_e - \sum_{i=1}^{n} W_i = 0.$$

Therefore,

$$\sum_{i=1}^{n} W_e = \sum_{i=1}^{n} W_i.$$

Since $\sum_{i=1}^{n} W_e = n W_e$,

$$W_e = \frac{1}{n}\sum_{i=1}^{n} W_i.$$

The right-hand side of the last equation is the average value of the measurements.

PROBLEM 8.5 The position of an object moving radially at a constant velocity is measured nine times at 1-sec intervals as shown in Table 8.2. Estimate the range at $t = 1$ sec by the method of least squares.

TABLE 8.2

Time t (sec)	-4	-3	-2	-1	0	1	2	3	4
Range R (ft)	4.0	5.1	6.3	6.9	7.9	8.7	9.9	11.1	12.0

Solution: Since the object is moving at a constant velocity, the estimate is

$$R_e(t) = A_0 + A_1 t.$$

The data are in symmetrical form so that, from (8.8-9), substituting R for x, and calculating the appropriate sums and products of R and t from Table 8.3,

$$A_0 = \frac{1}{n} \sum_{i=1}^{n} R_i = \frac{1}{9}(71.9) = 7.99, \qquad A_1 = \frac{\sum_{i=1}^{n} R_i t_i}{\sum_{i=1}^{n} t_i^2} = \frac{59}{60}.$$

Hence,

$$R_e(t) = 7.99 + \frac{59}{60} t.$$

Therefore, the estimate of the range at $t = 1$ sec is

$$R_e(1) = 7.99 + \frac{59}{60} = 8.97.$$

TABLE 8.3

i	t_i	R_i	$R_i t_i$	t_i^2
1	-4	4.0	-16	16
2	-3	5.1	-15.3	9
3	-2	6.3	-12.6	4
4	-1	6.9	-6.9	1
5	0	7.9	0	0
6	1	8.7	8.7	1
7	2	9.9	19.8	4
8	3	11.1	33.3	9
9	4	12.0	48.0	16
Totals		71.9	59.0	60

PROBLEM 8.6 Boyle's law relates the pressure p of a gas to its volume v by an equation of the form $pv^a = b$. Determine a and b when an experiment yields the following values.

p	1.5	2	2.5	0.6	1	3.5
v	0.8	1	1.6	0.2	1	0.4

Solution: With v as the independent variable, the prediction equation becomes $p = bv^{-a}$. Taking logarithms to the base 10,

$$\log p = \log b - a \log v.$$

Estimates of $\log b$ and a are found by applying (8.6-7) to the points $(\log p_i, \log v_i)$. Hence, the normal equations are

$$\sum_{i=1}^{6} \log p_i = n \log b - a \sum_{i=1}^{6} \log v_i,$$

$$\sum_{i=1}^{6} \log p_i \log v_i = \log b \sum_{i=1}^{6} \log v_i - a \sum_{i=1}^{6} (\log v_i)^2.$$

The logarithms of the p_i's and v_i's are, respectively, 0.1761, 0.3010, 0.3979, -0.2218, 0.0000, 0.5441, and -0.0969, 0.0000, 0.2041, -0.6990, 0.0000, -0.3979. The summations required for substitution into the normal equations are

$$\sum_{i=1}^{6} \log p_i = 1.2973, \quad \sum_{i=1}^{6} \log p_i \log v_i = -0.1369, \quad \sum_{i=1}^{6} \log v_i = -0.1808, \quad \sum_{i=1}^{6} (\log v_i)^2 = 0.6980.$$

Hence, the normal equations are

$$1.2973 = 6 \log b + 0.1808 \, a, \qquad -0.1369 = -0.1808 \log b - 0.6980 \, a.$$

Solving this system of equations, $a = 0.141$ and $\log b = 0.2119$; hence, $b = 3.26$. The required curve is $pv^{0.141} = 3.26$.

Paired data is often plotted on various kinds of graph paper to determine if the points will fall close to a straight line for suitably transformed scales. If this is so, then the transformation leads to a functional form of the regression equation, and the necessary parameters can be determined by using the normal equations developed in (8.6-7).

The regression curve of y on x is said to be *exponential* if a set of data consisting of n points (x_i, y_i) "straightens out" when plotted on semilog paper. The mean of the distribution of the y's is given by $A_0 A_1^x$. Taking logarithms to the base 10 (or any other base) of both sides of the predicting equation $y = A_0 A_1^x$,

$$\log y = \log A_0 + x \log A_1.$$

Estimates of $\log A_0$ and $\log A_1$, and hence of A_0 and A_1, are obtained from applying (8.6-7) to the n pairs of values $(x_i, \log y_i)$. The normal equations in this case are

$$\sum_{i=1}^{n} \log y_i = n \log A_0 + \log A_1 \sum_{i=1}^{n} x_i, \quad \sum_{i=1}^{n} x_i \log y_i = \log A_0 \sum_{i=1}^{n} x_i + \log A_1 \sum_{i=1}^{n} x_i^2.$$

If the relationship between x and $1/y$ is linear, then the suitable transformation is the *reciprocal function* $y = 1/(A_0 + A_1 x)$, and A_0 and A_1 are estimated by applying (8.6-7) to the n pairs of points $(x_i, 1/y_i)$.

If the relationship between $\log x$ and $\log y$ is linear, then the suitable transformation is the *power function* $y = A_0 x^{A_1}$; that is, taking logarithms, $\log y = \log A_0 + A_1 \log x$. The estimates $\log A_0$ and A_1, and hence A_0 and A_1, are obtained by applying (8.6-7) to the n pairs of points $(\log x_i, \log y_i)$.

PROBLEM 8.7 The following observations are made of the weights of 10 metal specimens when treated by a chemical for varying periods of time:

Weight (lb), y	19	16	15	5	15	9	11	13	8	10
Time (sec), x	5	10	15	20	25	30	35	40	45	50

(a) Fit an exponential curve of the form $y = A_0 A_1^x$ using the method of least squares. (b) Fit a curve of the form $y = \dfrac{1}{A_0 + A_1 x}$.

Solution: (a) The logarithms of the y's are 1.2788, 1.2041, 1.1761, 0.6990, 1.1461, 0.9542, 1.0414, 1.1139, 0.9031, 1.0000, and the summations required for substitution into the normal equations are

$$\sum_{i=1}^{10} x_i = 275, \qquad \sum_{i=1}^{10} \log y_i = 10.5167, \qquad \sum_{i=1}^{10} x_i^2 = 9625, \qquad \sum_{i=1}^{10} x_i \log y_i = 278.9795.$$

The normal equations are

$$10.5167 = 10 \log A_0 + 275 \log A_1, \qquad 278.9795 = 275 \log A_0 + 9625 \log A_1,$$

and solving this system of equations,

$$\log A_0 = -0.0049, \qquad \log A_1 = 1.1396.$$

Hence, $A_0 = 0.99$ and $A_1 = 13.8$, and the least-squares exponential curve is

$$y = (0.99)(13.8)^x.$$

(b) The points under consideration here are $(x_i, 1/y_i)$, and hence, the normal equations are

$$\sum_{i=1}^{10} \frac{1}{y_i} = n A_0 + A_1 \sum_{i=1}^{10} x_i, \qquad \sum_{i=1}^{10} \frac{x_i}{y_i} = A_0 \sum_{i=1}^{10} x_i + A_1 \sum_{i=1}^{10} x_i^2.$$

The reciprocals of the y's are 0.053, 0.063, 0.067, 0.200, 0.071, 0.111, 0.091, 0.077, 0.125, 0.100, and the summations required for substitution into the normal equations are

$$\sum_{i=1}^{10} x_i = 275, \qquad \sum_{i=1}^{10} \frac{1}{y_i} = 0.96, \qquad \sum_{i=1}^{10} x_i^2 = 9625, \qquad \sum_{i=1}^{10} \frac{x_i}{y_i} = 27.92.$$

The normal equations are

$$0.96 = 10 A_0 + 275 A_1, \qquad 27.92 = 275 A_0 + 9625 A_1,$$

and solving this system of equations, $A_0 = 0.0758$ and $A_1 = 0.0007$. The least-squares reciprocal function curve is

$$y = \frac{1}{0.0758 + 0.0007x} = \frac{10000}{758 + 7x}.$$

PROBLEM 8.8 Show that the line of regression passes through the point $(\bar{t}, \bar{x})$.

Solution: From (8.10), the equation for the line of regression is

$$x_e(t) = \frac{1}{n} \sum_{i=1}^{n} x_i + \frac{\displaystyle\sum_{i=1}^{n} x_i t_i}{\displaystyle\sum_{i=1}^{n} t_i^2} \, t,$$

where the data is assumed to be symmetrical in t. Because of this symmetry,

$$\bar{t} = \frac{1}{n}(t_1 + t_2 + \cdots + t_n) = 0.$$

At $t = 0$,

$$x_e(t) = \frac{1}{n} \sum_{i=1}^{n} x_i.$$

The right-hand side of this equation is $\bar{x}$ so that the regression line passes through the point $t = \bar{t}, x = \bar{x}$.

PROBLEM 8.9   A set of measured points $x_1, x_2, \cdots, x_n$ is smoothed by least-squares smoothing, as shown in Fig. 8.5. Using a parabolic estimate,

$$x_e(t_i) = A_0 + A_1 t_i + A_2 t_i^2, \quad i = 1, 2, \cdots, n,$$

determine the normal equations that will give the values of A_0, A_1, and A_2 in terms of the measured data. Assume that the t_i's are equally spaced.

Solution: The constants A_0, A_1, and A_2 are chosen so that

$$e^2 = \sum_{i=1}^{n} (x_i - x_e)^2$$

is a minimum. Substituting for $x_e(t)$,

$$e^2 = \sum_{i=1}^{n} [x_i - (A_0 + A_1 t_i + A_2 t_i^2)]^2.$$

For e^2 to be a minimum,

$$\frac{\partial e^2}{\partial A_0} = 0, \qquad \frac{\partial e^2}{\partial A_1} = 0, \qquad \frac{\partial e^2}{\partial A_2} = 0.$$

Differentiating e^2 with respect to A_0,

$$\frac{\partial e^2}{\partial A_0} = -2 \sum_{i=1}^{n} [x_i - (A_0 + A_1 t_i + A_2 t_i^2)] = 0.$$

Hence,

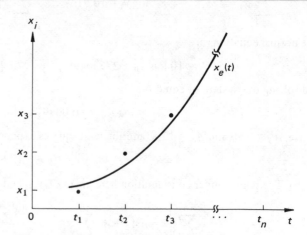

Fig. 8.5   Least-mean-squares smoothing of a set of measured points $x_1, x_2, \ldots, x_n$.

$$\sum_{i=1}^{n} x_i = \sum_{i=1}^{n} (A_0 + A_1 t_i + A_2 t_i^2) = nA_0 + \sum_{i=1}^{n} (A_1 t_i + A_2 t_i^2).$$

Differentiating e^2 with respect to A_1,

$$\frac{\partial e^2}{\partial A_1} = -2 \sum_{i=1}^{n} [x_i - (A_0 + A_1 t_i + A_2 t_i^2)] (t_i) = 0.$$

Hence,

$$\sum_{i=1}^{n} x_i t_i = \sum_{i=1}^{n} A_0 t_i + \sum_{i=1}^{n} A_1 t_i^2 + \sum_{i=1}^{n} A_2 t_i^3.$$

Differentiating e^2 with respect to A_2,

$$\frac{\partial e^2}{\partial A_2} = -2 \sum_{i=1}^{n} [x_i - (A_0 + A_1 t_i + A_2 t_i^2)] (t_i^2) = 0.$$

Hence,

$$\sum_{i=1}^{n} x_i t_i^2 = \sum_{i=1}^{n} A_0 t_i^2 + \sum_{i=1}^{n} A_i t_i^3 + \sum_{i=1}^{n} A_2 t_i^4.$$

The normal equations are

$$\sum_{i=1}^{n} x_i = nA_0 + A_1 \sum_{i=1}^{n} t_i + A_2 \sum_{i=1}^{n} t_i^2,$$

$$\sum_{i=1}^{n} x_i t_i = A_0 \sum_{i=1}^{n} t_i + A_1 \sum_{i=1}^{n} t_i^2 + A_2 \sum_{i=1}^{n} t_i^3,$$

$$\sum_{i=1}^{n} x_i t_i^2 = A_0 \sum_{i=1}^{n} t_i^2 + A_1 \sum_{i=1}^{n} t_i^3 + A_2 \sum_{i=1}^{n} t_i^4.$$

PROBLEM 8.10 Fit a second degree parabola to the following data.

t	0	1	2	3	4	5
x	6	7	4	9	12	11.5

Solution: For the given data, $n = 6$, $\sum_{i=1}^{6} x_i = 49.5$, $\sum_{i=1}^{6} t_i = 15$,

$\sum_{i=1}^{6} t_i^2 = 55$, $\sum_{i=1}^{6} t_i^3 = 225$, $\sum_{i=1}^{6} t_i^4 = 979$, $\sum_{i=1}^{6} x_i t_i = 147.5$,

$\sum_{i=1}^{6} x_i t_i^2 = 583.5$. Substituting these values in the normal equations of Prob. 8.9,

$$49.5 = 6A_0 + 15A_1 + 55A_2,$$
$$147.5 = 15A_0 + 55A_1 + 225A_2,$$
$$583.5 = 55A_0 + 225A_1 + 979A_2.$$

Solving these equations simultaneously, $A_0 = 5.85$, $A_1 = -0.15$, and $A_2 = 0.3$. Hence, the equation of the parabolic curve is

$$x_e(t) = 5.85 - 0.15t + 0.3t^2.$$

The graph is shown in Fig. 8.6.

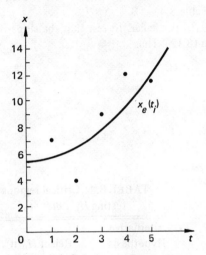

Fig. 8.6 Solution to Prob. 8.10.

8.3 Regression Line Slope Test

Student's t-distribution can be used to determine whether the difference between the slopes of a sample and a theoretical regression line can be reasonably caused by sampling variation.

The regression line for a set of n samples with cordinates (x_i, y_i), $i = 1, 2, \cdots, n$, is

$$y_e(x) = \frac{1}{n} \sum_{i=1}^{n} y_i + \frac{\sum_{i=1}^{n} x_i y_i}{\sum_{i=1}^{n} x_i^2} x, \qquad [8.10]$$

where the variable x is measured from its mean and the variables y_i are assumed to be independently distributed with normal distributions and common variance. Then the slope of the regression line is

$$m = \frac{\sum_{i=1}^{n} x_i y_i}{\sum_{i=1}^{n} x_i^2}. \qquad (8.12)$$

If $m = 0$, the regression line is horizontal and the mean of y does not depend linearly on x.

The quantity m is an unbiased estimate of the theoretical slope m_0 and

$$t = (m - m_0) \sqrt{\frac{(n - 2) \sum_{i=1}^{n} x_i^2}{\sqrt{\sum_{i=1}^{n} (y_i - y_e)^2}}} \qquad (8.13)$$

possesses Student's t-distribution having $v = n - 2$ degrees of freedom. Equation (8.13) is used to test the hypothetical values of regression slopes and to find confidence limits.

Equation (8.10) is used to test the null hypothesis $H_0 : m = m_0$. The resulting critical regions are shown in Table 8.4.

In particular, to test that the slope of the regression line does not differ from zero significantly, set $m_0 = 0$ in (8.13). Thus,

$$t = m \sqrt{\frac{(n - 2) \sum_{i=1}^{n} x_i^2}{\sqrt{\sum_{i=1}^{n} (y_i - y_e)^2}}} . \qquad (8.14)$$

TABLE 8.4   Critical regions for testing $H_0 : m = m_0$.

Alternative Hypothesis	Reject H_0 if[a]
$m > m_0$	$t > t_0$
$m < m_0$	$t < -t_0$
$m \neq m_0$	$t < -t_0$ or $t > t_0$

[a]Obtain t_0 from Table V in the Appendix for $n - 2$ d.f.

TABLE 8.5

Time x' (sec)	0	1	2	3	4
Position y (ft)	0	9	20	33	43

PROBLEM 8.11 The position of an object moving along the y-axis at constant velocity at 1-sec intervals is shown in Table 8.5. At the 5% level of significance, determine if the hypothesis that the target is moving at a speed of 10 ft/sec is reasonable.

Solution: The sums are computed in Table 8.6.

TABLE 8.6

Time x' (sec)	Position y (ft)	$x = x' - \overline{x'}$	x^2	xy	y_e	$y - y_e$	$(y - y_e)^2$
0	0	-2	4	0	-1	1	1
1	9	-1	1	-9	10	-1	1
2	20	0	0	0	21	-1	1
3	33	1	1	33	32	1	1
4	43	2	4	86	43	0	0
10	105	0	10	110	105	0	4

From column 1, the mean $\overline{x'} = (\Sigma x')/n = \frac{10}{5} = 2$. With $n = 5$, the equation of the regression line is

$$y_e(x) = \frac{1}{5} \sum_{i=1}^{n} y_i + \frac{\sum_{i=1}^{5} y_i x_i}{\sum_{i=1}^{5} x_i^2} x = \left(\frac{1}{5}\right)(105) + \left(\frac{110}{10}\right) x = 21 + 11x.$$

Since the hypothesis to be tested is $m_0 = 10$, the value t is calculated from (8.13). Thus, with $n = 5$,

$$t = (11 - 10) \sqrt{\frac{(5 - 2) \sum_{i=1}^{5} x_i^2}{\sum_{i=1}^{5} [y_i - y_e(x_i)]^2}} = \sqrt{\frac{(3)(10)}{4}} = 2.74.$$

From Table V in the Appendix, for $\nu = n - 2 = 3$ d.f., at the 5% level of significance, $t = 3.182$. Since the calculated value does not exceed the tabulated value, the hypothesis of a 10-ft/sec speed is reasonable. However, note that many other hypotheses are also reasonable.

PROBLEM 8.12 Determine the 95% confidence interval for the true slope of the regression line of Prob. 8.11.

Solution: With $n = 5$,

$$t = |m - m_0| \sqrt{\frac{(n - 2) \sum_{i=1}^{n} x_i^2}{\sum_{i=1}^{n} (y_i - y_e)^2}} = 3.182,$$

and the corresponding values of m_0 give the 95% confidence limits for the true slope m_0. From Prob. 8.11,

$$\sqrt{\frac{(n - 2) \sum_{i=1}^{n} x_i^2}{\sum_{i=1}^{n} (y_i - y_e)^2}} = 2.74;$$

hence,

$$|m - m_0| = \frac{3.182}{2.74} = 1.16.$$

Therefore, the confidence limits are

$$m_0 = m \pm 1.16.$$

Since $m = 11$, there is a 95% probability that the true slope lies in the interval

$$9.84 < m_0 < 12.16.$$

PROBLEM 8.13 Determine the 99% confidence interval for the true slope of the regression line of Prob. 8.11.

Solution. From Table V of the Appendix for $\nu = n - 2 = 3$ d.f., at the 99% confidence interval (i.e., the probability of $|t| < 0.01$), $t = 5.841$. From Prob. 8.11,

$$t = |m - m_0| \sqrt{\frac{(n - 2) \sum_{i=1}^{n} x_i^2}{\sum_{i=1}^{n} (y_i - y_e)^2}} = (11 - 10) \sqrt{\frac{(5 - 2)(10)}{4}} = 2.74.$$

The 99% confidence limits are

$$|m - m_0| = \frac{5.841}{2.74} = 2.13.$$

Therefore, the confidence limits are

$$m_0 = m \pm 2.13 = 11 \pm 2.13 = 13.13 \text{ or } 8.87.$$

Thus, the 99% confidence interval is

$$8.87 < m_0 < 13.13.$$

8.4   Correlation

Correlation is a measure of the relationship between two variables.

Two variables x and y are in *perfect correlation* if all data points lie on the regression line, and y can be perfectly predicted from x (see Fig. 8.7). If y is *totally* unpredictable from x, there is *no correlation* between x and y.

If y increases as x increases, in *direct* proportion, x and y are in *positive* or *direct correlation* (shown in Figs. 8.8–9). If y decreases as x increases, in *inverse* proportion, x and y are in *negative* or *inverse correlation* (shown in Figs. 8.10–11).

Covariance of a *random sample* with n pairs of values (x_i, y_i) is defined by

$$C_{xy} = \frac{1}{n} \sum_{i=1}^{n} (x_i - \overline{x})(y_i - \overline{y}), \tag{8.15}$$

where $\overline{x} = \dfrac{1}{n} \sum_{i=1}^{n} x_i$ and $\overline{y} = \dfrac{1}{n} \sum_{i=1}^{n} y_i$. The covariance of a *population* is obtained from (8.15) by substituting population means μ_x and μ_y for the sample means $\overline{x}$ and $\overline{y}$.

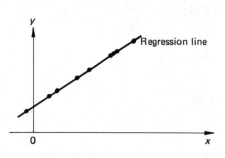

Fig. 8.7   Perfect correlation.

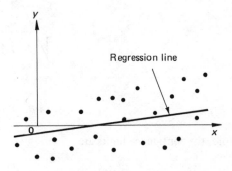

Fig. 8.8   Low position correlation.

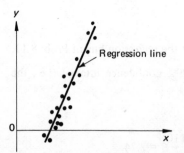

Fig. 8.9   High positive or direct correlation.

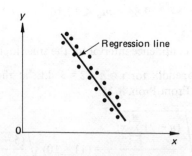

Fig. 8.10   High negative or inverse correlation.

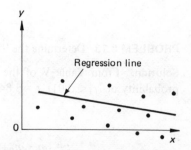

Fig. 8.11   Low negative correlation.

Thus, the *population correlation coefficient* of two variables x and y with population means μ_x and μ_y and variances σ_x^2 and σ_y^2 is

$$\rho = \frac{C_{xy}}{\sigma_x \sigma_y} = \frac{\sum\limits_{i=1}^{N} (x_i - \mu_x)(y_i - \mu_y)}{\sqrt{\sum\limits_{i=1}^{N} (x_i - \mu_x)^2}\ \sqrt{\sum\limits_{i=1}^{N} (y_i - \mu_y)^2}}. \tag{8.16}$$

The *correlation coefficient r of a random sample* (which is generally much smaller than the total population) *estimates* the population correlation coefficient ρ. Thus, if $y_e(x)$ is the y-value taken from the equation of the regression line in (8.10), and (x_i, y_i) are the coordinates of each of the n data points, the sample correlation coefficient is

$$r = \sqrt{1 - \frac{\sum\limits_{i=1}^{n} (y_i - y_e)^2}{\sum\limits_{i=1}^{n} (y_i - \bar{y})^2}}, \tag{8.17}$$

where $\bar{y} = \dfrac{1}{n} \sum\limits_{i=1}^{n} y_i$. Alternatively, r can be defined as

$$r = \frac{\sum\limits_{i=1}^{n} (x_i - \bar{x})(y_i - \bar{y})}{n s_x s_y}, \tag{8.18}$$

where

$$s_x^2 = \frac{1}{n} \sum\limits_{i=1}^{n} (x_i - \bar{x})^2, \qquad s_y^2 = \frac{1}{n} \sum\limits_{i=1}^{n} (y_i - \bar{y})^2. \tag{8.19}$$

The sample correlation coefficient r has the following properties:
(1) It is dimensionless.
(2) Its absolute value cannot exceed unity, that is, $-1 \leqslant r \leqslant 1$.
(3) If all points in a scatter diagram lie on one straight line (the line of regression), the two variables are in perfect correlation and $r = \pm 1$ as the slope of the line is positive or negative, respectively.
(4) If all points in a scatter diagram do not lie on one line, the regression line is the best representation of the data in a linear fashion and in a mean-squared sense, and $-1 < r < 1$.
(5) If $r > 0$, the regression line slopes upward to the right; if $r < 0$, the regression line slopes downward to the right.
(6) Note that the magnitude of r does not indicate the steepness or slope of the regression line, rather r is a measure of how closely the data points cluster about the line.
(7) If $|r|$ is near zero, the points in the scatter diagram show no straight-line trend, i.e., no linear correlation.

Table 8.7 shows the meaning of the value of r in terms of the closeness of the points in the bivariate population to the regression line.

TABLE 8.7 Meaning of r

r	Clustering tendency about regression line
$r = 0$	No correlation
$\lvert r \rvert \ll 1, r > 0$	Low positive correlation
$1 - r \ll 1$	High positive correlation
$\lvert r \rvert \ll 1, r < 0$	Low negative correlation
$1 + r \ll 1$	High negative correlation

The equation of the regression line is expressed explicitly in terms of the correlation coefficient by

$$y_e(x) = \bar{y} + r\frac{s_y}{s_x}(x - \bar{x}).$$ (8.20)

PROBLEM 8.14 The simultaneous temperatures of two cities are recorded on four different days (at random times during the day). Calculate the covariance and the correlation coefficient for the recorded values shown in Table 8.8.

Solution: If x_i are taken to denote the temperatures in city A, and y_i denote the temperatures in city B, then

$$x_1 = 50, \quad x_2 = 34, \quad x_3 = 62, \quad x_4 = 30,$$
$$y_1 = 56, \quad y_2 = 42, \quad y_3 = 64, \quad y_4 = 42.$$

The calculations for $\bar{x}, \bar{y}, s_x$, and s_y are shown in Table 8.9.

TABLE 8.8

City	Temperatures (in degrees)
A	50 34 62 28
B	56 42 64 42

TABLE 8.9   Calculations for Problem 8.14

x	y	$x' = x - \bar{x}$	$y' = y - \bar{y}$	x'^2	y'^2	$x'y'$
50	56	6	5	36	25	30
34	42	-10	-9	100	81	90
62	64	18	13	324	169	234
30	42	-14	-9	196	81	126

$\Sigma x = 176, \ \Sigma y = 204, \ \bar{x} = 44, \ \bar{y} = 51, \ \Sigma x'^2 = 656, \ \Sigma y'^2 = 356, \ \Sigma x'y' = 480.$

From Table 8.9,

$$s_x^2 = \frac{1}{n}x'^2 = \frac{1}{4}(656) = 164, \quad s_y^2 = \frac{1}{n}y'^2 = \frac{1}{4}(356) = 89.$$

The covariance is

$$C_{xy} = \frac{1}{n}\sum_{i=1}^{4} x_i'y_i' = \frac{480}{4} = 120,$$

and using (8.18) with $n = 4$, the correlation coefficient is

$$r = \frac{\sum_{i=1}^{4}(x_i - \bar{x})(y_i - \bar{y})}{ns_x s_y} = \frac{C_{xy}}{s_x s_y} = \frac{120}{\sqrt{(164)(89)}} = \frac{120}{120.8} = 0.993.$$

Thus, the data exhibits high positive correlation.

PROBLEM 8.15 The ages and Political Science grades of eight students taken at random from a freshman class are shown in Table 8.10.

TABLE 8.10

x (age in years)	18	19	20	16	21	17	18	19
y (grade in percentages)	70	90	90	50	80	60	80	70

Compute the coefficient of correlation and discuss its significance in regard to the bivariate parent population from which this sample was taken.

Solution: Table 8.11 shows the computations for the coefficient of correlation.

TABLE 8.11

x	y	$x' = x - \bar{x}$	$y' = y - \bar{y}$	$x'y'$	x'^2	y'^2
18	70	-0.5	-5	2.5	0.25	25
19	90	0.5	15	7.5	0.25	225
20	90	1.5	15	22.5	2.25	225
16	60	-2.5	-15	37.5	6.25	225
21	80	2.5	5	12.5	6.25	25
17	60	-1.5	-15	22.5	2.25	225
18	80	-0.5	5	2.5	0.25	25
19	70	0.5	-5	-2.5	0.25	25

$\Sigma x = 148, \ \Sigma y = 600, \ \Sigma x'y' = 105.0, \ \Sigma x'^2 = 18.00, \ \Sigma y'^2 = 1000, \ \bar{x} = \dfrac{148}{8} = 18.5, \ \bar{y} = \dfrac{600}{8} = 75.$

Hence from Table 8.11,

$$s_x^2 = \frac{1}{n}x'^2 = \frac{1}{8}(18.00) = 2.25, \quad s_y^2 = \frac{1}{n}y'^2 = \frac{1}{8}(1000.00) = 125.00.$$

The covariance is

$$C_{xy} = \frac{1}{n}\sum_{i=1}^{n} x_i' y_i' = \frac{1}{8}(105.00) = 13.13,$$

and using (8.18) with $n = 4$, the correlation coefficient is

$$r = \frac{C_{xy}}{s_x s_y} = \frac{13.13}{\sqrt{(2.25)(125)}} = \frac{13.13}{16.77} = 0.78.$$

Thus, there is a high positive correlation between age and grades for this course. Hence, it can be concluded that older students tend to do better in Political Science.

PROBLEM 8.16 Determine the equation of the regression line for the data of Prob. 8.14.

Solution: From (8.20), the equation of the regression line is

$$y_e(x) = \bar{y} + r\frac{s_y}{s_x}(x - \bar{x}).$$

Using the values for $r, \bar{y}, \bar{x}, s_y,$ and s_x calculated in Prob. 8.14,

$$y_e(x) = 51 + 0.993 \sqrt{\frac{89}{164}}(x - 44) = 51 + 0.73 \, (x - 44).$$

PROBLEM 8.17 Show that $-1 \leqslant r \leqslant 1$.

Solution: From (8.17), the square of the correlation coefficient is

$$r^2 = 1 - \frac{\sum\limits_{i=1}^{n} (y_i - y_e)^2}{\sum\limits_{i=1}^{n} (y_i - \overline{y})^2} .$$

The value of the least-squares estimate of y, or the y coordinate of the regression line, that corresponds to the data point y_i is y_e. Thus,

$$\sum_{i=1}^{n} (y_i - y_e)^2 \leqslant \sum_{i=1}^{n} (y_i - \overline{y})^2$$

because, by definition, y_e minimizes the sum of the squared errors. Thus, $r^2 \leqslant 1$, and, hence,

$$-1 \leqslant r \leqslant 1.$$

PROBLEM 8.18 Show that the correlation coefficient r is the geometric mean of the slopes b and b' of the regression lines

$$y_e = a + bx, \qquad x_e = a' + b'x,$$

that is, show that $r = \sqrt{bb'}$.

Solution: From (8.20), the equations of the regression lines can be written in terms of the correlation coefficient r, i.e.,

$$y_e - \overline{y} = r \frac{s_y}{s_x} (x - \overline{x}), \qquad x_e - \overline{x} = r \frac{s_x}{s_y} (y - \overline{y}).$$

Equating these slopes to b and b',

$$b = r \frac{s_y}{s_x}, \qquad b' = r \frac{s_x}{s_y} .$$

Hence,

$$\sqrt{bb'} = \sqrt{\left(r \frac{s_y}{s_x} \right) \left(r \frac{s_x}{s_y} \right)} = \sqrt{r^2} = r.$$

8.5   Correlation Coefficient Significance Test

Since the value of the correlation coefficient r is calculated from a finite number of samples, it is a random variable which estimates the true correlation coefficient ρ. There are three specific cases where it is necessary to test r in order to determine whether it differs significantly from what is expected due to chance.

Case 1: As a result of chance variations, even two uncorrelated random variables (i.e., $\rho = 0$) will generally have $r \neq 0$. To test whether the null hypothesis appears true, the statistic

$$t = \frac{r\sqrt{n-2}}{\sqrt{1-r^2}} , \tag{8.21}$$

which has Student's t-distribution with $\nu = n - 2$ degrees of freedom, is tested where n is the number of data points. It is assumed in (8.21) that the data is taken from a bivariate normal population.

Case 2: When $\rho \neq 0$, the statistic

$$z = \frac{1}{2} \ln \left(\frac{1+r}{1-r} \right), \tag{8.22}$$

which is approximately normal with mean $\mu_z = \frac{1}{2} \ln [(1 + \rho)/(1 - \rho)]$ and variance $\sigma_z^2 = 1/(n-3)$, is tested.

Case 3: If the sample correlation coefficients are calculated from two independent sets of data consisting of n_1 and n_2 samples, the results r_1 and r_2 will, in general, differ even if the actual correlation coefficients ρ_1 and ρ_2 are equal. To test whether the difference between r_1 and r_2 is significant (i.e., the null hypothesis $r_1 = r_2$ is tested), the statistic

$$z = z_1 - z_2, \tag{8.23}$$

which is approximately normally distributed with zero mean and variance $\sigma_z^2 = [1/(n_1 - 3) + 1/(n_2 - 3)]$, and where $z_1 = \frac{1}{2} \ln [(1 + r_1)/(1 - r_1)]$ and $z_2 = \frac{1}{2} \ln [(1 + r_2)(1 - r_2)]$, is tested. Hence, (8.23) can be written as

$$z = \frac{1}{2} \ln \left[\frac{(1 + r_1)(1 - r_2)}{(1 - r_1)(1 + r_2)} \right]. \tag{8.24}$$

PROBLEM 8.19 (a) The simultaneous temperatures of two cities are recorded on four different days (at random times during the day). The correlation coefficient r for the recorded values is 0.987. Does r differ significantly from zero? Use both the 5 and 1% levels of significance. (b) At the 0.10 level of significance, determine whether there is a significant difference between the correlation coefficients $r_1 = 0.9$ and $r_2 = 0.1$ of two samples of sizes $n_1 = 52$ and $n_2 = 19$.

Solution: (a) Since the amount of data ($n = 4$) used is so small, it does not necessarily imply that $r = 0.987$ indicates high correlation. Using Table IX of the Appendix with $\nu = n - 2 = 2$ degrees of freedom,

$$r = 0.950 \quad \text{at 5\% level of significance}$$

$$= 0.990 \quad \text{at 1\% level of significance.}$$

Thus, the calculated value is significant at the 5% level but not at the 1% level since 0.987 exceeds 0.950 but not 0.990. Hence, the given value of r is probably significant and more data would be desirable to substantiate the conclusion that the data is highly correlated.

(b) The z-statistics for the two samples of sizes $n_1 = 52$ and $n_2 = 19$ are

$$z_1 = \frac{1}{2} \ln \left(\frac{1 + r_1}{1 - r_1} \right) = \frac{1}{2} \ln \left(\frac{1 + 0.9}{1 - 0.9} \right) = \frac{1}{2} \ln 19 = \frac{1}{2}(2.944) = 1.472,$$

$$z_2 = \frac{1}{2} \ln \left(\frac{1 + r_2}{1 - r_2} \right) = \frac{1}{2} \ln \left(\frac{1 + 0.1}{1 - 0.2} \right) = \frac{1}{2} \ln (1.375) = \frac{1}{2}(0.322) = 0.161.$$

The variances of z_1 and z_2 are

$$\sigma_{z_1}^2 = \frac{1}{n_1 - 3} = \frac{1}{49}, \qquad \sigma_{z_2}^2 = \frac{1}{n_2 - 3} = \frac{1}{16}.$$

From (8.23), the statistic for testing the hypothesis that $\mu_{z_1} = \mu_{z_2}$ is

$$z = z_1 - z_2 = 1.311.$$

From Table VI of the Appendix, at the 0.10 level of significance, $z = 0.24$. Since the calculated value of z is so close to 1.24, the hypothesis that $\mu_{z_1} = \mu_{z_2}$ cannot be accepted or rejected without further testing.

PROBLEM 8.20 Use the t-statistic (8.21) to solve Prob. 8.19(a).

Solution: Since $r = 0.987$ and $n = 4$, from (8.21), the statistic

$$t = \frac{r\sqrt{n - 2}}{\sqrt{1 - r^2}} = \frac{0.987\sqrt{2}}{\sqrt{1 - (0.987)^2}} = 8.65$$

possesses Student's t-distribution. From Table V of the Appendix with $\nu = n - 2 = 2$ degrees of freedom,

$$t = 4.303 \quad \text{at 5\% level of significance}$$

$$= 9.925 \quad \text{at 1\% level of significance.}$$

Thus, the conclusion is the same as that of Prob. 8.19(a).

PROBLEM 8.21 Determine the approximate number of samples of two variables required to establish that the correlation coefficient between them is 0.20.

Solution: From Table IX of the Appendix, the value $r = 0.20$ is reached when the number of degrees ν is between 90 and 100 at the 5% level of significance, and when ν is between 150 and 200 at the 1% level of significance. Since $\nu = n - 2$, the number of samples that would be used would be $n = \nu + 2$; that is,

$$n \approx 100 \quad \text{at the 5\% level of significance}$$
$$\approx 200 \quad \text{at the 1\% level of significance.}$$

PROBLEM 8.22 The correlation coefficient of a sample with $n = 39$ is 0.8. Determine whether this sample was taken from a population whose correlation coefficient is 0.6 at the 5% significance level.

Solution: Since $n = 39, r = 0.8$, and $\rho = 0.6$, from (8.22),

$$z = \frac{1}{2} \ln\left(\frac{1 + r}{1 - r}\right) = \frac{1}{2} \ln\left(\frac{1 + 0.8}{1 - 0.8}\right) = \frac{1}{2} \ln 9 = \frac{1}{2}(2.197) = 1.099,$$

$$\mu_z = \frac{1}{2} \ln\left(\frac{1 + \rho}{1 - \rho}\right) = \frac{1}{2} \ln\left(\frac{1 + 0.6}{1 - 0.6}\right) = \frac{1}{2} \ln 4 = \frac{1}{2}(1.386) = 0.693,$$

$$\sigma_z = \frac{1}{\sqrt{n - 3}} = \frac{1}{\sqrt{39 - 3}} = \frac{1}{6} = 0.167.$$

The quantity

$$Z = \frac{z - \mu_z}{\sigma_z} = \frac{1.099 - 0.693}{0.167} = 2.43$$

is the value of the normal variate with zero mean and unit variance. At the 5% level of significance from Table VI of the Appendix, $Z = 1.96$. Since the calculated value is greater than 1.96, the hypothesis that the population correlation coefficient is 0.6 is rejected.

8.6 Supplementary Problems

PROBLEM 8.23 The distance between two points is independently measured n times. If the measured values are denoted by $d_1, d_2, \cdots, d_n$, determine the best estimate (in a mean-squared sense) of the true distance.

Answer: $d = \dfrac{1}{n} \sum_{i=1}^{n} d_i.$

PROBLEM 8.24 If the measurement errors corresponding to the distances $d_1, d_2, \cdots, d_n$ in Prob. 8.23 are denoted by $e_1, e_2, \cdots, e_n$ and are independently distributed with mean zero and variance σ^2, determine the expected value of the variance of the least mean-squares estimate of d.
Answer: $\sigma^2/n.$

PROBLEM 8.25 A function $x(t_i), i = 0, \pm 1, \pm 2, \cdots$, is approximated by

$$x_e(t_i) = \sum_{j=1}^{2} A_j \phi_j(t_i),$$

where ϕ_1 and ϕ_2 are arbitrary functions. If a least squares estimate for $x(t_i)$ is made, determine the normal equations for the coefficients A_1 and A_2.

Answer: $\sum_i x(t_i)\phi_1(t_i) = A_1 \sum_i \phi_1^2(t_i) + A_2 \sum_i \phi_1(t_i)\phi_2(t_i), \quad \sum_i x(t_i)\phi_2(t_i) = A_1 \sum_i \phi_1(t_i)\phi_2(t_i) + A_2 \sum_i \phi_2^2(t_i).$

PROBLEM 8.26 A function $x(t_i), i = 0, \pm1, \pm2, \cdots$, is approximated by

$$x_e(t_i) = \sum_{j=1}^{n} A_j \phi_j(t_i),$$

where $\phi_1, \phi_2, \cdots, \phi_n$ are arbitrary functions. If a least squares estimate for $x(t_i)$ is made, determine the normal equations for the coefficients $A_1, A_2, \cdots, A_n$.

Answer: $\sum_i x(t_i)\phi_k(t_i) = A_1 \sum_i \phi_1(t_i)\phi_k(t_i) + \cdots + A_n \sum_i \phi_n(t_i)\phi_k(t_i), \quad k = 1, 2, \cdots, n.$

PROBLEM 8.27 A least squares approximation of a function $x(t_i)$ is made by

$$x_e(t_i) = \sum_{j=1}^{n} A_j \phi_j(t_i).$$

If the functions $\phi_1, \phi_2, \cdots, \phi_n$ are chosen to be orthonormal, i.e.,

$$\sum_i \phi_m(t_i)\phi_n(t_i) = 1 \quad \text{for } m = n$$

$$= 0 \quad \text{for } m \neq n,$$

find expressions for the coefficients $A_1, A_2, \cdots, A_n$.

Answer: $A_j = \sum_i x(t_i)\phi_j(t_i), j = 1, 2, \cdots, n.$

PROBLEM 8.28 Show that if all points of a scatter diagram lie on a straight line, the magnitude of the correlation coefficient r is equal to one.

PROBLEM 8.29 Show that if all points of a scatter diagram lie on a circle, the correlation coefficient is equal to zero.

PROBLEM 8.30 A random variable y is generated from the normally distributed random variable x by $y = -5x + 3$. Determine the population correlation coefficient ρ.
Answer: $\rho = -1$.

PROBLEM 8.31 A random variable y is generated from the random variable x by $y = -5|x| + 3$. If x is normally distributed with zero mean, determine the population correlation coefficient ρ.
Answer: $\rho = 0$.

PROBLEM 8.32 A random variable y is generated from $y = x + z$, where x and z are independent, normally distributed random variables with mean zero and variance σ^2. Determine the population correlation coefficient ρ.
Answer: $\rho = \sqrt{2}/2$.

PROBLEM 8.33 The random variables x and y are normally distributed with variances 4 and 9, respectively. If the regression line relating y_e and x is given by $y_e(x) = 0.4 + 0.6x$, determine the correlation coefficient r.
Answer: $r = 0.4$.

PROBLEM 8.34 Show that the correlation coefficient r can be written as

$$r = \frac{n \sum_i x_i y_i - \sum_i x_i \sum_i y_i}{\sqrt{\left[n \sum_i x_i^2 - \left(\sum_i x_i\right)^2\right]\left[n \sum_i y_i^2 - \left(\sum_i y_i\right)^2\right]}}$$

PROBLEM 8.35 Equation (8.22) can be transformed to test the null hypothesis $\rho = 0$ with the statistic

$$z = \frac{\sqrt{n-3}}{2} \ln\left(\frac{1+r}{1-r}\right),$$

whose sampling distribution is approximately the standard normal distribution. Determine approximately the 99% confidence interval for r when $\rho = 0$ and $n = 103$.

Answer: $-0.252 < r < 0.277$.

PROBLEM 8.36 Determine approximately how many samples are required to obtain a 95% confidence interval for $-0.05 < r < 0.05$ for $\rho = 0$. (Cf., Prob. 8.35.)

Answer: $n = 1540$.

CONTINUOUS RANDOM PROCESSES

9.1 Stationary and Ergodic Processes

A *random* or *stochastic process* is a process that assigns, according to a certain rule, a (real or complex) continuous time function $f(t)$ to every outcome ξ of an experiment. It can be viewed as a function of two variables: time t and outcome ξ. Note that $f(t)$ represents:

(1) a family of functions with both t and ξ variables;

(2) a random variable, that is, for a fixed time t, $f(t)$ is dependent on ξ;

(3) a single time function, that is, for a fixed outcome ξ, $f(t)$ signifies a single time function;

(4) a single number, that is, $f(t)$ is a (real or complex) number when both t and ξ are fixed.

If the outcome is defined only for discrete values of t, the process is called a *random series* or a *discrete parameter random process*. (Cf., Chap. 11.)

Two stochastic processes are said to be *equal* if and only if their respective functions are equal for each and every outcome ξ.

The *sum* $f(t) + g(t)$, the *product* $f(t)g(t)$, and any operation (for example, *differentiation* and *integration*) involving one or more processes are obtained by operating on each of the functions of the processes.

The *first-order distribution* $P(x, t)$ of a stochastic process $f(t)$ is the probability that at a given time t, the functions $f(t)$ of the process do not exceed x. The corresponding density is obtained by partially differentiating $P(x, t)$ with respect to x; that is,

$$p(x, t) = \frac{\partial P(x, t)}{\partial x}. \tag{9.1}$$

The *second-order distribution* $P(x_1, x_2; t_1, t_2)$ of a stochastic process $f(t)$ is a joint distribution which is the probability that, at time t_1, the functions $f(t)$ of the process do not exceed x_1 and at time t_2, the $f(t)$ do not exceed the value x_2. The corresponding density is obtained by partial differentiation of $P(x_1, x_2; t_1, t_2)$ with respect to both x_1 and x_2; that is,

$$p(x_1, x_2; t_1, t_2) = \frac{\partial^2 P(x_1, x_2; t_1, t_2)}{\partial x_1 \partial x_2}. \tag{9.2}$$

The *nth-order distribution* is similarly defined.

A real stochastic process is statistically determined if its nth-order distribution $P(x_1, x_2, \cdots, x_n)$ = Prob. $\{f(t_1) \leqslant x_1, f(t_2) \leqslant x_2, \cdots, f(t_n) \leqslant x_n\}$ for any n, and $t_1, t_2, \cdots, t_n$ are known. Note that a distribution of a given order can be determined from a distribution of a higher order.

The statistics of a random process can be determined by observing the outputs of a large number of identical but independent systems which generate the random process. For example, as shown in Fig. 9.1, a large number of 1-Ω resistors generate the *ensemble* (outputs) of noise voltages $\xi_1(t), \xi_2(t), \cdots, \xi_n(t)$. If each member of the ensemble is sampled at $t = t_1$, the first-order probability density function $p(x, t_1)$ is calculated from the resulting set of numbers. In general, $p(x, t_1)$ will depend on the particular value selected for t. Similar remarks apply to all possible higher-order probability distributions.

An *n-dimensional process* consists of the n processes $f_1(t), f_2(t), \cdots, f_n(t)$ and is statistically determined if the joint distribution of the random variable

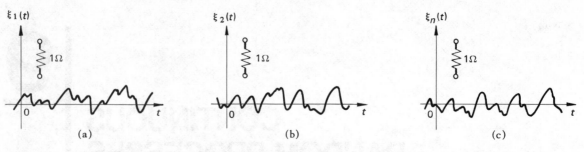

Fig. 9.1 A number of 1-Ω resistors generating the ensemble of noise voltages $\xi_1(t)$, $\xi_2(t)$, $\cdots$, $\xi_n(t)$.

$$\prod_{i=1}^{m_1} f_1(t_{1i}) \prod_{i=1}^{m_2} f_2(t_{2i}) \cdots \prod_{i=1}^{m_n} f_n(t_{ni})$$

is known.

A *complex process*

$$z(t) = f(t) + jg(t), \quad j = \sqrt{-1},$$

is a family of complex functions and is statistically determined in terms of the two-dimensional process $f(t)$, $g(t)$.

A process $f(t)$ is said to be *normal* if the random variables $f(t_1), f(t_2), \cdots, f(t_n)$ are jointly normal for any $n, t_1, t_2, \cdots, t_n$. Note that for $f(t)$ to be normal, densities of all orders must be normal.

Stationary processes can be defined in several ways as follows:

(1) *Strict sense definition:* A stochastic process is said to be stationary in the strict sense if its statistics (that is, probability density functions) are invariant to a shift in the time origin. That is, the two processes $f(t)$ and $f(t + \epsilon)$ have the same statistics for any arbitrary ϵ. Consequently, for a stationary process, the nth-order density must be such that

$$p(x_1, x_2, \cdots, x_n; t_1, t_2, \cdots, t_n) = p(x_1, x_2, \cdots, x_n; t_1 + \epsilon, t_2 + \epsilon, \cdots, t_n + \epsilon). \tag{9.3}$$

This shows that the first-order density $p(x, t)$ of a stationary process is *independent* of t since $p(x; t) = p(x; t + \epsilon)$. Consequently, the expected value $E[f(t)]$ of $f(t)$ is a constant.

The *second-order density* is the joint density of the random variables $f(t)$ and $f(t + t_2 - t_1)$ since the distribution of order two is

$$P(x_1, x_2; t_1, t_2) = P(x_1, x_2; t_1 + \epsilon, t_2 + \epsilon),$$

and, hence $p(x_1, x_2; t_1, t_2) = p(x_1, x_2; t_2 - t_1)$.

1(a) Two processes $f(t)$ and $g(t)$ are said to be *jointly* stationary if the joint statistics of $f(t)$, $g(t)$ are the same as those of $f(t + \epsilon)$, $g(t + \epsilon)$.

The complex process $z(t) = f(t) + jg(t)$ is stationary if and only if $f(t)$ and $g(t)$ are jointly stationary. Note that the process $f(t)$ might be individually, and not jointly, stationary.

(2) *Finite-order stationary definition:* A stochastic process is said to be stationary of order k if and only if (9.3) is true for *only* $n \leqslant k$.

(3) *Wide-sense stationary definition:* A stochastic process $f(t)$ is said to be stationary in the wide-sense (or *weakly* stationary) if its first- and second-order probability density functions are independent of t. That is, the expected value of $f(t)$ is a constant. Clearly, $f(t)$ is stationary in the wide-sense if it is stationary of order two; however, the converse is not true.

(4) *Periodically stationary definition:* A process $f(t)$ is said to be periodically stationary in the strict sense with period T if (9.3) is true for $\epsilon = nT$.

(5) *Stationary in an interval definition:* A process $f(t)$ is said to be stationary in an interval (a, b) if (9.3) is satisfied for all t in the interval (a, b).

(6) *Stationary increments definition:* A process $f(t)$ is said to possess stationary increments if the process $g(t) = f(t + h) - f(t)$ is stationary for every h.

(7) *Asymptotically stationary definition:* A process $f(t)$ is said to be asymptotically stationary if

$$\lim_{\epsilon \to \infty} p(x_1, x_2, \cdots, x_n; t_1 + \epsilon, t_2 + \epsilon, \cdots, t_n + \epsilon)$$

exists and is independent of ϵ.

Note that if $f(t)$ is normal and stationary in the wide-sense, then it is also stationary in the strict sense.

A random process $f(t)$ is said to be *ergodic* if all its statistics can be determined from a single outcome ξ of the process with probability 1. Thus, the first-order distribution and joint distributions of a process can be deduced by either examining one member of the process over a long time or the entire process once or twice. If a process is ergodic then time and ensemble averages (that is, expected values) are equal.

Note that all ergodic processes are stationary; however, all stationary processes are not ergodic.

PROBLEM 9.1 What is the frequency interpretation of the first-order distribution $P(x; t)$?

Solution: An experiment is performed n times and at each trial a time function $f(t)$ is observed. Thus n functions are obtained. Selecting two numbers x and t arbitrarily, let $n_t(x)$ be the total number of trials for which the observed functions $f(t) \leqslant x$ at time t. Then, the first-order distribution is

$$P(x; t) = \lim_{n \to \infty} \frac{n_t(x)}{n}.$$

PROBLEM 9.2 A biased coin is tossed once, and a process is defined by

$$f(t) = \cos \pi t \quad \text{if the outcome is heads}$$
$$= t - \tfrac{1}{2} \quad \text{if the outcome is tails.}$$

Find its distribution function $P(x; t)$ for (a) $t = \tfrac{1}{6}$, (b) $t = \tfrac{1}{3}$, and (c) $t = 1$.

Solution: (a) If $x \geqslant \dfrac{\sqrt{3}}{2}$, then $\{f(t) \leqslant x\}$ is a certain event because

$$f(t) = \frac{\sqrt{3}}{2} \quad \text{if the outcome is heads}$$
$$= -\tfrac{1}{3} \quad \text{if the outcome is tails.}$$

If $-\dfrac{1}{3} \leqslant x < \dfrac{\sqrt{3}}{2}$, then $P\{f(t) \leqslant x\} = P\{\text{tails}\} = q$. Finally, if $x < -\dfrac{1}{3}$, $\{f(t) \leqslant x\}$ is an impossible event. Thus, the complete probability distribution function is

$$P\left(x; \tfrac{1}{6}\right) = 1 \quad \text{for } x \geqslant \frac{\sqrt{3}}{2}$$
$$= q \quad \text{for } -\frac{1}{3} \leqslant x < \frac{\sqrt{3}}{2}$$
$$= 0 \quad \text{for } x < -\tfrac{1}{3}.$$

(b) If $x \geqslant \tfrac{1}{2}$, then $\{f(t) \leqslant x\}$ is a certain event because

$$f(t) = \tfrac{1}{2} \quad \text{if the outcome is heads}$$
$$= -\tfrac{1}{6} \quad \text{if the outcome is tails.}$$

If $-\tfrac{1}{6} \leqslant x < \tfrac{1}{2}$, then $P\{f(t) \leqslant x\} = P\{\text{tails}\} = q$. If $x < -\tfrac{1}{6}$, then $\{f(t) \leqslant x\}$ is an impossible event. Now, the complete distribution function is

$$P(x; \tfrac{1}{3}) = 1 \quad \text{for } x \geqslant \tfrac{1}{2}$$
$$= q \quad \text{for } -\tfrac{1}{6} \leqslant x < \tfrac{1}{2}$$
$$= 0 \quad \text{for } x < -\tfrac{1}{6}.$$

(c) For $t = 1$,

$$f(t) = -1 \quad \text{if the outcome is heads}$$
$$= \tfrac{1}{2} \quad \text{if the outcome is tails.}$$

The distribution function is then

$$P(x; 1) = 1 \qquad \text{for } x \geqslant \tfrac{1}{2}$$
$$= 1 - q \quad \text{for } -1 \leqslant x < \tfrac{1}{2}$$
$$= 0 \qquad \text{for } x < -1.$$

PROBLEM 9.3 Show that $\Phi(1) = 0$ is a necessary condition for the process $f(t) = \sin(\lambda t + \phi)$, where λ is a constant and ϕ is a random variable whose characteristic function is

$$\Phi(\omega) = E[e^{j\omega\phi}] = E[\cos \omega\phi] + jE[\sin \omega\phi], \quad j = \sqrt{-1},$$

to be stationary in the wide-sense.

Solution: For $f(t)$ to be stationary in the wide-sense, its expected value must be independent of t; that is, $E\{f(t)\} = \text{const.}$ Now,

$$E[f(t)] = E[\sin(\lambda t + \phi)] = E[\sin \lambda t \cos \phi + \cos \lambda t \sin \phi] = \sin \lambda t\, E[\cos \phi] + \cos \lambda t\, E[\sin \phi].$$

If $f(t)$ is stationary, the equation will be equal to a constant. This is possible only when the coefficients of $\sin \lambda t$ and $\cos \lambda t$ are zero; that is,

$$E[\cos \phi] = E[\sin \phi] = 0.$$

Since $\Phi(1) = E[\cos \phi] + jE[\sin \phi]$, it follows that $\Phi(1) = 0$.

PROBLEM 9.4 Show that if the process $f(t) = a \cos \lambda t + b \sin \lambda t$ is stationary in the wide-sense where a and b are random variables, then

$$E[a] = E[b] = 0.$$

Solution: If $f(t)$ is stationary in the wide-sense, then $E[f(t)]$ must be independent of t. Thus,

$$E[f(t)] = E[a \cos \lambda t + b \sin \lambda t] = \cos \lambda t\, E[a] + \sin \lambda t\, E[b] = \text{const.}$$

This is possible only if the coefficients of $\cos \lambda t$ and $\sin \lambda t$ are zero; that is,

$$E[a] = E[b] = 0,$$

which proves the result.

PROBLEM 9.5 Describe (a) the Poisson process, (b) Poisson impulses, (c) Poisson increments, (d) shot noise, (e) random telegraph signal, (f) random walk, (g) the Wiener-Lévy process as a limiting form of random walk, and (h) semirandom and random binary transmissions.

Solution: (a) Select n points at random in the interval $\left(-\dfrac{T}{2}, \dfrac{T}{2}\right)$. If $n \to \infty$ and $T \to \infty$ such that $n/T \to \lambda$, then the probability of having k points in an interval of length t is

$$\frac{e^{-\lambda t}(\lambda t)^k}{k!}.$$

(Cf., Chap. 3.)

Now define the stochastic process $f(t)$ as follows: Assume that $f(0) = 0$ and that $f(t)$ is equal to the number of points in the interval $(0, t)$ if $t > 0$. When $t < 0$, $-f(t)$ is equal to the number of points in the interval. The family of functions thus obtained is called a Poisson process. [Cf., Fig. 9.2(a).]

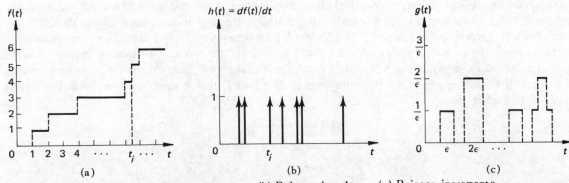

Fig. 9.2 (a) A Poisson process. (b) Poisson impulses. (c) Poisson increments.

(b) Let t_i be the points in time, $f(t)$, the process of part (a), and form the process

$$h(t) = \sum_i \delta(t - t_i),$$

where $\delta(t - t_i)$ is the delta function and

$$h(t) = \frac{df(t)}{dt} = \lim_{\epsilon \to 0} \frac{f(t + \epsilon) - f(t)}{\epsilon}.$$

This family of functions is called Poisson impulses. [Cf., Fig. 9.2(b).]

(c) Poisson increments are formed with the process

$$g(t) = \frac{f(t + \epsilon) - f(t)}{\epsilon},$$

where $f(t)$ is a Poisson process defined in part (a) and $\epsilon > 0$ is a given constant.

Clearly, $g(t) = k/\epsilon$, where k is the number of points in the interval $(t, t + \epsilon)$. [Cf., Fig. 9.2(c).] Note that, from part (b), $h(t) = \lim_{\epsilon \to 0} g(t)$.

(d) Shot noise $s(t)$ can be considered as the output of a linear system whose input is a Poisson sequence of impulses $h(t) = \sum_i \delta(t - t_i)$ and whose impulse response is given by a real time function $z(t)$. (Cf., Fig. 9.3.) Thus, shot noise is the process

$$s(t) = \sum_i z(t - t_i),$$

where the points t_i are Poisson distributed.

(e) The random telegraph signal is a stochastic process $f(t)$ which assumes the values +1 or −1 and whose zero crossings are Poisson distributed. (Cf., Fig. 9.4.)

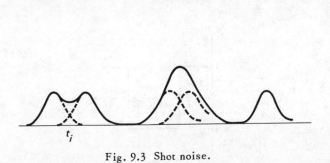

Fig. 9.3 Shot noise.

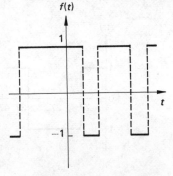

Fig. 9.4 Random telegraph signal.

(f) Random walk is a stochastic process $f(t)$ obtained as follows: A fair coin is tossed every T sec an infinite number of times, and a step is taken at each tossing—a step to the right if heads show and to the left if tails show. Then, $f(t)$ represent the position t sec after the tossing began. Clearly, $f(t)$ depends on the outcomes of the tossings, that is, on the particular sequence that the heads and tails occur. The resulting function is in the form of a staircase, as shown in Fig. 9.5(a), with discontinuities at $t = nT$. The steps are taken instantly and are of length s. If k heads appear in the first n tossings in time $t = nT$, then k steps have been taken to the right and $n - k$ to the left. Hence,

$$f(t) = ks - (n - k)s$$
$$= (2k - n)s$$
$$= rs,$$

where $r = 2k - n$, and $f(t)$ is a random variable which assumes the values rs with $r = n, n - 2, n - 4, \cdots, -n$.

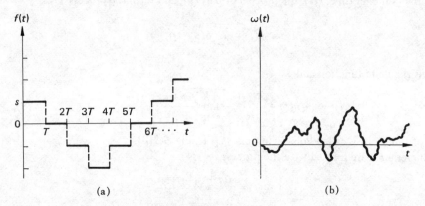

(a)   (b)

Fig. 9.5 (a) Random walk. (b) Wiener-Levy process.

(g) The Wiener-Lévy process, also known as *Brownian motion,* is defined by

$$\omega(t) = \lim_{T \to 0} f(t),$$

where the process $f(t)$ is that of a random walk. It is also assumed that $s^2 \propto T$, where s and T are the length of the steps and the time between the tossings of the fair coin. [Cf., Fig. 9.5(b).]

This process, for example, defines (1) the ceaseless irregular motions exhibited by a very small particle immersed in a liquid or gas, and (2) thermal noise in electric circuits.

(h) A fair coin is tossed an infinite number of times at intervals of T sec. Then, the semirandom binary transmission is the process defined by

$$f(t) = 1 \qquad \text{for heads at } n\text{th toss}$$
$$= -1 \qquad \text{for tails at } n\text{th toss,}$$

and where $(n - 1)T < t < nT$. [Cf., Fig. 9.6(a).]

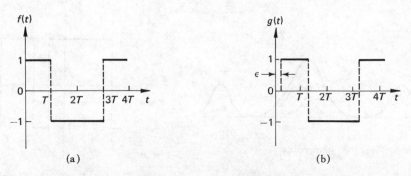

(a)   (b)

Fig. 9.6 (a) Semirandom binary transmission. (b) Random binary transmission.

The random binary transmission is obtained by shifting the semirandom binary transmission $f(t)$ by a random variable ϵ, which is uniformly distributed in the interval $(0, T)$ and is independent of $f(t)$. Thus, as shown in Fig. 9.6(b), the random binary transmission is the process

$$g(t) = f(t - \epsilon).$$

PROBLEM 9.6 An ensemble of signals is defined by $y_i = A_i \cos \omega t$, where A_i are random variables with uniform probability density

$$p(A) = \frac{1}{|A_0|} \quad \text{for } 0 \leqslant A \leqslant |A_0|$$

$$= 0 \quad \text{elsewhere.}$$

Is the process ergodic?

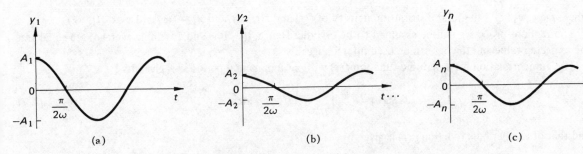

Fig. 9.7 Typical members of the ensemble of Prob. 9.6.

Solution: Typical members of the ensemble are shown in Fig. 9.7. It is seen that the probability density function taken across the ensemble at $t = \pi/2\omega$ and $t = 0$ is, respectively,

$$p_y(y, \pi/2\omega) = \delta(y) \quad \text{and} \quad p_y(y, 0) = p(A)|_{A=y}.$$

Thus, the process is not stationary and, therefore, not ergodic.

PROBLEM 9.7 An ensemble of signals is defined by $y_i = A_i$, where the A_i are independent random variables with uniform probability density

$$p(A) = \frac{1}{|A_i|} \quad \text{for } 0 \leqslant A_i \leqslant |A_0|$$

$$= 0 \quad \text{elsewhere.}$$

Is the process ergodic?

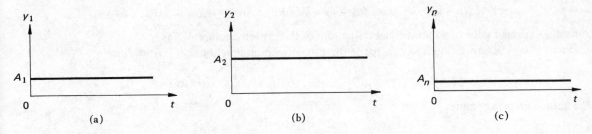

Fig. 9.8 Typical members of the ensemble of Prob. 9.7.

Solution: Typical members of the ensemble are shown in Fig. 9.8. The probability density across the ensemble is $p_y(y) = p(A)|_{A=y}$, and is seen from Fig. 9.8 to be independent of time, so that the process is stationary. However, the probability density functions for the members of the ensemble are $p_{y_i}(y) = \delta(y - A_i)$, which are, in general, all different. Therefore, the ensemble is not ergodic.

9.2 Autocorrelation and Autocovariance

The *autocorrelation* $R_y(\tau)$ of a random process $f(t)$ is defined by

$$R_y(\tau) = \lim_{T \to \infty} \frac{1}{2T} \int_{-T}^{T} f(t)f(t + \tau)dt \tag{9.4}$$

$$= \overline{f(t)f(t + \tau)}, \tag{9.5}$$

where the bar denotes the time average as opposed to the expected value, which denotes an ensemble average.

If the process $f(t)$ is ergodic, the autocorrelation $R_y(\tau)$ can be calculated by taking the joint moments of the random variables $f(t)$ and $f(t + \tau)$; that is,

$$R_f(\tau) = E[f(t)f(t + \tau)] = \int_{-\infty}^{\infty} x_1 x_2 \, p(x_1, x_2 ; \tau)dx_1 dx_2, \tag{9.6}$$

where $p(x_1, x_2 ; \tau)$ is the joint distribution density of $f(t)$ and $f(t + \tau)$, and $x_1 = f(t)$ and $x_2 = f(t + \tau)$.

The random processes will be assumed to be ergodic. Hence, the time and ensemble averages are equal and the expected value and the bar can be used interchangeably.

The autocorrelation for a periodic function $f(t)$ with a fundamental period T is given by

$$R_f(\tau) = \frac{1}{T} \int_{-T/2}^{T/2} f(t)f(t + \tau)dt, \tag{9.7}$$

and that of an aperiodic function $g(t)$ is given by

$$R_g(\tau) = \int_{-\infty}^{\infty} g(t)g(t + \tau)dt. \tag{9.8}$$

The *autocovariance* $\rho_f(\tau)$ of a random process $f(t)$ is

$$\rho_f(\tau) = E\{[f(t) - m][f(t + \tau) - m]\}, \tag{9.9}$$

where m denotes the mean value of $f(t)$.

The *normalized autocovariance* $\rho_{f_n}(\tau)$ of a random process $f(t)$, with a variance σ_f^2, is

$$\rho_{f_n}(\tau) = \frac{1}{\sigma_f^2} \, \rho_f(\tau). \tag{9.10}$$

The autocovariance and autocorrelation of a process $f(t)$ are equal when the average value of $f(t)$ is zero.

PROBLEM 9.8 Determine the relationship between the autocorrelation and autocovariance functions.

Solution: Let $u = f(t)$, $v = f(t + \tau)$, $\overline{u} = m$, and $\overline{v} = m$. Then, from (9.9), the autocovariance is

$$\rho_f(\tau) = E[(u - \overline{u})(v - \overline{v})] = E(uv - \overline{u}v - \overline{v}u + \overline{u}\overline{v}) = E(uv) - E(\overline{u}v) - E(\overline{v}u) + E(\overline{u}\overline{v})$$

since the expected value of a sum is equal to the sum of the expected values.

From (9.6), the term $E(uv)$ is recognized as the autocorrelation function $R_f(\tau)$. Also, since

$$E(\overline{u}v) = \overline{u}E(v) = \overline{u}\overline{v}, \qquad E(\overline{v}u) = \overline{v}E(u) = \overline{v}\overline{u}, \qquad E(\overline{u}\overline{v}) = \overline{u}\overline{v},$$

the autocovariance becomes

$$\rho_f(\tau) = R_f(\tau) - \overline{u}\overline{v}.$$

Since $\overline{u} = \overline{v} = m$,

$$\rho_f(\tau) = R_f(\tau) - m^2.$$

PROBLEM 9.9 Calculate the autocorrelation of the periodic function $f(t) = A \sin(\omega_0 t + \phi)$.

Solution: Since the period is $T = 2\pi/\omega_0$, from (9.5), the autocorrelation is

$$R_f(\tau) = \frac{A^2}{T} \int_{-T/2}^{T/2} \sin(\omega_0 t + \phi) \sin[\omega_0(t + \tau) + \phi]\, dt$$

$$= \frac{A^2}{T} \int_{-T/2}^{T/2} \sin(\omega_0 t + \phi)[\sin(\omega_0 t + \phi)\cos\omega_0\tau + \cos(\omega_0 t + \phi)\sin\omega_0\tau]\, dt$$

$$= \frac{A^2}{T}\left[\cos\omega_0\tau \int_{-T/2}^{T/2} \sin^2(\omega_0 t + \phi)\, dt\right.$$

$$\left. + \sin\omega_0\tau \int_{-T/2}^{T/2} \sin(\omega_0 t + \phi)\cos(\omega_0 t + \phi)\, dt\right]$$

$$= \frac{A^2}{T}\left[\cos\omega_0\tau\left(\frac{T}{2}\right) + (\sin\omega_0\tau)\cdot 0\right]$$

$$= \frac{A^2}{2}\cos\omega_0\tau.$$

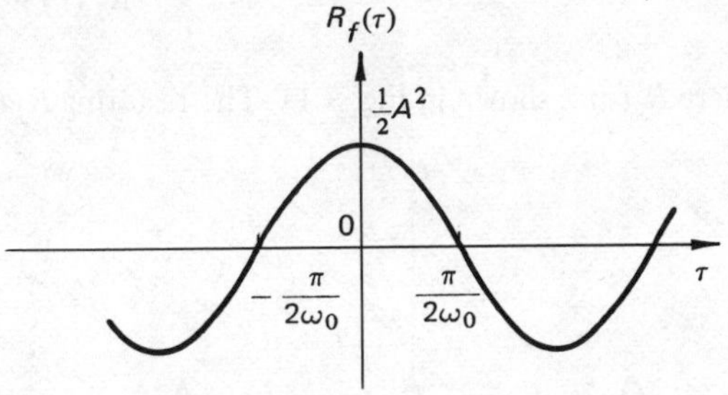

Figure 9.9 shows the graph of $R_f(\tau)$.

Fig. 9.9 Solution to Prob. 9.9.

PROBLEM 9.10 Calculate the autocorrelation of the rectangular pulse shown in Fig. 9.10(a); that is,

$$g(t) = A \quad \text{for } 0 \leqslant t \leqslant T_0$$
$$= 0 \quad \text{elsewhere.}$$

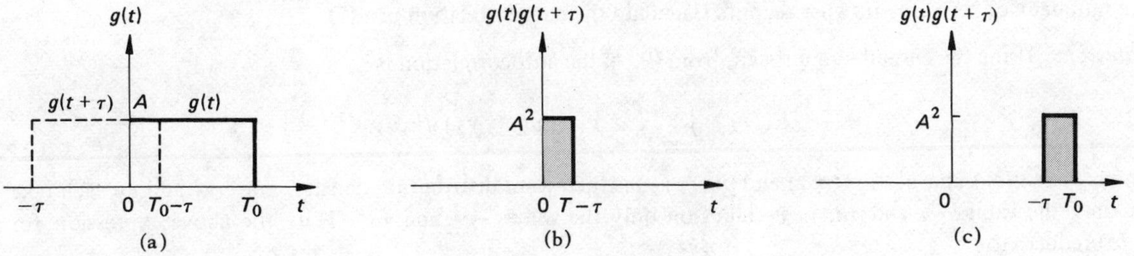

Fig. 9.10 (a) Rectangular pulse of Prob. 9.10. (b) Area under $g(t)g(t + \tau)$ for $0 \leq \tau \leq T_0$.
(c) Area under $g(t)g(t + \tau)$ for $-T_0 \leq \tau \leq 0$.

Solution: Using (9.8), $R_g(\tau)$ is seen to be equal to the area under $g(t)g(t + \tau)$ for $0 \leqslant \tau \leqslant T_0$, as shown in Fig. 9.10(b). Thus, $R_g(\tau) = A^2(T_0 - \tau)$ for $0 \leqslant \tau \leqslant T_0$. For $-T_0 \leqslant \tau \leqslant 0$, Fig. 9.10(c) shows that $R_g(\tau) = A^2(T_0 + \tau)$. When $|\tau| > T_0$, $R_g(\tau) = 0$. Thus,

$$R_g(\tau) = A^2(T_0 - |\tau|) \quad \text{for } |\tau| \leqslant T_0$$
$$= 0 \quad \text{elsewhere,}$$

as shown in Fig. 9.11.

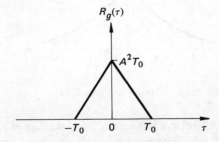

Fig. 9.11 Solution to Prob. 9.10.

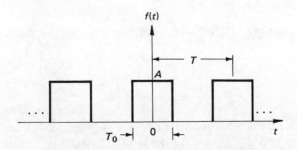

Fig. 9.12 Periodic signal of Prob. 9.11.

PROBLEM 9.11   Calculate the autocorrelation function of the periodic signal shown in Fig. 9.12.

Solution: Using (9.7) for $|\tau| \leqslant T_0$, the results of Prob. 9.10 can be used since

$$R_f(\tau) = \frac{1}{T} R_g(\tau) \quad \text{for } |\tau| \leqslant T_0$$

$$= 0 \qquad \text{for } |\tau| < T - T_0.$$

Since $f(t)$ is periodic, $R_f(\tau)$ is periodic with the same fundamental period T. Thus,

$$R_f(\tau) = \frac{1}{T} \sum_{n=-\infty}^{\infty} R_g(\tau - nT),$$

where $R_g(\tau)$ is shown in Fig. 9.11. The resulting $R_f(\tau)$ is shown in Fig. 9.13.

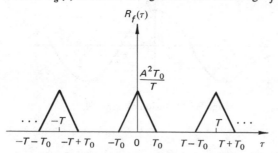

Fig. 9.13   Solution to Prob. 9.11.

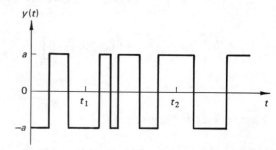

Fig. 9.14   Random telegraph signal.

PROBLEM 9.12   The random telegraph signal shown in Fig. 9.14 is a random process $y(t) = f(t)$, where $f(t)$ alternately takes on the value $+a$ or $-a$. The interval between zero crossings is Poisson distributed with an average number ν of zero crossings per second. Calculate the autocorrelation of $y(t)$.

Solution: Using the ensemble approach, from (9.6), the autocorrelation is

$$R_y(\tau) = \int_{-\infty}^{\infty} \int_{-\infty}^{\infty} y_1 y_2 \, p(y_1, y_2) \, dy_1 dy_2,$$

where $y_1 = y(t_1)$ and $y_2 = y(t + \tau)$ and $p(y_1, y_2)$ is their joint distribution density. Since y_1 and y_2 each take on only the values $-a$ and $+a$, $y_1 y_2$ takes on only the values $-a^2$ and $+a^2$. Thus, the above expression for $R_y(\tau)$ reduces to

$$R_y(\tau) = a^2 P(y_1 y_2 = a^2) - a^2 P(y_1 y_2 = -a^2).$$

The quantity $P(y_1 y_2 = a^2)$ is the probability of an even number of zero crossings (including zero) between t_1 and t_2, while $P(y_1 y_2 = -a^2)$ is the probability of an odd number of zero crossings. Thus,

$$P(y_1 y_2 = a^2) = P(0) + P(2) + P(4) + \cdots, \qquad P(y_1 y_2 = -a^2) = P(1) + P(3) + P(5) + \cdots.$$

From Chap. 3, the Poisson distribution is

$$P(k) = \frac{(\nu\tau)^k}{k!} e^{-\nu\tau},$$

where $\tau = t_2 - t_1$ and k = number of zero crossings in time τ. Therefore, for $\tau \geqslant 0$,

$$R_y(\tau) = a^2 [P(0) - P(1) + P(2) - P(3) + \cdots]$$

$$= a^2 e^{-\nu\tau} \left[1 - \nu\tau + \frac{(\nu\tau)^2}{2!} - \frac{(\nu\tau)^3}{3!} + \cdots \right]$$

$$= a^2 e^{-\nu\tau} e^{-\nu\tau} = a^2 e^{-2\nu\tau}.$$

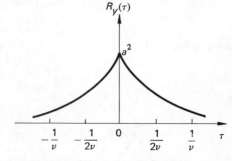

Fig. 9.15   Solution to Prob. 9.12.

Since the number of zero crossings in an interval τ is dependent only on $|\tau|$ and is independent of the sign of τ, $R_y(\tau) = a^2 e^{-2\nu|\tau|}$, and $R_y(\tau)$ is an even function of τ, as shown in Fig. 9.15. This property holds, in general, for the autocorrelation of an arbitrary waveform.

PROBLEM 9.13 A function $y(t)$ consists of an infinite sequence of identical rectangular pulses of duration T_0, as shown in Fig. 9.16(a). The possible locations for the centers of each of the pulses are $\pm nT$, $n = 0, 1, 2, \cdots$. If the probability that a pulse is present at any given location is P_0 and is independent of the presence or absence of all other pulses, determine the autocorrelation of $y(t)$. Show that the autocorrelation function is composed of a periodic function of τ plus an aperiodic part which is zero except in the interval $-T_0 < \tau < T_0$.

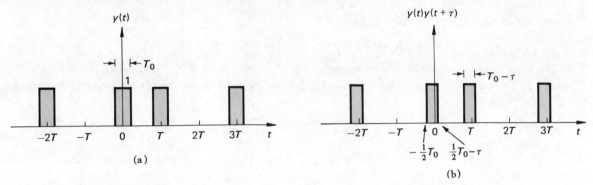

Fig. 9.16 (a) Rectangular pulses $y(t)$ of duration T_0. (b) Product $y(t)y(t + \tau)$ for $0 \le \tau \le T_0$.

Solution: From (9.5), the autocorrelation is $R_y(\tau) = \overline{y(t)y(t + \tau)}$. When $0 \le \tau \le T_0$, the product $y(t)y(t+\tau)$ is as shown in Fig. 9.16(b). If pulses at each possible location were present, then $\overline{y(t)y(t + \tau)}$ would simply be the fraction of time the product $y(t)y(t + \tau)$ is nonzero since the pulse height equals one. Thus, for this case,

$$\overline{y(t)y(t + \tau)} = \frac{\frac{1}{2}T_0 - \tau - (-\frac{1}{2}T_0)}{T} = \frac{T_0 - \tau}{T}.$$

Similar reasoning for the interval $-T_0 \le \tau \le 0$ yields $\overline{y(t)y(t + \tau)} = (T_0 + \tau)/T$. However, for the case of Fig. 9.16(a), the average value of this product is reduced since only the fraction P_0 of the pulses are present. Therefore,

$$R_y(\tau) = P_0 \frac{T_0 - |\tau|}{T} \quad \text{for } -T_0 \le \tau \le T_0.$$

In the intervals $nT + T_0 \le \tau \le (n + 1)T - T_0$ for $n = 0, \pm 1, \pm 2, \cdots$, $y(t)y(t + \tau) = 0$. Hence.

$$R_y(\tau) = 0 \quad \text{for } nT + T_0 \le \tau \le (n + 1)T - T_0, \text{ where } n = 0, \pm 1, \pm 2, \cdots.$$

In the intervals $nT - T_0 \le \tau \le nT + T_0$ for $n = \pm 1, \pm 2, \cdots$, the quantity $\overline{y(t)y(t + \tau)}$ is reduced by the factor P_0^2 from $(T_0 - |\tau|)/T$ since only the fraction P_0^2 of the pulses are present in pairs with the separation nT, where $n = 1, 2, \cdots$. Therefore,

$$R_y(\tau) = P_0^2 \frac{T_0 - |\tau - nT|}{T} \quad \text{for } nT - T_0 \le \tau \le nT + T_0, \text{ where } n = \pm 1, \pm 2, \cdots.$$

The autocorrelation $R_y(\tau)$ is shown in Fig. 9.17 and can be separated into the sum of a periodic function $R_{y_p}(\tau)$ plus an aperiodic function $R_{y_a}(\tau)$, where $R_{y_p}(\tau)$ and $R_{y_a}(\tau)$ are shown in Figs. 9.18(a–b).

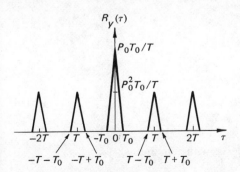

Fig. 9.17 Autocorrelation $R_y(\tau)$ of Prob. 9.13.

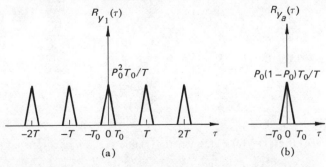

Fig. 9.18 (a) Periodic component $R_{y_p}(\tau)$ of $R_y(\tau)$ of Fig. 9.17. (b) Aperiodic component $R_{y_a}(\tau)$ of $R_y(\tau)$ of Fig. 9.17.

PROBLEM 9.14 Determine the mean value and autocorrelation of the random binary transmission. (Cf., Prob. 9.5.)

Solution: Since at any arbitrary time, a random binary transmission $g(t)$ takes on the values $+1$ or -1 with equal likelihood,

$$\overline{g(t)} = 0.$$

The autocorrelation of the process is given by

$$R_g(\tau) = E[g(t_1)g(t_2)] \quad \text{for } \tau = t_2 - t_1.$$

Since the value of $g(t_2)$ is statistically independent of $g(t_1)$ when $t_2 - k_1 > T$, $R_g(\tau) = [\overline{g(t)}]^2 = 0$ for $\tau > T$. When $\tau \leqslant T$, $R_g(\tau)$ is equal to the probability that the interval (t_1, t_2) does not contain the point $nT + \epsilon$, where n is any integer. Thus,

$$R_g(\tau) = 1 - \frac{|\tau|}{T} \quad \text{for } |\tau| \leqslant T$$

$$= 0 \qquad\qquad \text{for } |\tau| > T.$$

9.3   Properties of Autocorrelation Functions

The *mean-squared value* of a stochastic process $f(t)$ is its autocorrelation $R_f(\tau)$ when $\tau = 0$; that is, from (9.4),

$$R_f(0) = \lim_{T \to \infty} \frac{1}{2T} \int_{-T}^{T} f^2(t)dt \tag{9.11}$$

$$= \overline{f^2(t)}. \tag{9.12}$$

The *average power* (into a 1-Ω resistor) of a random process $f(t)$, when it represents voltage or current, is the mean-squared value $R_f(0)$ of $f(t)$.

Two processes $f(t)$ and $g(t)$ are said to be *uncorrelated* processes if $E[f(t_1)g(t_2)] = 0$.

The properties of the autocorrelation function $R_f(\tau)$ of a real stochastic process $f(t)$ are:

(1) The mean-squared value of $f(t)$ is always nonnegative; that is, $R_f(0) \geqslant 0$.

(2) $R_f(\tau)$ is always real and even; that is,

$$R_f(\tau) = R_f(-\tau). \tag{9.13}$$

This follows immediately on substituting $-\tau$ for τ in (9.4).

(3) $R_f(\tau)$ is a maximum at the origin; that is,

$$R_f(\tau) \leqslant R_f(0). \tag{9.14}$$

(Cf., Prob. 9.15.)

(4) If $z(t) = df(t)/dt$ is the derivative of $f(t)$,

$$R_z(\tau) = -\frac{d^2 R_f(\tau)}{d\tau^2}. \tag{9.15}$$

(Cf., Prob. 9.16.)

(5) If $f(t) = \int_{-\infty}^{t} g(t)dt$,

$$R_f(\tau) = -\int_{-\infty}^{\tau} \int_{-\infty}^{v} R_g(u)du\,dv. \tag{9.16}$$

(Cf., Prob. 9.17.)

(6) If $z(t) = f(t) + g(t)$, where $f(t)$ and $g(t)$ are uncorrelated processes with zero means,

$$R_z(\tau) = R_f(\tau) + R_g(\tau). \tag{9.17}$$

(Cf., Prob. 9.18.)

(7) If $z(t) = f(t)g(t)$, where $f(t)$ and $g(t)$ are statistically independent processes,

$$R_z(\tau) = R_f(\tau)R_g(\tau). \tag{9.18}$$

(Cf., Prob. 9.19.)

PROBLEM 9.15 (a) Prove Schwartz's inequality

$$\int f^2(t)dt \int g^2(t)dt \geqslant \left[\int f(t)g(t)dt\right]^2, \tag{9.19}$$

where $f(t)$ and $g(t)$ are arbitrary real functions integrated over arbitrary limits. (b) Establish (9.14) using (9.19).

Solution: (a) Consider the function $\int [\lambda f(t) + g(t)]^2 \, dt$ of the variable λ. Then,

$$\int [\lambda f(t) + g(t)]^2 \, dt = \int [\lambda^2 f^2(t) + 2\lambda f(t)g(t) + g^2(t)] \, dt = \lambda^2 \int f^2(t)dt + 2\lambda \int f(t)g(t)dt + \int g^2(t)dt \geqslant 0$$

since the square of any number is always nonnegative. Thus, the integral $\int [\lambda f(t) + g(t)]^2 \, dt$ is a positive definite quadratic in λ. Hence,

$$\left[2\int f(t)g(t)dt\right]^2 - 4\int f^2(t)dt \int g^2(t)dt \leqslant 0 \quad \text{or} \quad \left[\int f(t)g(t)dt\right]^2 \leqslant \int f^2(t)dt \int g^2(t)dt.$$

Note that the equality in (9.19) holds if and only if $f(t)$ and $g(t)$ are proportional.

(b) Substituting $g(t) = f(t + \tau)$ in (9.19),

$$\left[\frac{1}{2T} \int_{-T}^{T} f(t)f(t+\tau)dt\right]^2 \leqslant \frac{1}{2T} \int_{-T}^{T} f^2(t)dt \, \frac{1}{2T} \int_{-T}^{T} f^2(t+\tau)dt.$$

Taking the limit as $T \to \infty$, $R_f^2(\tau) \leqslant R_f^2(0)$; that is, $|R_f(\tau)| \leqslant R_f(0)$ since, from (9.7), $R_f(0)$ is always positive. Thus, $|R_f(\tau)/R_f(0)| \leqslant 1$.

PROBLEM 9.16 Prove (9.15).

Solution: From (9.1), the autocorrelation function of $f'(t) = df/dt$ is

$$R_g(\tau) = \overline{f'(t)f'(t+\tau)}.$$

Since by the definition of the derivative,

$$f'(t) = \lim_{\Delta t \to 0} \left[\frac{f(t+\Delta t) - f(t)}{\Delta t}\right],$$

the autocorrelation function becomes

$$R_g(\tau) = \lim_{\Delta t \to 0} \left\{\frac{\overline{[f(t+\Delta t) - f(t)][f(t+\tau+\Delta t) - f(t+\tau)]}}{(\Delta t)^2}\right\}$$

$$= \lim_{\Delta t \to 0} \left\{\frac{1}{(\Delta t)^2} [\overline{f(t+\Delta t)f(t+\tau+\Delta t)} + \overline{f(t)f(t+\tau)} - \overline{f(t)f(t+\tau+\Delta t)} - \overline{f(t+\Delta t)f(t+\tau)}]\right\}$$

$$= \lim_{\Delta t \to 0} \left\{\frac{1}{(\Delta t)^2} [R_f(\tau) + R_f(\tau) - R_f(\tau+\Delta t) - R_f(\tau-\Delta t)]\right\}$$

$$= \lim_{\Delta t \to 0} \left\{\frac{1}{\Delta t}\left[-\frac{dR_f(\tau)}{d\tau} + \frac{dR_f(\tau-\Delta t)}{d\tau}\right]\right\}$$

$$= -\frac{d^2 R_f(\tau)}{d\tau^2}.$$

PROBLEM 9.17 Prove (9.16).

Solution: From (9.15), since $g = df/dt$,

$$R_g(\tau) = -\frac{d^2 R_f(\tau)}{d\tau^2} \, .$$

Integrating,

$$\frac{dR_f(\tau)}{d\tau} = \int_{-\infty}^{\tau} R_g(u)\,du,$$

$$R_f(\tau) = \int_{-\infty}^{\tau} d\tau \int_{-\infty}^{\tau} R_g(u)\,du = \int_{-\infty}^{\tau} dv \int_{-\infty}^{v} R_g(u)\,du = \int_{-\infty}^{\tau}\int_{-\infty}^{v} R_g(u)\,du\,dv.$$

PROBLEM 9.18   Prove (9.17).

Solution: If $z(t) = f(t) + g(t)$, then

$$R_z(\tau) = \overline{z(t)z(t + \tau)}$$

$$= \overline{[f(t) + g(t)][f(t + \tau) + g(t + \tau)]}$$

$$= \overline{f(t)f(t + \tau) + g(t)g(t + \tau) + g(t)f(t + \tau) + f(t)g(t + \tau)}.$$

Since the average value of a sum is the sum of the average values,

$$R_z(\tau) = \overline{f(t)f(t + \tau)} + \overline{g(t)g(t + \tau)} + \overline{g(t)g(t + \tau)} + \overline{f(t)g(t + \tau)}.$$

The first two terms on the right-hand side of the preceding equation are seen to be $R_f(\tau)$ and $R_g(\tau)$, respectively. The last two terms are equal to zero since $f(t)$ and $g(t)$ are uncorrelated random processes with zero means. (These terms are known as cross-correlation functions and are discussed in Sec. 9.5.) Therefore,

$$R_z(\tau) = R_f(\tau) + R_g(\tau).$$

PROBLEM 9.19   Prove (9.18).

Solution: The autocorrelation function of $z(t) = f(t) \cdot g(t)$ is

$$R_z(\tau) = \overline{z(t)z(t + \tau)} = \overline{f(t)g(t)f(t + \tau)g(t + \tau)}.$$

Since $x(t)$ and $y(t)$ are statistically independent,

$$R_z(\tau) = \overline{[f(t)f(t + \tau)]}\,\overline{[g(t)g(t + \tau)]} = R_f(\tau)R_g(\tau).$$

9.4   Gaussian Processes

A real stochastic process $f(t)$ is said to be *Gaussian*, or *normal*, if the random variables $f(t_1)$, $f(t_2)$, $\cdots$, $f(t_n)$ are jointly normal for any n, t_1, t_2, $\cdots$, t_n.

Two real stochastic processes $f(t)$ and $g(t)$ are said to be *Gaussian*, or *normal*, if the random variables $f(t_1)$, $f(t_2)$, $\cdots$, $f(t_n)$, $g(t_1')$, $g(t_2')$, $\cdots$, $g(t_m')$ are jointly normal for any m, n, t_1, t_2, $\cdots$, t_n, t_1', t_2', $\cdots$, t_m'; that is, the joint distribution of the random variables is Gaussian.

The *joint probability density function* $p(u, v; \tau)$ for a Gaussian process $u = f(t)$ with $\overline{f(t)} = 0$ and $\sigma^2 = \overline{f^2(t)}$ $= 1$ is

$$p(u, v; \tau) = \frac{1}{2\pi\sqrt{1 - \rho_f^2(\tau)}} \, \exp\left\{ -\frac{1}{2[1 - \rho_f^2(\tau)]} [u^2 - 2\rho_f(\tau)uv + v^2] \right\}, \qquad (9.20)$$

where $v = f(t + \tau)$ and $\rho_f(\tau)$ is the autocovariance of $f(t)$. (Cf., Chap. 4.) The moments μ_{02}, μ_{20}, and μ_{11} are given by

$$\mu_{02} = \overline{f^2(t)} = \sigma^2 = 1, \qquad \mu_{20} = \overline{f^2(t + \tau)} = \sigma^2 = 1, \qquad \mu_{11} = \overline{f(t)f(t + \tau)} = \rho_f(\tau).$$

If the random processes $f_1(t)$, $f_2(t)$, $f_3(t)$, and $f_4(t)$ are jointly Gaussian with $\overline{f_1(t)} = \overline{f_2(t)} = \overline{f_3(t)} = \overline{f_4(t)}$, then

$$\overline{f_1(t)f_2(t)f_3(t)f_4(t)} = [\overline{f_1(t)f_2(t)}][\overline{f_3(t)f_4(t)}] + [\overline{f_1(t)f_3(t)}][\overline{f_2(t)f_4(t)}] + [\overline{f_1(t)f_4(t)}][\overline{f_2(t)f_3(t)}]. \quad (9.21)$$

A Gaussian process $f(t)$ can be transformed into a new process $g(t)$ by means of the transformation

$$g(t) = F[f(t)].$$

If the transformation is *linear*, then the process $g(t)$ is also Gaussian. If the transformation is *nonlinear*, $g(t)$ is non-Gaussian, but if $F(f)$ is *memoryless* [i.e., for any $t = t_0$, $g(t_0)$ depends only on $f(t_0)$], the normalized autocovariance function $\rho_{g_n}(\tau)$ of $g(t)$ is related to the normalized autocovariance function $\rho_{f_n}(\tau)$ of $f(t)$ by

$$\frac{\partial^k[\rho_{g_n}(\tau)]}{\partial[\rho_{f_n}(\tau)]^k} = \overline{F^k[f(t)]F^k[f(t+\tau)]}, \quad (9.22)$$

where the superscript k on the right-hand side of (9.22) denotes k differentiations with respect to f.

As an ensemble average, (9.22) can be written as

$$\frac{\partial^k[\rho_{g_n}(\tau)]}{\partial[\rho_{f_n}(\tau)]^k} = \int_{-\infty}^{\infty} \int_{-\infty}^{\infty} F^k(u)F^k(v)p(u, v; \tau)du\,dv, \quad (9.23)$$

where $u = f(t)$, $v = f(t + \tau)$ and $p(u, v; \tau)$ is given by (9.20).

Equations (9.22-3) are a special form of *Price's theorem*.

Several common nonlinear transformations are:

(1) *square-law transformation*:

$$g(t) = f^2(t);$$

(2) *linear detector—full wave*:

$$g(t) = f(t) \quad \text{for } f(t) \geqslant 0$$
$$= -f(t) \quad \text{for } f(t) < 0;$$

(3) *linear detector—half wave*:

$$g(t) = f(t) \quad \text{for } f(t) \geqslant 0$$
$$= 0 \quad \text{for } f(t) < 0;$$

(4) *hard limiter*:

$$g(t) = 1 \quad \text{for } f(t) \geqslant 0$$
$$= -1 \quad \text{for } f(t) < 0.$$

(Cf., Figs. 9.19-21.) (Cf., Probs. 9.20-4.)

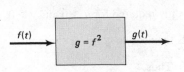

Fig. 9.19 Square-law transformation of a Gaussian process $f(t)$.

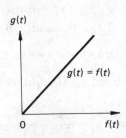

Fig. 9.20 Transformation of Prob. 9.22.

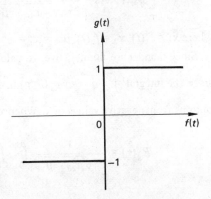

Fig. 9.21 Transformation of Prob. 9.23.

PROBLEM 9.20 A stationary Gaussian process $f(t)$ with mean zero and variance σ^2 is passed through a square-law transformation, as shown in Fig. 9.19. Show that

$$R_g(\tau) = R_f^2(0) + 2R_f^2(\tau) = \sigma^4 + 2R_f^2(\tau) \qquad \text{and} \qquad \sigma_g^2 = 2R_f^2(0),$$

where $g(t)$ is the output with variance σ_g^2.

Solution: Using (9.21) with $f_1(t) = f_2(t) = f(t)$ and $f_3(t) = f_4(t) = f(t + \tau)$,

$$\overline{f^2(t)f^2(t+\tau)} = \overline{f^2(t)}\,\overline{f^2(t+\tau)} + \overline{f(t)f(t+\tau)}\ \overline{f(t)f(t+\tau)} + \overline{f(t)f(t+\tau)}\ \overline{f(t)f(t+\tau)}.$$

Since $R_g(\tau) = \overline{g(t)g(t+\tau)} = \overline{f^2(t)f^2(t+\tau)}$ and $R_f(\tau) = \overline{f(t)f(t+\tau)}$, substituting in the above equation gives

$$R_g(\tau) = R_f^2(0) + 2R_f^2(\tau) = \sigma^4 + 2R_f^2(\tau).$$

In particular, since $R_g(0) = \overline{g^2(t)}$,

$$\overline{g^2(t)} = R_g(0) = R_f^2(0) + 2R_f^2(0) = 3R_f^2(0).$$

Hence, the variance of $g(t)$ is

$$\sigma_g^2 = \overline{g^2(t)} - \left[\overline{g(t)}\right]^2 = 3R_f^2(0) - R_f^2(0) = 2R_f^2(0)$$

since $\overline{g(t)} = \overline{f^2(t)} = R_f(0)$.

PROBLEM 9.21 If $y(t)$ is a Gaussian process with zero mean and variance σ^2, determine $\overline{y^4}$.

Solution: Using (9.21) with $f_1(t) = f_2(t) = f_3(t) = f_4(t) = y$,

$$\overline{y^4} = \overline{y^2}\,\overline{y^2} + \overline{y^2}\,\overline{y^2} + \overline{y^2}\,\overline{y^2} = 3\left[\overline{y^2}\right]^2 = 3\sigma^4.$$

PROBLEM 9.22 A Gaussian process $f(t)$ with mean zero and variance σ^2 is passed through the nonlinear transformation given by

$$g(t) = f(t) \quad \text{for } f(t) \geqslant 0$$
$$= 0 \quad \text{for } f(t) < 0.$$

(Cf., Fig. 9.20.) Express $R_g(\tau)$ in terms of an integral containing $R_f(\tau)$ using (9.6). (Cf., Fig. 9.21.)

Solution: From (9.6), the autocorrelation function of $g(t)$ is

$$R_g(\tau) = \int_{-\infty}^{\infty} \int_{-\infty}^{\infty} uv\, p_g(u, v)\, du\, dv,$$

where $u = g(t)$ and $v = g(t + \tau)$. The joint probability density function of the input is given by

$$p_f(x_1, x_2) = \frac{1}{2\pi\sqrt{\mu_{20}\mu_{02} - \mu_{11}^2}} \exp\left[\frac{-1}{2(\mu_{20}\mu_{02} - \mu_{11}^2)}(\mu_{02}x_1^2 - 2\mu_{11}x_1 x_2 + \mu_{20}x_2^2)\right],$$

where $x_1 = f_1(t)$, $x_2 = f_2(t)$, $\mu_{20} = \overline{x_1^2} = \sigma^2 = R_f(0)$, $\mu_{02} = \overline{x_2^2} = \sigma^2 = R_f(0)$, $\mu_{11} = \overline{x_1 x_2} = R_f(\tau)$.

Since u and v are nonnegative, to calculate $R_g(\tau)$, the quantity $p_g(u, v)$ is only required for $u > 0$ and $v > 0$ since the integral $\int_{-\infty}^{\infty} \int_{-\infty}^{\infty} uv\, p_g(u, v)\, du\, dv$ is zero when $u = v = 0$. This avoids the need to consider the contributions from negative values of x. When $x_1 > 0$ and $x_2 > 0$, $p_g(u, v) = p_f(u, v)$. Thus,

$$R_g(\tau) = \frac{1}{2\pi\sqrt{\mu_{20}^2 - \mu_{11}^2}} \int_0^\infty \int_0^\infty uv \exp\left[\frac{-1}{2(\mu_{20}^2 - \mu_{11}^2)}(\mu_{20}u^2 - 2\mu_{11}uv + \mu_{20}v^2)\right] du\, dv$$

$$= \frac{1}{2\pi}\left\{[R_f^2(0) - R_f^2(\tau)]^{1/2} + R_f(\tau)\cos^{-1}\left[-\frac{R_f(\tau)}{R_f(0)}\right]\right\}.$$

PROBLEM 9.23 A stationary Gaussian process $f(t)$ with zero mean and unit variance is passed through the nonlinear transformation

$$g(t) = 1 \quad \text{for } f(t) \geqslant 0$$
$$= -1 \quad \text{for } f(t) < 0.$$

(Cf., Fig. 9.21.) Show that

$$\rho_g(\tau) = \frac{2}{\pi} \arcsin \left[\rho_f(\tau)\right].$$

Solution: Since $F' = dg/df = 2\delta(f)$, where $\delta(f)$ is the delta function, using (9.22) with $k = 1$,

$$\frac{\partial \rho_g(\tau)}{\partial \rho_f(\tau)} = 4 \int_{-\infty}^{\infty} \int_{-\infty}^{\infty} \delta(u)\delta(v)p(u, v; \tau)du\, dv = 4p(0, 0; \tau).$$

From (9.20), $p(0, 0; \tau) = \dfrac{1}{2\pi\sqrt{1 - \rho_f^2(\tau)}}$; hence,

$$\frac{\partial \rho_g(\tau)}{\partial \rho_f(\tau)} = \frac{2}{\pi\sqrt{1 - \rho_f^2(\tau)}}.$$

Integrating,

$$\rho_g(\tau) = \frac{2}{\pi} \int_0^{\rho_f(\tau)} \frac{d\rho_f(\tau)}{\sqrt{1 - \rho_f^2(\tau)}}.$$

The lower limit is determined from the fact that when $\rho_f(\tau)$ is zero [that is, $f(t) = 0$], $\rho_g(\tau)$ is zero since $g(t)$ is nonfluctuating. Thus,

$$\rho_g(\tau) = \frac{2}{\pi} \arcsin \left[\rho_f(\tau)\right].$$

PROBLEM 9.24 Show that the result of Prob. 9.23 can be expressed as the series

$$\rho_g(\tau) = \frac{2}{\pi} \sum_{n=1}^{\infty} \frac{1}{n} \left[J_0(n\pi) - (-1)^n\right] \sin \left[n\pi\rho_f(\tau)\right],$$

where $J_0(x)$ is the Bessel function of order zero, given by

$$J_0(x) = \frac{1}{\pi} \int_{-\pi/2}^{\pi/2} \cos (x \sin y)dy.$$

Solution: Since the function $\arcsin \rho_f(\tau)$ is odd, its Fourier expansion in a sine series for $|\rho_f(\tau)| \leqslant 1$ is

$$\arcsin \rho_f(\tau) = \sum_{n=1}^{\infty} b_n \sin n\pi\rho_f(\tau),$$

where, on integrating by parts,

$$b_n = \int_{-1}^{1} \arcsin \rho_f(\tau) \sin n\pi\rho_f(\tau)d\rho_f(\tau)$$

$$= \frac{-\arcsin \rho_f(\tau) \cos n\pi\rho_f(\tau)}{n\pi} \bigg|_{-1}^{1} + \frac{1}{n\pi} \int_{-\pi/2}^{\pi/2} \cos n\pi\rho_f(\tau)d\left[\arcsin \rho_f(\tau)\right]$$

$$= -\frac{\cos n\pi}{n} + \frac{1}{n\pi} \int_{-\pi/2}^{\pi/2} \cos \{n\pi \sin \left[\arcsin \rho_f(\tau)\right]\}\, d\left[\arcsin \rho_f(\tau)\right]$$

$$= -\frac{(-1)^n}{n} + \frac{1}{n}J_0(n\pi).$$

Substituting in the result of Prob. 9.23 yields the required result.

9.5   Linear System Relationships

The output $g(t)$ from a time-invariant linear system due to an arbitrary input $f(t)$ is given by either of the two forms of the *convolution integral*

$$g(t) = f(\tau) * h(\tau) = \int_{-\infty}^{\infty} f(\tau)h(t - \tau)d\tau \qquad (9.24)$$

$$= h(\tau) * f(\tau) = \int_{-\infty}^{\infty} h(\tau)f(t - \tau)d\tau, \qquad (9.25)$$

where $h(t)$ is the impulse response of the linear system, and the $*$ denotes convolution.

When $f(t)$ is a stationary random process, (9.25) gives

$$R_g(\tau) = \overline{g(t)g(t + \tau)}$$

$$= \overline{\left[\int_{-\infty}^{\infty} h(u)f(t - u)du\right]\left[\int_{-\infty}^{\infty} h(v)f(t + \tau - v)dv\right]}$$

$$= \int_{-\infty}^{\infty}\int_{-\infty}^{\infty} h(u)h(v)\,\overline{f(t - u)f(t + \tau - v)}\,du\,dv$$

$$= \int_{-\infty}^{\infty}\int_{-\infty}^{\infty} h(u)h(v)R_f(\tau - v + u)du\,dv \qquad (9.26)$$

since $\overline{f(t - u)f(t + \tau - v)} = R_f(\tau - v + u)$.

The impulse response $h(t)$ of a linear system is *physically realizable* if and only if $h(t) = 0$ for $t < 0$.

A random process $f(t)$ is called *white noise* if its autocorrelation function is equal to a delta function. (Cf., Prob. 9.29.)

PROBLEM 9.25   Show that if the impulse response $h(t)$ of a linear system $f(t)$ is physically realizable, then (9.24-5) reduce to

$$g(t) = \int_{-\infty}^{t} f(\tau)h(t - \tau)d\tau, \qquad (9.27)$$

$$= \int_{0}^{\infty} h(\tau)f(t - \tau)d\tau. \qquad (9.28)$$

Solution: Since $h(t) = 0$ for $t < 0$, $h(t - \tau) = 0$ for $\tau > t$. Hence, the limits of integration in (9.24-5) change from $-\infty$ and ∞ to $-\infty$ and t, and 0 and ∞, respectively.

PROBLEM 9.26   If the impulse response of a linear system is physically realizable and the input is zero for $t < 0$, show that (9.24-5) reduce to

$$g(t) = \int_{0}^{t} f(\tau)h(t - \tau)d\tau \qquad (9.29)$$

$$= \int_{0}^{t} h(\tau)f(t - \tau)d\tau. \qquad (9.30)$$

Solution: Since $f(\tau) = 0$ for $\tau < 0$, the lower limit of integration in (9.27) changes from $-\infty$ to 0, and (9.24) reduces to (9.29).

Similarly, since $f(\tau) = 0$ for $\tau < 0$, $f(t - \tau) = 0$ for $\tau > t$; hence, (9.25) reduces to (9.30) on substituting in (9.28).

PROBLEM 9.27   The output $g(t)$ of a linear system is k times the input $f(t)$. (Cf., Fig. 9.22.) Show that

$$R_g(\tau) = k^2 R_f(\tau).$$

Solution: Since $g(t) = k f(t)$, the unit impulse response $h(t)$ is found by setting $f(t) = \delta(t)$. Therefore, $h(t) = k\delta(t)$. From (9.26),

$$R_g(\tau) = \int_{-\infty}^{\infty} \int_{-\infty}^{\infty} h(u)h(v)R_f(\tau - v + u)du\, dv$$

$$= k^2 \int_{-\infty}^{\infty} \int_{-\infty}^{\infty} \delta(u)\delta(v)R_f(\tau - v + u)du\, dv$$

$$= k^2 \int_{-\infty}^{\infty} R_f(\tau - v)\delta(v)dv$$

$$= k^2 R_x(\tau),$$

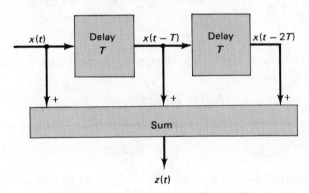

Fig. 9.22 Linear system of Prob. 9.27.

where the sifting property $\int_{-\infty}^{\infty} f(x)\delta(x)dx = f(0)$ of $\delta(x)$ has been used.

PROBLEM 9.28 A random process $x(t)$ is passed through the delay lines shown in Fig. 9.23. The output $z(t)$ is

$$z(t) = x(t) + x(t - T) + x(t - 2T).$$

(a) Determine $R_z(\tau)$ in terms of $R_x(\tau)$. (b) Evaluate $\overline{z^2(t)}$.

Fig. 9.23 Linear system of Prob. 9.28.

Solution: (a) The response of the linear system of Fig. 9.23 to a unit impulse is

$$h(t) = \delta(t) + \delta(t - T) + \delta(t - 2T).$$

Using (9.26),

$$R_z(\tau) = \int_{-\infty}^{\infty} \int_{-\infty}^{\infty} [\delta(u) + \delta(u - T) + \delta(u - 2T)][\delta(v) + \delta(v - T) + \delta(v - 2T)]R_x(\tau - v + u)du\,dv$$

$$= \int_{-\infty}^{\infty} du[\delta(u) + \delta(u - T) + \delta(u - 2T)][R_x(\tau + u) + R_x(\tau - T + u) + R_x(\tau - 2T + u)],$$

where the sifting property $\int_{-\infty}^{\infty} f(x)\delta(x - x_0)dv = f(x_0)$ of $\delta(x)$ has been used. Integrating,

$$R_z(\tau) = R_x(\tau) + R_x(\tau - T) + R_x(\tau - 2T) + R_x(\tau + T) + R_x(\tau) + R_x(\tau - T) + R_x(\tau + 2T) + R(\tau + T) + R_x(\tau)$$

$$= 3R_x(\tau) + 2R_x(\tau - T) + 2R_x(\tau + T) + R_x(\tau + 2T) + R_x(\tau - 2T).$$

(b) Since $\overline{z^2(t)} = R_z(0)$, using part (a),

$$\overline{z^2(t)} = 3R_x(0) + 2R_x(-T) + 2R_x(T) + R_x(2T) + R_x(-2T) = 3R_x(0) + 4R_x(T) + 2R_x(2T).$$

PROBLEM 9.29 If $z(t)$, $x(t)$, and $h(t)$ denote the output, input, and impulse response of a linear system, respectively, show that

$$R_z(\tau) = h(\tau) * h(\tau) * R_x(\tau) = \int_{-\infty}^{\infty} R_x(t - \tau)R_h(t)dt,$$

where the $*$ denotes convolution.

Solution: Making the change of variable $t = u - v$ and, hence, $dt = du$ in (9.26),

$$R_z(\tau) = \int_{-\infty}^{\infty} \int_{-\infty}^{\infty} h(v)h(v + t)R_x(\tau - t)dv\,dt = \int_{-\infty}^{\infty} R_x(\tau - t)dt \int_{-\infty}^{\infty} h(v)h(v + \tau)dv.$$

The integral $\int_{-\infty}^{\infty} h(v)h(v + \tau)dv$ can be written as $h(\tau) * h(-\tau)$; hence,

$$R_z(\tau) = \int_{-\infty}^{\infty} R_x(\tau - t)[h(t) * h(-t)]\,dt,$$

which is the convolution of R_x and $h(\tau) * h(-\tau)$. Thus,

$$R_z(\tau) = h(-\tau) * h(\tau) * R_x(\tau).$$

Since $R_h(\tau) = \int_{-\infty}^{\infty} h(v)h(v + \tau)dv$,

$$R_z(\tau) = \int_{-\infty}^{\infty} R_x(\tau - t)R_h(t)dt = \int_{-\infty}^{\infty} R_x(t - \tau)R_h(t)dt$$

because $R_x(\tau - t) = R_x(t - \tau)$.

PROBLEM 9.30 The input $x(t)$ to a linear system, whose impulse response is $h(t)$, is a random process whose autocorrelation function is given by

$$R_x(\tau) = R_0\,\delta(\tau),$$

where $\delta(\tau)$ is a delta function. Determine the autocorrelation of the output.

Solution: Using (9.26),

$$R_z(\tau) = \int_{-\infty}^{\infty} \int_{-\infty}^{\infty} h(u)h(v)R_x(\tau - v + u)du\,dv = R_0 \int_{-\infty}^{\infty} \int_{-\infty}^{\infty} h(u)h(v)\delta(\tau - v + u)du\,dv.$$

Since $\int_{-\infty}^{\infty} \delta(x - x_0)f(x)dx = f(x_0)$, for the integral with respect to u,

$$\int_{-\infty}^{\infty} h(u)\delta(\tau - v + u)du = h(v - \tau).$$

Hence,

$$R_z(\tau) = R_0 \int_{-\infty}^{\infty} h(v)h(v - \tau)dv = R_0[h(\tau) * h(-\tau)]$$

using the basic definition of the convolution integral where the $*$ denotes convolution.

9.6 Cross-Correlation Function of Two Random Processes

The *cross-correlation function* $R_{xy}(\tau)$ of two stationary ergodic processes $x(t)$ and $y(t)$ (not necessarily statistically independent) is given by

$$R_{xy}(\tau) = E[x(t)y(t + \tau)] \tag{9.31}$$

$$= \int_{-\infty}^{\infty} \int_{-\infty}^{\infty} x_1 y_2 p(x_1, y_2)dx_1\,dy_2, \tag{9.32}$$

where $x_1 = x(t)$, $y_2 = y(t + \tau)$, and $p(x_1, y_2)$ is the joint probability density function of x_1 and y_2. Equations (9.31-2) give $R_{xy}(\tau)$ *in terms of ensemble averages.*

The cross-correlation functions $R_{xy}(\tau)$ and $R_{yx}(\tau)$ of $x(t)$ and $y(t)$ *in terms of time averages* are given by

$$R_{xy}(\tau) = \lim_{T \to \infty} \frac{1}{2T} \int_{-T}^{T} x(t)y(t + \tau)dt, \tag{9.33}$$

$$R_{yx}(\tau) = \lim_{T \to \infty} \frac{1}{2T} \int_{-T}^{T} y(t)x(t + \tau)dt. \tag{9.34}$$

PROBLEM 9.31 Show that $R_{xy}(\tau) = R_{yx}(-\tau)$.

Solution: Substituting $u = t - \tau$ and, hence, $du = dt$ in (9.34),

$$R_{yx}(-\tau) = \lim_{T \to \infty} \frac{1}{2T} \int_{-T-\tau}^{T-\tau} y(u + \tau)x(u)du.$$

As $T \to \infty$, the shift in the limits of the integral by τ does not change the value of the integral. Therefore,

$$R_{yx}(-\tau) = \lim_{T \to \infty} \frac{1}{2T} \int_{-T}^{T} y(u + \tau)x(u)du = R_{xy}(\tau).$$

PROBLEM 9.32 Show that if $x(t)$ and $y(t)$ are random processes with the autocorrelation functions $R_x(\tau)$ and $R_y(\tau)$, then

$$|R_{xy}(\tau)| \leqslant \tfrac{1}{2}[R_x(0) + R_y(0)].$$

Solution: Since the square of any number is always nonnegative, the expression $\displaystyle\lim_{T \to \infty} \frac{1}{2T} \int_{-T}^{T} [x(t) \pm y(t + \tau)]^2 dt$ is nonnegative; that is,

$$\lim_{T \to \infty} \frac{1}{2T} \int_{-T}^{T} [x(t) \pm y(t + \tau)]^2 dt \geqslant 0.$$

Expanding,

$$\lim_{T \to \infty} \frac{1}{2T} \int_{-T}^{T} x^2(t)dt + \lim_{T \to \infty} \frac{1}{2T} \int_{-\infty}^{\infty} y^2(t + \tau)dt \pm 2\lim_{T \to \infty} \frac{1}{2T} \int_{-T}^{T} x(t)y(t + \tau)dt \geqslant 0.$$

The first two integrals are equal to $R_x(0)$ and $R_y(0)$, respectively, while the third integral is $2R_{xy}(\tau)$. Thus,

$$R_x(0) + R_y(0) \pm 2R_{xy}(\tau) \geqslant 0, \quad \text{or} \quad \pm R_{xy}(\tau) \leqslant \tfrac{1}{2}[R_x(0) + R_y(0)].$$

Hence,

$$|R_{xy}(\tau)| \leqslant \tfrac{1}{2}[R_x(0) + R_y(0)].$$

PROBLEM 9.33 The autocorrelation of a random process $x(t)$ is $R_x(\tau)$. Determine $R_{xy}(\tau)$ if $y(t) = x(t - T)$.

Solution: From (9.33), on substituting $y(t) = x(t - T)$,

$$R_{xy}(\tau) = \lim_{T \to \infty} \frac{1}{2T} \int_{-T}^{T} x(t)y(t + \tau)dt$$

$$= \lim_{T \to \infty} \frac{1}{2T} \int_{-T}^{T} x(t)x(t + \tau - T)dt.$$

Since the autocorrelation of x is $R_x(\tau) = \displaystyle\lim_{T \to \infty} \frac{1}{2T} \int_{-T}^{T} x(t)x(t + \tau)dt,$

$$R_{xy}(\tau) = R_x(\tau - T).$$

9.7   Cross-Correlation Function of Periodic and Aperiodic Functions

If $x(t)$ and $y(t)$ are *periodic* functions with the same fundamental period T, then

$$R_{xy}(\tau) = \frac{1}{T} \int_0^T x(t)y(t+\tau)dt, \tag{9.35}$$

$$R_{yx}(\tau) = \frac{1}{T} \int_0^T y(t)x(t+\tau)dt. \tag{9.36}$$

Note that $R_{xy}(\tau)$ and $R_{yx}(\tau)$ are antisymmetric; that is,

$$R_{xy}(\tau) = R_{yx}(-\tau). \tag{9.37}$$

If $x(t)$ and $y(t)$ are *aperiodic* functions, then

$$R_{xy}(\tau) = \int_{-\infty}^{\infty} x(t)y(t+\tau)dt, \tag{9.38}$$

$$R_{yx}(\tau) = \int_{-\infty}^{\infty} y(t)x(t+\tau)dt. \tag{9.39}$$

Again, $R_{xy}(\tau)$ and $R_{yx}(\tau)$ are antisymmetric; that is,

$$R_{xy}(\tau) = R_{yx}(-\tau).$$

The cross-correlation function $R_{xy}(\tau)$, unlike the autocorrelation function, is *not* an even function of τ (cf., Prob. 9.34), and, in general, does not have a maximum value at $\tau = 0$ (cf., Prob. 9.35).

PROBLEM 9.34   Calculate $R_{xy}(\tau)$ for

$$x(t) = A_1 e^{-a_1 t} \quad \text{for } t \geqslant 0$$
$$ = 0 \qquad\quad \text{for } t < 0$$

and

$$y(t) = A_2 e^{-a_2 t} \quad \text{for } t \geqslant 0$$
$$ = 0 \qquad\quad \text{for } t < 0.$$

(See Fig. 9.24.)

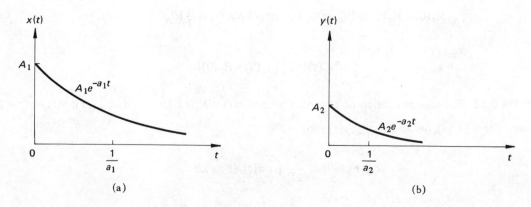

Fig. 9.24 Functions (a) $x(t)$ and (b) $y(t)$ of Prob. 9.34.

Solution: Since $x(t)$ and $y(t)$ are aperiodic, from (9.38),

$$R_{xy}(\tau) = \int_{-\infty}^{\infty} x(t)y(t+\tau)dt.$$

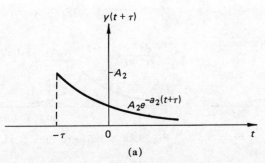

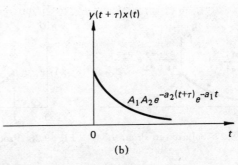

Fig. 9.25 (a) The quantity $y(t + \tau)$ for $\tau \geqslant 0$ of Prob. 9.34. (b) The product $x(t)y(t + \tau)$ for $\tau \geqslant 0$ of Prob. 9.34.

The quantities $y(t + \tau)$ and $x(t)y(t + \tau)$ are shown in Fig. 9.25 for $\tau \geqslant 0$. For this case,

$$R_{xy}(\tau) = \int_0^\infty A_1 A_2 e^{-a_2(t+\tau)} e^{-a_1 t} \, dt$$

$$= A_1 A_2 e^{-a_2\tau} \int_0^\infty e^{-(a_1+a_2)t} \, dt$$

$$= -A_1 A_2 e^{-a_2\tau} \left(\frac{1}{a_1 + a_2} \right) e^{-(a_1+a_2)t} \Big|_0^\infty$$

$$= \frac{A_1 A_2}{a_1 + a_2} e^{-a_2\tau}.$$

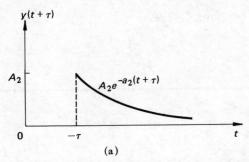

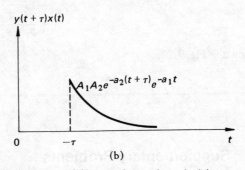

Fig. 9.26 (a) The quantity $y(t + \tau)$ for $\tau < 0$ of Prob. 9.34. (b) The product $y(t + \tau)x(t)$ for $\tau < 0$ of Prob. 9.34.

For $\tau < 0$, $y(t + \tau)$ and $y(t + \tau)x(t)$ are shown in Fig. 9.26. For this case,

$$R_{xy}(\tau) = \int_{-\tau}^\infty A_1 A_2 e^{-a_2(t+\tau)} e^{-a_1 t} \, dt = A_1 A_2 e^{-a_2\tau} \int_{-\tau}^\infty e^{-(a_1+a_2)t} \, dt$$

$$= A_1 A_2 e^{-a_2\tau} \left(\frac{-1}{a_1 + a_2} \right) e^{-(a_1+a_2)t} \Big|_{-\tau}^\infty$$

$$= \frac{A_1 A_2}{a_1 + a_2} e^{-a_2\tau} e^{(a_1+a_2)\tau}$$

$$= \frac{A_1 A_2}{a_1 + a_2} e^{a_1\tau}.$$

Thus, the cross-correlation of $x(t)$ and $y(t)$ is

$$R_{xy}(\tau) = \frac{A_1 A_2}{a_1 + a_2} e^{-a_2\tau} \quad \text{for } \tau \geqslant 0$$

$$= \frac{A_1 A_2}{a_1 + a_2} e^{a_1\tau} \quad \text{for } \tau < 0.$$

(Cf., Fig. 9.27.)

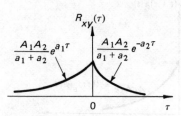

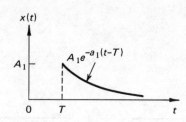

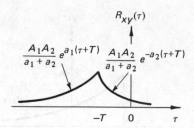

Fig. 9.27 Solution to Prob. 9.34.   Fig. 9.28 Process $x(t)$ of Prob. 9.35.   Fig. 9.29 Solution to Prob. 9.35.

PROBLEM 9.35 If the process $x(t)$ of Prob. 9.34 is defined by

$$x(t) = A_1 e^{-a_1(t-T)} \quad \text{for } t \geqslant T$$
$$= 0 \qquad\qquad \text{for } t < T,$$

and if $y(t)$ is unchanged, determine $R_{xy}(\tau)$. (Cf., Fig. 9.28.)

Solution: Substituting $t = u + T$ and, hence, $dt = du$ in (9.38), the cross-correlation R'_{xy} of $x(t)$ and $y(t)$ is

$$R'_{xy}(\tau) = \int_{-\infty}^{\infty} x(t)y(t+\tau)dt = \int_{-\infty}^{\infty} x(u+T)y(u+\tau+T)du.$$

A comparison with Prob. 9.34 shows that $R'_{xy}(\tau)$ is equal to $R_{xy}(\tau + T)$. Thus,

$$R'_{xy}(\tau) = \frac{A_1 A_2}{a_1 + a_2} e^{-a_2(\tau+T)} \quad \text{for } \tau \geqslant -T$$

$$= \frac{A_1 A_2}{a_1 + a_2} e^{a_1(\tau+T)} \quad \text{for } \tau < -T,$$

as shown in Fig. 9.29.

9.8 Supplementary Problems

PROBLEM 9.36 A biased coin is tossed once, and a process is defined by

$$f(t) = \sin \pi t \quad \text{if the outcome is heads}$$
$$= \tfrac{1}{2}t \qquad \text{if the outcome is tails.}$$

Find its distribution function $P(x; t)$ for (a) $t = \tfrac{1}{4}$, (b) $t = \tfrac{1}{2}$, and (c) $t = 1$.
Answer: If q is the probability of obtaining tails,

(a) $P(x; t) = 1$ for $x \geqslant \tfrac{1}{2}\sqrt{2}$ (b) $P(x; t) = 1$ for $x \geqslant 1$ (c) $P(x; t) = 1$ for $x \geqslant \tfrac{1}{2}$

$\quad = q$ for $\tfrac{1}{8} \leqslant x < \tfrac{1}{2}\sqrt{2}$ $\quad = q$ for $\tfrac{1}{4} \leqslant x < 1$ $\quad = q$ for $0 \leqslant x \leqslant \tfrac{1}{2}$

$\quad = 0$ for $x < \tfrac{1}{8}$, $\quad = 0$ for $x < \tfrac{1}{4}$, $\quad = 0$ for $x < 0$.

PROBLEM 9.37 Determine the autocorrelation function of

$$x(t) = \sum_{i=1}^{n} a_i \cos(\omega_i t + \phi_i),$$

where $\omega_1 \neq \omega_2 \neq \cdots \neq \omega_n \neq 0$.

Answer: $R_x(\tau) = \displaystyle\sum_{i=1}^{n} \frac{a_i^2}{2} \cos \omega_i \tau$.

PROBLEM 9.38 Determine the autocorrelation function of the real function

$$x(t) = \sum_{n=-\infty}^{\infty} a_n e^{j2\pi n f_0 t},$$

where f_0 is a constant.

Answer: $R_x(\tau) = \sum_{n=-\infty}^{\infty} |a_n|^2 e^{-j2\pi n f_0}.$

PROBLEM 9.39 Show that if $x(t)$ and $y(t)$ are sample functions of stationary random processes, then

$$R_{xy}(\tau) \leqslant \sqrt{R_x(0)R_y(0)}.$$

PROBLEM 9.40 A random process is applied as the input to a linear system whose impulse response is

$$h(t) = (1/T)e^{-t/T} \quad \text{for } t \geqslant 0$$
$$= 0 \quad \text{for } t < 0.$$

If the autocorrelation function of the input is

$$\phi_f(\tau) = \delta(\tau),$$

determine the autocorrelation function of the output $g(t)$.
Answer: $\phi_g(\tau) = (1/2T)e^{-|\tau|/T}.$

PROBLEM 9.41 Determine the autocorrelation function of

$$x(t) = y(t) \sin (\omega t + \phi),$$

where $y(t)$ has an autocorrelation function equal to $Ae^{-\alpha|\tau|}$ and ϕ and ω are constants.
Answer: $R_x(\tau) = \frac{1}{2}Ae^{-\alpha|\tau|} \cos \omega\tau.$

PROBLEM 9.42 The sample function $x(t)$ of a stationary process $y(t)$ is given by

$$x(t) = y(t) \sin (\omega t + \phi).$$

If $y(t)$ and ϕ are statistically independent, ϕ is uniformly distributed over the interval $0 \leqslant \phi \leqslant 2\pi$, and ω is a constant, show that

$$R_x(\tau) = \frac{1}{2}R_y(\tau) \cos \omega\tau.$$

PROBLEM 9.43 Determine an expression for the cross-correlation function $R_{xy}(\tau)$ between the periodic signals

$$x(t) = a_{x_0} + \sum_{n=1}^{\infty} (a_{x_n} \cos n\omega_0 t + b_{x_n} \sin n\omega_0 t),$$

$$y(t) = a_{y_0} + \sum_{n=1}^{\infty} (a_{y_n} \cos n\omega_0 t + b_{y_n} \sin n\omega_0 t).$$

Answer: $R_{xy}(\tau) = a_{x_0}b_{x_0} + \dfrac{1}{2}\sum_{n=1}^{\infty} C_{x_n}C_{y_n} \cos (n\omega_0\tau + \theta_{y_n} - \theta_{x_n}),$ where

$$C_{x_n} = \sqrt{a_{x_n}^2 + b_{x_n}^2}, \qquad C_{y_n} = \sqrt{a_{y_n}^2 + b_{y_n}^2}, \qquad \theta_{y_n} = \tan^{-1}\left(-\frac{b_{y_n}}{a_{y_n}}\right), \qquad \theta_{x_n} = \tan^{-1}\left(-\frac{b_{x_n}}{a_{x_n}}\right).$$

PROBLEM 9.44 If the amplitude a and average number ν of zero crossings per second are equal for two independent random telegraph signals, determine the autocorrelation function of their sum.
Answer: $R(\tau) = 2a^2 e^{-2\nu|\tau|}.$

PROBLEM 9.45   Repeat Prob. 9.44 for the product of two random telegraph signals.
Answer: $R(\tau) = a^4 e^{-4\nu|\tau|}$.

PROBLEM 9.46   Let $x(t)$ and $y(t)$ be sample functions of jointly Gaussian processes with zero means. If the autocorrelation and cross-correlation functions of x and y are denoted by $R_x(\tau), R_y(\tau)$, and $R_{xy}(\tau)$, determine the cross-correlation function between $x^2(t)$ and $y^2(t)$.
Answer: $R_{x^2 y^2}(\tau) = R_x(0)R_y(0) + 2R_{xy}^2(\tau)$.

PROBLEM 9.47   Let $x(t)$ be a sample function of a Gaussian process. Express the cross-correlation between $x(t)$ and $x^3(t)$ in terms of the autocorrelation of $x(t)$.
Answer: $R_{xx^3}(\tau) = 3R_x(0)R_x(\tau)$.

PROBLEM 9.48   Show that if either $R_x(\tau)$ or $R_y(\tau)$ is continuous at $\tau = 0$, then $R_{xy}(\tau)$ is continuous in the range $-\infty < \tau < \infty$.

PROBLEM 9.49   Show that if $R_x(\tau)$ is continuous at $\tau = 0$, it is continuous everywhere.

PROBLEM 9.50   Show that the correlation function of a Gaussian-shaped pulse is Gaussian in form.

PROBLEM 9.51   Show that the autocorrelation of the output of a linear system whose impulse response is $h(t)$ is given by

$$R_g(\tau) = \int_{-\infty}^{\infty} R_h(t)R_f(\tau + t)dt,$$

where

$$R_h(\tau) = \int_{-\infty}^{\infty} h(t)h(t + \tau)dt,$$

and $R_f(\tau)$ is the autocorrelation of the input.

PROBLEM 9.52   Show that the cross-correlation between an input f and output g of a linear system is

$$\phi_{fg}(\tau) = \int_{-\infty}^{\infty} h(t)\phi_f(\tau - t)dt,$$

where $h(t)$ represents the system impulse response and $\phi_f(\tau)$ is the autocorrelation of the input.

PROBLEM 9.53   Express the cross-correlation between the outputs $g_1(t)$ and $g_2(t)$ of two linear systems whose impulse responses are $h_1(t)$ and $h_2(t)$, respectively, in terms of the cross-correlation between the corresponding inputs $f_1(t)$ and $f_2(t)$.
Answer: $R_{g_1 g_2}(\tau) = \int_{-\infty}^{\infty} \int_{-\infty}^{\infty} h_1(u)h_2(v)R_{f_1 f_2}(\tau + u - v)dudv$.

PROBLEM 9.54   Show that an alternate form for $R_{g_1 g_2}(\tau)$ in Prob. 9.53 is

$$R_{g_1 g_2}(\tau) = \int_{-\infty}^{\infty} R_{h_1 h_2}(\tau)R_{f_1 f_2}(\tau - t)dt,$$

where

$$R_{h_1 h_2}(\tau) = \int_{-\infty}^{\infty} h_1(t)h_2(\tau + t)dt.$$

PROBLEM 9.55   A nonstationary stochastic process $f(t)$ is said to be *continuous* at a point t in the mean-square sense if and only if the expected value

$$E[\{f(t + \tau) - f(t)\}^2] \to 0 \quad \text{as } \tau \to 0.$$

Show that $f(t)$ is continuous for every t if its autocorrelation $R_f(t_1, t_2)$ is continuous everywhere along the line $t_1 = t_2$.

PROBLEM 9.56 Show that the Poisson process is continuous in the mean-square sense for every t.

PROBLEM 9.57 Show that the expected value of a process $f(t)$ must be continuous if $f(t)$ is continuous. (Cf., Prob. 9.55.)

PROBLEM 9.58 Determine the relationship between the continuity of a stationary process $f(t)$ and its autocorrelation $R(\tau)$.
Answer: The continuity of one implies the continuity of the other for $\tau = 0$.

PROBLEM 9.59 A stationary process $f(t)$ is said to be *differentiable* in the mean-square, or Cauchy, sense if and only if

$$\lim_{h_1, h_2 \to 0} \left[\frac{f(t+h_1) - f(t)}{h_1} - \frac{f(t+h_2) - f(t)}{h_2} \right]^2 \to 0.$$

Show that if $R(\tau)$ is the autocorrelation of $f(t)$, then $f(t)$ is differentiable if and only if

$$R'(\tau) = 0 \quad \text{and} \quad \lim_{h \to 0} \frac{R(\tau + h) - R(\tau)}{h^2} = \frac{R''(\tau)}{2} \quad \text{for } \tau = 0.$$

PROBLEM 9.60 Show that

$$E[f'(t)] = \frac{dE[f(t)]}{dt}, \qquad E[\{f'(t)\}^2] = R_{f'}(0) = -\frac{d^2 R_f(0)}{d\tau^2},$$

where $R_f(t_1, t_2) = E[f(t_1)f(t_2)]$, $R_{f'}(t_1, t_2) = E[f'(t_1)f'(t_2)]$, $t_1 - t_2 = \tau$, and $f'(t) = df/dt$.

10 POWER SPECTRA

10.1 Periodic and Aperiodic Functions: Fourier Series

A real-valued function $x(t)$ of the real variable t is said to be *periodic with period T*, where T is a real constant, if

$$x(t) = x(t + T). \tag{10.1}$$

In general, by iteration of (10.1),

$$x(t) = x(t + nT), \quad n = 0, \pm 1, \pm 2, \cdots.$$

An example of a periodic function is shown in Fig. 10.1.

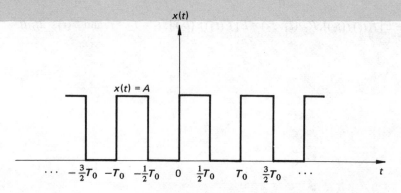

Fig. 10.1 A periodic function with period T.

A function that is not periodic is called *aperiodic* or *nonperiodic*.

The *Fourier series* of a periodic function $f(t)$ with period T is the trigonometric series

$$x(t) = \tfrac{1}{2}a_0 + \sum_{n=1}^{\infty} [a_n \cos(n\omega t) + b_n \sin(n\omega t)], \tag{10.2}$$

where $\omega = 2\pi/T$ is called the *fundamental angular* or *radian* frequency of $x(t)$, and a_n and b_n, given by

$$a_0 = \frac{1}{T} \int_{-\frac{1}{2}T}^{\frac{1}{2}T} x(t)dt,$$

$$a_n = \frac{2}{T} \int_{-\frac{1}{2}T}^{\frac{1}{2}T} x(t) \cos(n\omega t)dt, \quad n = 1, 2, \cdots, \tag{10.3}$$

$$b_n = \frac{2}{T} \int_{-\frac{1}{2}T}^{\frac{1}{2}T} x(t) \sin(n\omega t)dt, \quad n = 1, 2, \cdots, \tag{10.4}$$

are called the *Fourier coefficients* of $x(t)$.

The *complex Fourier series* of a periodic function $x(t)$ with period T is given by

$$x(t) = \sum_{n=-\infty}^{\infty} c_n \, e^{j2\pi n f_0 t},$$ (10.5)

where $f_0 = 1/T$ is called the *fundamental frequency* of $x(t)$, $j = \sqrt{-1}$ and c_n are the complex *Fourier coefficients* given by

$$c_n = \frac{1}{T} \int_0^T x(t) e^{-j2\pi n f_0 t} \, dt,$$ (10.6)

and providing that

$$\int_0^T x^2(t) dt < \infty.$$ (10.7)

The *Fourier transform* of a real and aperiodic function is the function $X(\omega)$ defined by

$$X(\omega) = \int_{-\infty}^{\infty} x(t) e^{-j\omega t} \, dt,$$ (10.8)

where the radian frequency $\omega = 2\pi f_0$.

The inverse Fourier transform is the inverse operation of obtaining $x(t)$ from its transform $X(\omega)$, and is given by

$$x(t) = \frac{1}{2\pi} \int_{-\infty}^{\infty} X(\omega) e^{j\omega t} \, d\omega.$$ (10.9)

Note that $X(\omega)$ and $x(t)$ are often called *Fourier transform* pairs, and it is assumed that

$$\int_{-\infty}^{\infty} x^2(t) dt < \infty \qquad \text{and} \qquad \int_{-\infty}^{\infty} |X(\omega)|^2 \, d\omega < \infty.$$

A short table of common Fourier transforms is given in Table 10.1, and Table 10.2 gives some general properties of the Fourier transform.

The *amplitude spectrum* of a function $x(t)$ is a plot of the magnitudes of the complex coefficients c_n versus the frequency nf_0 if $x(t)$ is periodic, or a plot of $|X(\omega)|$ versus ω if $x(t)$ if aperiodic.

Since the *phase angle* ϕ_n of c_n is obtained from $c_n = |c_n| \, e^{j\phi n}$, the *phase spectrum* of the periodic function $x(t)$ is a plot of ϕ_n versus the frequency nf_0.

The *phase spectrum* of an aperiodic function $x(t)$ is a plot of the amplitude of $/X(\omega)$ versus ω.

Now, the index n assumes only integral values; thus, the amplitude and phase spectra exist *only* at the discrete variable nf_0 for a periodic function. These, therefore, are referred to as *complex line spectra* since they consist of lines at nf_0.

When $x(t)$ is aperiodic, (10.9) shows that $[1/(2\pi)] \, |X(\omega)| \, d\omega$ represents the infinitesimal magnitude of a "harmonic" at the radian frequency ω. These harmonics have zero fundamental frequency and are "spaced" infinitesimally close together. Though $|X(\omega)| \, d\omega$ is infinitesimal, $X(\omega)$ is finite. The plot of $|X(\omega)|$ versus ω is called a *continuous spectrum*, and $|X(\omega)|$ is often called the *magnitude spectrum of $x(t)$*.

The *average power* or *power content* P of a real periodic function $x(t)$ is the mean-square value

$$P = \frac{1}{T} \int_0^T x^2(t) dt.$$ (10.10)

The *energy content* E of an aperiodic function $x(t)$ is defined by

$$E = \int_{-\infty}^{\infty} x^2(t) dt.$$ (10.11)

Parseval's theorem for periodic functions states that if $x(t)$ is a real periodic function with period T, then

TABLE 10.1

$x(t)$		$X(\omega)$
1. $u(t)$ (unit step)		$\dfrac{1}{j\omega}$
2. $\delta(t)$ (unit impulse)		1
3. $\begin{cases} t^k & t \geqslant 0,\ k = 1, 2, \cdots \\ 0 & t < 0 \end{cases}$		$\dfrac{k!}{(j\omega)^{k+1}}$
4. $\begin{cases} t^k e^{-\alpha t} & t > 0,\ k = 1, 2, \cdots \\ 0 & t \leqslant 0 \end{cases}$		$\dfrac{k!}{(j\omega + \alpha)^{k+1}}$
5. $\begin{cases} e^{-\alpha t} & t \geqslant 0 \\ 0 & t < 0 \end{cases}$		$\dfrac{1}{j\omega + \alpha}$
6. $\begin{cases} \sin \alpha t & t \geqslant 0 \\ 0 & t < 0 \end{cases}$		$\dfrac{\alpha}{(j\omega)^2 + \alpha^2}$
7. $\begin{cases} \cos \alpha t & t \geqslant 0 \\ 0 & t < 0 \end{cases}$		$\dfrac{j\omega}{(j\omega)^2 + \alpha^2}$
8. $\begin{cases} e^{j\omega_0 t} & t \geqslant 0 \\ 0 & t < 0 \end{cases}$		$\dfrac{1}{j\omega - j\omega_0}$
9. $\begin{cases} 1 & -\dfrac{T}{2} < t < \dfrac{T}{2} \\ 0 & \text{elsewhere} \end{cases}$		$T\,\dfrac{\sin(\omega T/2)}{\omega T/2}$
10. $e^{-\frac{1}{2}\left(\frac{t}{T}\right)^2}$		$T\sqrt{2\pi}\,e^{-\frac{1}{2}(\omega T)^2}$
11. $e^{-\alpha|t|}$		$\dfrac{2\alpha}{\alpha^2 + \omega^2}$

TABLE 10.2

$x(t)$	$X(\omega)$
1. Linear Addition $ax_1(t) + bx_2(t)$	$aX_1(\omega) + bX_2(\omega)$
2. Scale Change $x(\alpha t)$	$\dfrac{1}{|\alpha|}\, X\!\left(\dfrac{\omega}{\alpha}\right)$
3. Time Delay $x(t - \tau)$	$e^{-j\omega\tau} X(\omega)$
4. $x(t)e^{j\omega_1 t}$	$X(\omega - \omega_1)$
5. $x_1(t) \cdot x_2(t)$	$X_1(\omega) * X_2(\omega) = \dfrac{1}{2\pi} \displaystyle\int_{-\infty}^{\infty} X_1(y)X_2(\omega - y)\,dy$
6. $\displaystyle\int_{-\infty}^{\infty} x_1(\tau)x_2(t - \tau)\,d\tau$	$X_1(\omega) \cdot X_2(\omega)$
7. $x(t)$ real	$X(-\omega) = X^*(\omega)$, where $X^*(\omega)$ is complex conjugate of $X(\omega)$

$$\frac{1}{T} \int_0^T x^2(t)dt = \sum_{n=-\infty}^{\infty} |c_n|^2, \tag{10.12}$$

where c_n's are the complex Fourier coefficients of $x(t)$.

Parseval's theorem for aperiodic functions states that if $X(\omega)$ is the Fourier transform of the aperiodic function $x(t)$, then

$$\int_{-\infty}^{\infty} x^2(t)dt = \frac{1}{2\pi} \int_{-\infty}^{\infty} |X(\omega)|^2 \, d\omega = \int_{-\infty}^{\infty} |X(\omega)|^2 \, df. \tag{10.13}$$

Now, (10.11) and (10.13) show that the energy content E of $x(t)$ is $(1/2\pi)$ times the area under the $|X(\omega)|^2$ curve. For this reason, the quantity $|X(\omega)|^2$ is called the *energy spectrum* or *energy spectral density function* of $x(t)$.

PROBLEM 10.1 Show that if the function $x(t) = \cos \omega_1 t + \cos \omega_2 t$ is periodic with period T, then the ratio ω_1/ω_2 must be a rational number.

Solution: If $x(t)$ is periodic with period T, from (10.1),

$$x(t) = \cos \omega_1 t + \cos \omega_2 t = \cos \omega_1 (t + T) + \cos \omega_2 (t + T).$$

Since $\cos (\theta + 2m\pi) = \cos \theta$ for any integer m,

$$\omega_1 T = 2m\pi \qquad \text{and} \qquad \omega_2 T = 2n\pi,$$

where m and n are integers. Hence,

$$T = \frac{2m\pi}{\omega_1} = \frac{2n\pi}{\omega_2}.$$

Simplifying, the required ratio is

$$\frac{\omega_1}{\omega_2} = \frac{2m\pi}{2n\pi} = \frac{m}{n}.$$

Since m and n are integers, ω_1/ω_2 is rational.

PROBLEM 10.2 Determine whether the following functions are periodic:
  (a) $x(t) = c$, a constant;
  (b) $x(t) = (4 \sin t)^2$;
  (c) $x(t) = \cos t + \cos (4 + \pi)t$.

Solution: (a) Since $x(t) = c$, $x(t + T) = c$ for all values of T. Hence, it is periodic.
  (b) Using the trigonometric identity $\sin^2 t = \frac{1}{2}(1 - \cos 2t)$,

$$x(t) = (4 \sin t)^2 = 16 \sin^2 t = 16 \cdot \frac{1}{2}(1 - \cos 2t) = 8 - 8 \cos 2t.$$

Since a constant is periodic for any period T and the period of $\cos 2t$ is π, $x(t)$ is periodic with a period π.
  (c) Here $\omega_1 = 1$ and $\omega_2 = 4 + \pi$. Since

$$\frac{\omega_1}{\omega_2} = \frac{1}{4 + \pi}$$

is an irrational number, it is not possible to find a value of T which satisfies (10.1). Hence, $x(t)$ is not periodic.

PROBLEM 10.3 Find the Fourier series expansion of the function $x(t)$ which is periodic with period 2π and defined by

$$x(t) = -t \quad \text{for } -\pi < t < 0$$

$$= 0 \quad \text{for } 0 < t < \pi.$$

Solution: Since the period $T = 2\pi$, the Fourier coefficients $x(t)$ are given by

$$a_0 = \frac{1}{T}\int_{-\frac{1}{2}T}^{\frac{1}{2}T} x(t)dt = \frac{1}{2\pi}\left[\int_{-\pi}^0 (-t)dt + \int_0^\pi 0\, dt\right] = \frac{-1}{2\pi}\int_{-\pi}^0 t\, dt = +\frac{1}{2\pi}\left(\frac{\pi^2}{2}\right) = +\frac{1}{4}\pi^2,$$

$$a_n = \frac{2}{T}\int_{-\frac{1}{2}T}^{\frac{1}{2}T} x(t)\cos nt\, dt = \frac{2}{2\pi}\int_{-\pi}^0 (-t)\cos nt\, dt = -\frac{1}{\pi}\int_{-\pi}^0 t\cos nt\, dt = \frac{1}{\pi}\left(\frac{\cos n\pi + n\pi\sin n\pi - 1}{n^2}\right),$$

$$b_n = \frac{2}{T}\int_{-\frac{1}{2}T}^{\frac{1}{2}T} x(t)\sin nt\, dt = \frac{2}{2\pi}\int_{-\pi}^0 (-t)\sin nt\, dt = -\frac{1}{\pi}\int_\pi^0 t\sin nt\, dt = -\frac{1}{\pi}\left(\sin n\pi - \frac{\pi}{n}\cos n\pi\right),$$

where $n = 1, 2, \cdots$.
Since $\sin n\pi = 0$ and $\cos n\pi = (-1)^n$, $n = 0, 1, 2, \cdots$, the Fourier coefficients become

$$a_0 = \tfrac{1}{4}\pi^2, \qquad b_n = \frac{1}{n}(-1) \quad \text{for } n = 1, 2, \cdots,$$

$$a_n = 0 \quad \text{for } n \text{ even}$$

$$= \frac{-2}{\pi n^2} \quad \text{for } n \text{ odd},$$

Hence, the Fourier series expansion is

$$x(t) = \frac{\pi}{4} - \frac{2}{\pi}\left(\cos t + \frac{\cos 3t}{3^2} + \frac{\cos 5t}{5^2} + \cdots\right) + \left(\frac{-\sin t}{1} + \frac{\sin 2t}{2} - \frac{\sin 3t}{3} + \cdots\right)$$

$$= \frac{\pi}{4} - \frac{2}{\pi}\sum_{n=1}^\infty \frac{\cos(2n-1)t}{(2n-1)^2} + \sum_{n=1}^\infty \frac{(-1)^n \sin nt}{n}.$$

PROBLEM 10.4 Derive the complex Fourier series (10.5) of a periodic function from (10.2).

Solution: With $\omega = 2\pi/T$, from (10.2), the Fourier series expansion is

$$x(t) = \frac{1}{2}a_0 + \sum_{n=1}^\infty (a_n\cos n\omega t + b_n\sin n\omega t). \tag{10.2}$$

The sine and cosine terms in the Fourier expansion of a periodic function $x(t)$ can be expressed in terms of exponentials as

$$\cos n\omega t = \frac{1}{2}(e^{jn\omega t} + e^{-jn\omega t}), \qquad \sin n\omega t = \frac{1}{2j}(e^{jn\omega t} - e^{-jn\omega t}), \tag{10.14}$$

where $j = \sqrt{-1}$. Substituting (10.14) in (10.2),

$$x(t) = \frac{1}{2}a_0 + \sum_{n=1}^\infty \left[a_n\frac{1}{2}(e^{jn\omega t} + e^{-jn\omega t}) + b_n\frac{1}{2j}(e^{jn\omega t} - e^{-jn\omega t})\right]$$

$$= \frac{1}{2}a_0 + \sum_{n=1}^\infty \left[\frac{1}{2}(a_n - jb_n)e^{jn\omega t} + \frac{1}{2}(a_n + jb_n)e^{-jn\omega t}\right]$$

since $1/j = -j$. Now, if $c_0 = \frac{1}{2}a_0$, $c_n = \frac{1}{2}(a_n - jb_n)$, and $c_{-n} = \frac{1}{2}(a_n + jb_n)$,

$$x(t) = c_0 + \sum_{n=1}^\infty (c_n e^{jn\omega t} + c_{-n}e^{-jn\omega t}) = c_0 + \sum_{n=1}^\infty c_n e^{jn\omega t} + \sum_{n=-1}^{-\infty} c_n e^{jn\omega t} = \sum_{n=-\infty}^\infty c_n e^{jn\omega t}. \tag{10.5}$$

PROBLEM 10.5 Determine the complex Fourier expansion for the periodic function shown in Fig. 10.1.

Solution: The general complex Fourier series for a real periodic function of time is given by (10.5). The Fourier coefficients are, from (10.6),

$$c_n = \frac{1}{T} \int_0^T x(t) e^{-j2\pi n f_0 t} \, dt,$$

where the period T in this case equals T_0. Thus,

$$c_n = \frac{1}{T_0} \int_0^{T_0} x(t) e^{-j2\pi n f_0 t} \, dt.$$

Since $x(t) = 0$ in the interval $\frac{1}{2} T_0 < t < T_0$,

$$c_n = \frac{1}{T_0} \int_0^{T_0/2} e^{-j2\pi n f_0 t} \, dt = \frac{A}{T_0} \left(\frac{-1}{j2\pi n f_0} \right) e^{-j2\pi n f_0 t} \bigg|_0^{\frac{1}{2} T_0} = \frac{A}{j2\pi n f_0 T_0} (1 - e^{-j\pi n f_0 T_0}),$$

or since $f_0 = 1/T_0$,

$$c_n = \frac{A e^{-j\frac{1}{2}\pi n}}{j2\pi n} \left(e^{j\frac{1}{2}\pi n} - e^{-j\frac{1}{2}\pi n} \right).$$

Using the relation $e^{j\theta} = \cos\theta + j\sin\theta$,

$$c_n = \frac{A e^{-j\frac{1}{2}\pi n}}{2} \frac{\sin\frac{1}{2}\pi n}{\frac{1}{2}\pi n} .$$

Therefore, from (10.5),

$$x(t) = \sum_{n=-\infty}^{\infty} \frac{A e^{-j\frac{1}{2}n\pi}}{2} \frac{\sin\frac{1}{2}\pi n}{\frac{1}{2}\pi n} e^{j2\pi n f_0 t} .$$

PROBLEM 10.6 Derive the complex Fourier series of a periodic train of impulses given by

$$\delta_T(t) = \sum_{n=-\infty}^{\infty} \delta(t - nT),$$

where T is the period and $\delta(t)$ is Dirac delta function. [See Fig. 10.2(a).]

Solution: The Fourier coefficients c_n for the periodic train of unit impulses are, from (10.6) with $\omega_0 = 2\pi/T$,

$$c_n = \frac{1}{T} \int_{-\frac{1}{2}T}^{\frac{1}{2}T} \delta_T(t) e^{-jn\omega_0 t} \, dt$$

$$= \frac{1}{T} \int_{-\frac{1}{2}T}^{\frac{1}{2}T} \delta(t) e^{-jn\omega_0 t} \, dt$$

$$= \frac{1}{T} e^{-jn\omega_0 t} \bigg|_{t=0}$$

$$= \frac{1}{T} .$$

Hence, the complex Fourier series is

$$\sum_{n=-\infty}^{\infty} \delta(t - nT) = \frac{1}{T} \sum_{n=-\infty}^{\infty} e^{jn\omega_0 t} = \frac{1}{T} \sum_{n=-\infty}^{\infty} e^{jn(2\pi/T)t}.$$

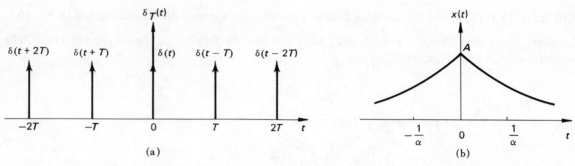

Fig. 10.2 (a) Periodic train of impulses. (b) Function for Prob. 10.7.

PROBLEM 10.7   Determine the Fourier transform of the function

$$x(t) = A e^{-\alpha |t|}, \quad \alpha > 0,$$

shown in Fig. 10.2(b).

Solution: From (10.8), the Fourier transform of $x(t)$ is given by

$$X(\omega) = \int_{-\infty}^{\infty} x(t) e^{-j\omega t}\, dt.$$

Substituting for $x(t)$,

$$X(\omega) = A \int_{-\infty}^{\infty} e^{-\alpha |t|} e^{-j\omega t}\, dt = A \int_{-\infty}^{0} e^{\alpha t} e^{-j\omega t}\, dt + A \int_{0}^{\infty} e^{-\alpha t} e^{-j\omega t}\, dt,$$

where the fact that $|t| = -t$ for $t \leqslant 0$ and $|t| = t$ for $t \geqslant 0$ is used. Carrying out the integration,

$$X(\omega) = A \left[\frac{1}{\alpha - j\omega}\, e^{(\alpha - j\omega)t} \,\Big|_{-\infty}^{0} + \frac{-1}{\alpha + j\omega}\, e^{-(\alpha + j\omega)t} \,\Big|_{0}^{\infty} \right] = A \left(\frac{1}{\alpha - j\omega} + \frac{1}{\alpha + j\omega} \right) = \frac{2\alpha A}{\alpha^2 + \omega^2}.$$

PROBLEM 10.8   If $X_1(\omega)$ and $X_2(\omega)$ are the Fourier transforms of the aperiodic functions $x_1(t)$ and $x_2(t)$, show that

$$\int_{-\infty}^{\infty} x_1(t) x_2(t)\, dt = \frac{1}{2\pi} \int_{-\infty}^{\infty} X_1(\omega) X_2(-\omega)\, d\omega.$$

Solution: From Table 10.2, the Fourier transform of $x_1(t) x_2(t)$ is

$$X[x_1(t) x_2(t)] = X_1(\omega) * X_2(\omega) = \frac{1}{2\pi} \int_{-\infty}^{\infty} X_1(y) X_2(\omega - y)\, dy;$$

that is,

$$\int_{-\infty}^{\infty} [x_1(t) x_2(t)]\, e^{-j\omega t} dt = \frac{1}{2\pi} \int_{-\infty}^{\infty} X_1(y) X_2(\omega - y)\, dy.$$

Now, letting $\omega = 0$ and changing the dummy variable of integration,

$$\int_{-\infty}^{\infty} x_1(t) x_2(t)\, dt = \frac{1}{2\pi} \int_{-\infty}^{\infty} X_1(\omega) X_2(-\omega)\, d\omega.$$

PROBLEM 10.9   If $X_1(\omega)$ and $X_2(\omega)$ are the Fourier transforms of the real functions $x_1(t)$ and $x_2(t)$, show that

$$\int_{-\infty}^{\infty} x_1(t) x_2(t)\, dt = \frac{1}{2\pi} \int_{-\infty}^{\infty} X_1(\omega) X_2^*(\omega)\, d\omega,$$

where $X_2^*(\omega)$ is the complex conjugate of $X_2(\omega)$.

Solution: Since $X(-\omega) = X^*(\omega)$ when $x(t)u$ is real, from Prob. 10.8,

$$\int_{-\infty}^{\infty} x_1(t)x_2(t)\, dt = \frac{1}{2\pi} \int_{-\infty}^{\infty} X_1(\omega)X_2(-\omega)d\omega = \frac{1}{2\pi} \int_{-\infty}^{\infty} X_1(\omega)X_2^*(\omega)d\omega.$$

PROBLEM 10.10 Verify property 1 of Table 10.2.

Solution: The Fourier transform of $x(t) = ax_1(t) + bx_2(t)$ is given by

$$X(\omega) = \int_{-\infty}^{\infty} x(t)e^{-j\omega t}\, dt = \int_{-\infty}^{\infty} (ax_1 + bx_2)e^{-j\omega t}\, dt = a\int_{-\infty}^{\infty} x_1(t)e^{-j\omega t}\, dt + b\int_{-\infty}^{\infty} x_2(t)e^{-j\omega t}dt.$$

The latter two integrals are just $X_1(\omega)$ and $X_2(\omega)$ so that

$$X(\omega) = aX_1(\omega) + bX_2(\omega).$$

PROBLEM 10.11 Verify property 2 of Table 10.2.

Solution: If the Fourier transform of $x(t)$ is $X(\omega)$, then the Fourier transform of $x(\alpha t)$ is

$$X_1(\omega) = \int_{-\infty}^{\infty} x(\alpha t)e^{-j\omega t}\, dt.$$

If $\alpha > 0$, substituting $\tau = \alpha t$, and hence, $d\tau = \alpha\, dt$,

$$X_1(\omega) = \frac{1}{\alpha} \int_{-\infty}^{\infty} x(\tau)e^{-j\omega(\tau/\alpha)}\, d\tau.$$

The integral is just $X(\omega/\alpha)$ so that

$$X_1(\omega) = \frac{1}{\alpha} X\!\left(\frac{\omega}{\alpha}\right) \quad \text{for } \alpha > 0.$$

If $\alpha < 0$,

$$X_1(\omega) = \frac{1}{\alpha} \int_{\infty}^{-\infty} x(\tau)e^{-j\omega(\tau/\alpha)}\, d\tau = \frac{-1}{\alpha} X\!\left(\frac{\omega}{\alpha}\right) \quad \text{for } \alpha < 0.$$

Thus,

$$X_1(\omega) = \frac{1}{|\alpha|} X\!\left(\frac{\omega}{\alpha}\right).$$

PROBLEM 10.12 Verify property 3 of Table 10.2.

Solution: If the Fourier transform of $x(t)$ is $X(\omega)$, then the Fourier transform of $x(t - \tau)$ is

$$X_1(\omega) = \int_{-\infty}^{\infty} x(t - \tau)e^{-j\omega t}\, dt.$$

Making the substitution $u = t - \tau$, and hence, $du = dt$,

$$X_1(\omega) = \int_{-\infty}^{\infty} x(u)e^{-j\omega(u+\tau)}\, du = e^{-j\omega\tau} \int_{-\infty}^{\infty} x(u)e^{-j\omega u}\, du.$$

The integral is just $X(\omega)$ so that $X_1(\omega) = e^{-j\omega\tau} X(\omega)$.

PROBLEM 10.13 Prove Parseval's theorem for periodic functions; that is, show that the average power of a periodic signal is given by (10.12).

Solution: Using (10.5), with m and n as integers,

$$\frac{1}{T}\int_0^T x^2(t)dt = \frac{1}{T}\int_0^T \sum_{n=-\infty}^\infty \sum_{m=-\infty}^\infty c_n c_m e^{j2\pi(n+m)f_0 t}\, dt = \frac{1}{T}\int_0^T \sum_{n=-\infty}^\infty c_n c_{-n}\, dt = \sum_{n=-\infty}^\infty c_n c_{-n},$$

since

$$\int_0^T e^{j2\pi k f_0 t}\, dt = 0 \quad \text{for } k = \pm 1, \pm 2, \cdots$$

$$= T \quad \text{for } k = 0.$$

From (10.6),

$$c_{-n} = \frac{1}{T}\int_0^T x(t)e^{j2\pi n f_0 t} = c_n^*,$$

where the star denotes the complex conjugate of c_n. Since $c_n c_{-n} = c_n c_n^* = |c_n|^2$,

$$\frac{1}{T}\int_0^T x^2(t)\, dt = \sum_{n=-\infty}^\infty |c_n|^2. \qquad [10.12]$$

Parseval's identity: If $x(t)$ is a real periodic function with period T, then

$$\frac{1}{T}\int_0^T x^2(t)dt = \frac{1}{4}a_0^2 + \frac{1}{2}\sum_{n=1}^\infty (a_n^2 + b_n^2).$$

PROBLEM 10.14 Establish Parseval's identity.

Solution: From Prob. 10.4, $c_0 = \frac{1}{2}a_0$, $c_n = \frac{1}{2}(a_n - jb_n)$, and $c_{-n} = \frac{1}{2}(a_n + jb_n)$; hence,

$$c_0^2 = \frac{1}{4}a_0^2, \qquad |c_n|^2 = \frac{1}{4}(a_n^2 + b_n^2) = |c_{-n}|^2.$$

Substituting in (10.12),

$$\frac{1}{T}\int_0^T x^2(t)dt = \sum_{n=-\infty}^\infty |c_n|^2 = |c_0|^2 + 2\sum_{n=1}^\infty |c_n|^2 = \frac{1}{4}a_0^2 + \frac{1}{2}\sum_{n=1}^\infty (a_n^2 + b_n^2).$$

PROBLEM 10.15 Prove Parseval's theorem for complex aperiodic functions; that is, show that

$$\int_{-\infty}^\infty x^2(t)dt = \frac{1}{2\pi}\int_{-\infty}^\infty |X(\omega)|^2\, d\omega, \qquad [10.13]$$

where $x(t)$ is, in general, a complex function of t.

Solution: If $X(\omega)$ is the Fourier transform of the complex function $x(t)$, the Fourier transform $X^*(\omega)$ of the complex conjugate $x^*(t)$ of $x(t)$ is

$$X[x^*(t)] = \int_{-\infty}^\infty x^*(t)e^{-j\omega t}\, dt = \int_{-\infty}^\infty [x(t)e^{j\omega t}]^*\, dt = \int_{-\infty}^\infty [x(t)e^{-j(-\omega)t}]^*\, dt = X^*(-\omega).$$

If $x_1(t) = x(t)$ and $x_2(t) = x^*(t)$ in the result of Prob. 10.8, then,

$$\int_{-\infty}^\infty x(t)x^*(t) = \frac{1}{2\pi}\int_{-\infty}^\infty X(\omega)X^*[-(-\omega)]\, d\omega = \frac{1}{2\pi}\int_{-\infty}^\infty X(\omega)X^*(\omega)\, d\omega.$$

Since $x(t)x^*(t) = |x(t)|^2$ and $X(\omega)X^*(\omega) = |X(\omega)|^2$,

$$\int_{-\infty}^\infty x^2(t)dt = \frac{1}{2\pi}\int_{-\infty}^\infty |X(\omega)|^2\, d\omega.$$

If $x(t)$ is real, the result follows immediately from Prob. 10.9.

PROBLEM 10.16 Verify Parseval's theorem for the aperiodic function

$$x(t) = A e^{-\alpha t} \quad \text{for } t \geq 0.$$
$$= 0 \qquad \text{for } t < 0.$$

Solution: From Table 10.1, $X(f) = \dfrac{A}{j2\pi f + \alpha}$. Substituting in (10.13),

$$\int_0^\infty A^2 e^{-2\alpha t}\, dt = \int_{-\infty}^\infty \frac{A^2}{(2\pi)^2 f^2 + \alpha^2}\, df.$$

Integrating,

$$\frac{1}{2\alpha} = \frac{1}{4\pi^2}\, \frac{1}{(\alpha/2\pi)}\, \tan^{-1}\!\left(\frac{f}{\alpha/2\pi}\right)\Big|_{-\infty}^{\infty} = \frac{1}{2\pi\alpha}\left[\frac{\pi}{2} - \left(-\frac{\pi}{2}\right)\right] = \frac{1}{2\alpha}.$$

10.2 Power Density Spectrum: Random Signals

In Sec. 10.1, it is assumed that the energy content of an aperiodic function $x(t)$ is finite; that is,

$$\int_{-\infty}^\infty x^2(t)\, dt = \text{finite},$$

and the average power of $x(t)$ approaches zero over the interval T as T approaches infinity, that is

$$\lim_{T \to \infty} \frac{1}{T} \int_0^T x^2(t)\, dt = 0.$$

For noise calculations, the signals that occur do not have finite energy content. In this case, the *power density spectrum* can be defined in two ways:

(1) Since the average power of an aperiodic function $x(t)$ with period T is given by

$$\lim_{T \to \infty} \frac{1}{2T} \int_{-T}^T x^2(t)\, dt,$$

the *power density spectrum* of $x(t)$ is defined by

$$G(\omega) = \lim_{T \to \infty} \frac{1}{2T}\, |F(\omega)|^2, \tag{10.15}$$

where

$$F(\omega) = \int_{-T}^T x(t) e^{-j\omega t}. \tag{10.16}$$

The *total power* in the band $\omega_1 \leq \omega \leq \omega_2$ is given by

$$\text{Total power} = \frac{1}{2\pi} \int_{\omega_1}^{\omega_2} G(\omega)\, d\omega: \tag{10.17}$$

The power density spectrum possesses the following properties:

$$G(\omega) \geq 0 \quad \text{for all } \omega, \tag{10.18a}$$

$$G(-\omega) = G(\omega). \tag{10.18b}$$

The definition of $G(\omega)$ as given in (10.15) is useful mainly when $x(t)$ is an explicit time function.

(2) If $x(t)$ is a random process, then the power density spectrum $G_0(\omega)$ of $x(t)$ is defined by the *Wiener-Khintchine theorem*, which states that the autocorrelation function $R_x(\tau)$ of $x(t)$ and $G_0(\omega)$ constitute a Fourier transform pair; i.e.,

$$G_0(\omega) = \int_{-\infty}^{\infty} R_x(\tau) e^{-j\omega\tau}\, d\tau, \qquad (10.19)$$

$$R_x(\tau) = \frac{1}{2\pi} \int_{-\infty}^{\infty} G_0(\omega) e^{j\omega\tau}\, d\omega, \qquad (10.20)$$

where $R_x(\tau)$ is the autocorrelation function of the random process $x(t)$.

White noise is any random signal whose power spectral density is equal to a constant, independent of frequency. (Cf., Fig. 10.3.)

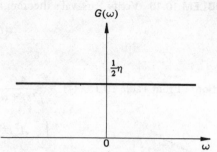

Fig. 10.3 Power density spectrum of white noise.

PROBLEM 10.17 Show that the average power of a random process $x(t)$ is

$$\lim_{T\to\infty} \frac{1}{2T} \int_{-T}^{T} x^2(t)\,dt = \frac{1}{2\pi} \int_{-\infty}^{\infty} G_0(\omega)\,d\omega = \int_{-\infty}^{\infty} G_0(2\pi f)\,df, \qquad (10.21)$$

where $\omega = 2\pi f$.

Solution: For $\tau = 0$, from (10.20),

$$R_x(0) = \frac{1}{2\pi} \int_{-\infty}^{\infty} G_0(\omega)\,d\omega = \int_{-\infty}^{\infty} G_0(2\pi f)\,df.$$

Now, in Chap. 9, the autocorrelation function of $x(t)$ is also defined as the limit

$$R_x(\tau) = \lim_{T\to\infty} \frac{1}{2T} \int_{-T}^{T} x(t)x(t+\tau)\,dt.$$

Hence, at $\tau = 0$,

$$R_x(0) = \lim_{T\to\infty} \frac{1}{2T} \int_{-T}^{T} x^2(t)\,dt.$$

Therefore,

$$\lim_{T\to\infty} \frac{1}{2T} \int_{-T}^{T} x^2(t)\,dt = \frac{1}{2\pi} \int_{-\infty}^{\infty} G_0(\omega)\,d\omega = \int_{-\infty}^{\infty} G_0(2\pi f)\,df.$$

PROBLEM 10.18 The random telegraph signal is a random process $y(t) = f(t)$, where $f(t)$ alternatively takes on the values $+a$ or $-a$. The interval between crossings is Poisson distributed with an average of ν zero crossings per second. Its autocorrelation of $y(t)$ is given by $R_y(\tau) = a^2 e^{-2\nu|\tau|}$. Determine the power density spectrum of the random telegraph signal. (Cf., Prob. 9.7.)

Solution: Since the autocorrelation of $y(t)$ is $R_y(\tau) = a^2 e^{-2\nu|\tau|}$, from (10.19), the power density spectrum is

$$G_0(\omega) = \int_{-\infty}^{\infty} a^2 e^{-2\nu|\tau|} e^{-j\omega\tau}\, d\tau = a^2 \int_{0}^{\infty} e^{-2\nu\tau} e^{-j\omega\tau}\, d\tau + a^2 \int_{-\infty}^{0} e^{2\nu\tau} e^{-j\omega\tau}\, d\tau$$

$$= a^2 \left[-\frac{e^{-(j\omega+2\nu)\tau}}{j\omega+2\nu}\bigg|_{0}^{\infty} - \frac{e^{-(j\omega-2\nu)\tau}}{j\omega-2\nu}\bigg|_{-\infty}^{0} \right]$$

$$= a^2 \left(\frac{1}{2\nu+j\omega} + \frac{1}{2\nu-j\omega} \right)$$

$$= \frac{4\nu a^2}{4\nu^2+\omega^2}$$

$$= \frac{a^2/\nu}{1+(\omega^2/2\nu)}.$$

The power density spectrum $G_0(\omega)$ is shown in Fig. 10.4.

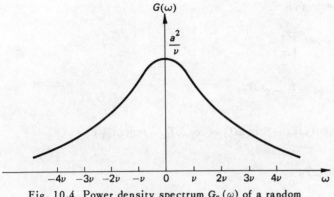

Fig. 10.4 Power density spectrum $G_0(\omega)$ of a random telegraph signal.

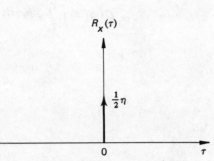

Fig. 10.5 Power density spectrum of white noise.

PROBLEM 10.19 Determine the autocorrelation of white noise.

Solution: Since the power density spectrum of white noise is $G_0(\omega) = \frac{1}{2}\eta$, from (10.20), the autocorrelation is

$$R_x(\tau) = \frac{1}{2\pi} \int_{-\infty}^{\infty} \frac{\eta}{2} \, e^{j\omega\tau} \, d\omega$$

$$= \frac{1}{2}\eta\delta(t),$$

where the delta function $\delta(x)$ is given by $\delta(x) = \dfrac{1}{2\pi} \displaystyle\int_{-\infty}^{\infty} e^{j\omega x} \, d\omega$. (Cf., Fig. 10.5.) The mean-square value of x which is the value of $R_x(\tau)$ at $\tau = 0$ is not finite. This can also be seen from (10.20) since

$$R_x(0) = \frac{1}{2\pi} \int_{-\infty}^{\infty} G(\omega)\,d\omega$$

is not finite for $G(\omega) = \frac{1}{2}\eta$. Thus, ideal white noise contains an infinite amount of power and is accordingly not physically realizable. However, many random processes are referred to as "white" in the sense that over the frequency band of interest, the power density function is constant.

PROBLEM 10.20 Is the function

$$R(\tau) = 1 \quad \text{for } |\tau| < T_0$$

$$= 0 \quad \text{elsewhere,}$$

as shown in Fig. 10.6, a realizable autocorrelation function?

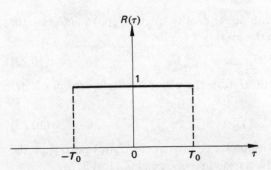

Fig. 10.6 Unrealizable autocorrelation function $R(\tau)$ of Prob. 10.20.

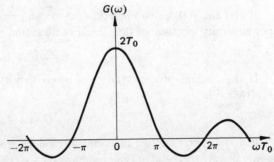

Fig. 10.7 Power density spectrum of the function of Fig. 10.6.

Solution: Using (10.19), the power density spectrum is

$$G(\omega) = \int_{-T_0}^{T_0} e^{-j\omega\tau} \, d\tau = \frac{-1}{j\omega} \, e^{-j\omega\tau} \, \Big|_{-T_0}^{T_0}$$

$$= -\frac{1}{j\omega} (e^{-j\omega T_0} - e^{j\omega T_0})$$

$$= \frac{-1}{j\omega} (\cos \omega T_0 - j \sin \omega T_0 - \cos \omega T_0 - j \sin \omega T_0)$$

$$= \frac{2}{\omega} \sin \omega T_0$$

$$= 2T_0 \left(\frac{\sin \omega T_0}{\omega T_0} \right) .$$

The power density spectrum $G(\omega)$ is shown in Fig. 10.7. Since $G(\omega) < 0$ for certain values of ω, condition (10.18a) is violated and $R(\tau)$ is not a realizable autocorrelation function. Property (10.18a) follows from (10.17) since $G(\omega)$ can be defined as the limit of a positive quantity.

PROBLEM 10.21 Is the function

$$R_0(\tau) = 2T_0 \left(1 - \frac{|\tau|}{2T_0} \right) \quad \text{for } |\tau| \leqslant 2T_0$$

$$= 0 \qquad\qquad \text{elsewhere,}$$

as shown in Fig. 10.8, a realizable autocorrelation function?

Solution: The function $R_0(\tau)$ is related to $R(\tau)$ by

$$R_0(\tau) = R(\tau) * R(\tau).$$

(Cf., Prob. 10.20.) Since convolution in the τ domain is equivalent to multiplication in the ω-domain,

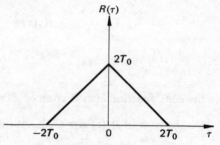

Fig. 10.8 Autocorrelation function $R_0(\tau)$ of Prob. 10.21.

$$G_0(\omega) = \int_{-\infty}^{\infty} R_0(\tau) e^{-j\omega\tau} \, d\tau = G^2(\omega),$$

where

$$G(\omega) = 2T_0 \left(\frac{\sin \omega T_0}{\omega T_0} \right),$$

as shown in Fig. 10.7. (See Table 10.2, property 6.) Since $G^2(\omega) \geqslant 0$ for all ω, $R_0(\tau)$ is a realizable autocorrelation function.

10.3 Power Density Relationships

If $x(t)$ and $y(t)$ are two independent random processes with power density spectra $G_x(\omega)$ and $G_y(\omega)$, the power density spectrum of their linear combination $z(t) = ax(t) + by(t)$ is

$$G_z(\omega) = a^2 G_x(\omega) + b^2 G_y(\omega). \tag{10.22}$$

If the random process $x(t)$ has a power density spectrum $G_x(\omega)$, the power density spectrum of $z(t) = x(t)e^{j\omega_0 t}$ is

$$G_z(\omega) = G_x(\omega - \omega_0). \tag{10.23}$$

If $x(t)$ and $y(t)$ are two independent random processes with power density spectra $G_x(\omega)$ and $G_y(\omega)$, the power density spectrum of their product $z(t) = x(t) \cdot y(t)$ is the convolution of G_x and G_y; that is,

$$G_z(\omega) = G_x(\omega) * G_y(\omega). \tag{10.24}$$

PROBLEM 10.22 Using the definition of the autocorrelation of a complex signal, that is, $R_z(\tau) = \overline{z^*(t)z(t + \tau)}$, where the * denotes the complex conjugate, verify (10.23).

Solution: The autocorrelation of $z(t)$ is

$$R_z(\tau) = \overline{[x(t)e^{-j\omega_0 t}][x(t + \tau)e^{j\omega_0(t+\tau)}]} = \overline{x(t)x(t + \tau)}\, e^{j\omega_0 \tau} = R_x(\tau)e^{j\omega_0 \tau}.$$

Since the Fourier transform of $R_x(\tau)$ is $G_x(\omega)$, property 4 of Table 10.2 gives $G_z(\omega) = G_x(\omega - \omega_0)$.

PROBLEM 10.23 If $z(t) = x(t)\cos\omega_0 t$, express $G_z(\omega)$ in terms of $G_x(\omega)$.

Solution: Since $\cos\omega_0 t = \frac{1}{2}(e^{j\omega_0 t} + e^{-j\omega_0 t})$,

$$z(t) = \tfrac{1}{2}x(t)(e^{j\omega_0 t} + e^{-j\omega_0 t}),$$

$$R_z(\tau) = \overline{z^*(t)z(t + \tau)}$$

$$= \tfrac{1}{4}\overline{x(t)x(t + \tau)(e^{-j\omega_0 t} + e^{j\omega_0 t})[e^{-j\omega_0(t+\tau)} + e^{j\omega_0(t+\tau)}]}$$

$$= \tfrac{1}{4}R_x(\tau)\overline{(e^{-2j\omega_0 t}e^{-j\omega_0 \tau} + e^{j\omega_0 \tau} + e^{-j\omega_0 \tau} + e^{2j\omega_0 t}e^{j\omega_0 \tau})}$$

$$= \tfrac{1}{4}R_x(\tau)(e^{j\omega_0 \tau} + e^{-j\omega_0 \tau}).$$

From (10.19), the power density spectrum of $z(t)$ is

$$G_z(\omega) = \int_{-\infty}^{\infty} R_z(\tau)e^{-j\omega\tau}\,d\tau$$

$$= \tfrac{1}{4}\int_{-\infty}^{\infty} R_x(\tau)e^{j\omega_0 \tau}e^{-j\omega\tau}\,d\tau + \tfrac{1}{4}\int_{-\infty}^{\infty} R_x(\tau)e^{-j\omega_0 \tau}e^{-j\omega\tau}\,d\tau$$

$$= \tfrac{1}{4}G_x(\omega - \omega_0) + \tfrac{1}{4}G_x(\omega + \omega_0),$$

using property 4 of Table 10.2.

PROBLEM 10.24 Determine the autocorrelation function of band-limited white noise, that is, a random process whose power density spectrum is

$$G(\omega) = G_0 \quad \text{for } \omega_1 < |\omega| < \omega_2$$

$$= 0 \quad \text{elsewhere,}$$

as shown in Fig. 10.9.

Solution: Using (10.20), the autocorrelation of band-limited white noise is

$$R(\tau) = \frac{1}{2\pi}\int_{-\infty}^{\infty} G(\omega)e^{j\omega\tau}\,d\omega$$

$$= \frac{G_0}{2\pi}\int_{-\omega_2}^{-\omega_1} e^{j\omega\tau}\,d\omega + \frac{G_0}{2\pi}\int_{\omega_1}^{\omega_2} e^{j\omega\tau}\,d\omega$$

$$= \frac{G_0}{2\pi j\tau}\left(e^{j\omega\tau}\Big|_{-\omega_2}^{-\omega_1} + e^{j\omega\tau}\Big|_{\omega_1}^{\omega_2}\right)$$

$$= \frac{G_0}{2\pi j\tau}(e^{-j\omega_1 \tau} - e^{-j\omega_2 \tau} + e^{j\omega_2 \tau} - e^{j\omega_1 \tau}).$$

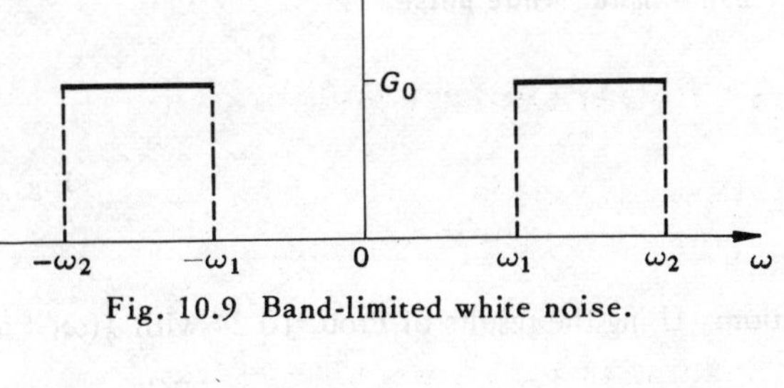

Fig. 10.9 Band-limited white noise.

Since $e^{jx} = \cos x + j\sin x$,

$$R(\tau) = \frac{G_0}{2\pi j\tau}(-2j\sin\omega_1 \tau + 2j\sin\omega_2 \tau) = \frac{G_0}{\pi\tau}(\sin\omega_2 \tau - \sin\omega_1 \tau).$$

Using the trigonometric identity $\sin A - \sin B = 2\cos\frac{1}{2}(A + B)\sin\frac{1}{2}(A - B)$, $R(\tau)$ becomes

$$R(\tau) = \frac{2G_0}{\pi\tau}\left[\cos\tfrac{1}{2}(\omega_1 + \omega_2)\tau \sin\tfrac{1}{2}(\omega_2 - \omega_1)\tau\right].$$

PROBLEM 10.25 Determine the autocorrelation function of low-pass band-limited white noise, that is, a random process whose power density spectrum is

$$G(\omega) = G_0 \quad \text{for } |\omega| < \omega_0$$
$$= 0 \quad \text{elsewhere,}$$

as shown in Fig. 10.10.

Solution: Using the results of Prob. 10.24, with $\omega_1 = 0$ and $\omega_2 = \omega_0$,

$$R(\tau) = \frac{2G_0}{\pi\tau} [\cos \tfrac{1}{2}(\omega_1 + \omega_2)\tau \sin \tfrac{1}{2}(\omega_2 - \omega_1)\tau]_{\substack{\omega_1=0 \\ \omega_2=\omega_0}}$$

$$= \frac{2G_0}{\pi\tau} (\cos \tfrac{1}{2}\omega_0\tau \sin \tfrac{1}{2}\omega_0\tau).$$

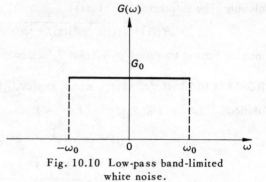

Fig. 10.10 Low-pass band-limited white noise.

Using the trigonometric identity $\sin 2A = 2 \sin A \cos A$, $R(\tau)$ becomes

$$R(\tau) = \frac{G_0}{\pi\tau} \sin \omega_0\tau.$$

PROBLEM 10.26 Determine the autocorrelation for the narrow-band case of band-limited white noise, that is, a random process whose power density spectrum is as shown in Fig. 10.11 ($\Delta\omega \ll \omega_0$). Sketch the result.

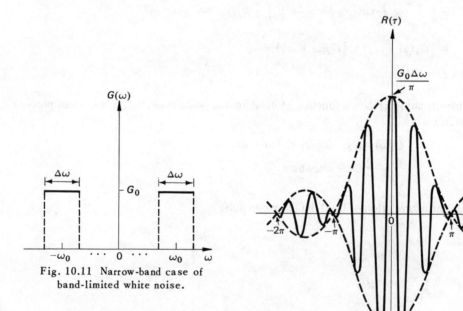

Fig. 10.11 Narrow-band case of band-limited white noise.

Fig. 10.12 Autocorrelation for the narrow-band case of band-limited white noise.

Solution: Using the results of Prob. 10.24 with $\tfrac{1}{2}(\omega_1 + \omega_2) = \omega_0$ and $\omega_2 - \omega_1 = \Delta\omega$, the autocorrelation is

$$R(\tau) = \frac{2G_0}{\pi\tau} [\cos \omega_0\tau \sin \tfrac{1}{2} (\Delta\omega)\tau],$$

which is sketched in Fig. 10.12.

PROBLEM 10.27 Determine the autocorrelation function of a random process whose spectral density is low-pass Gaussian; that is, $G(\omega) = G_0 e^{-\omega^2/(2\omega_0^2)}$, as shown in Fig. 10.13.

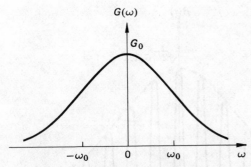

Fig. 10.13 Low-pass Gaussian spectral density of a random process.

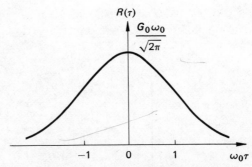

Fig. 10.14 Gaussian autocorrelation function of the Gaussian power density spectrum of Fig. 10.13.

Solution: The autocorrelation function is

$$R(\tau) = \frac{1}{2\pi} \int_{-\infty}^{\infty} G(\omega)e^{j\omega\tau} \, d\omega = \frac{G_0}{2\pi} \int_{-\infty}^{\infty} e^{-\omega^2/2\omega_0^2} e^{j\omega\tau} \, d\omega = \frac{G_0}{2\pi} \int_{-\infty}^{\infty} e^{-\omega^2/2\omega_0^2} (\cos \omega\tau + j \sin \omega\tau) d\omega.$$

Since $e^{-\omega^2/2\omega_0^2} \sin \omega\tau$ is an odd function of ω, its integral over symmetric limits is zero. Therefore,

$$R(\tau) = \frac{G_0}{2\pi} \int_{-\infty}^{\infty} e^{-\omega^2/2\omega_0^2} \cos \omega\tau \, d\omega.$$

Using a table of integrals,

$$\int_{-\infty}^{\infty} e^{-a^2 x^2} \cos bx \, dx = \frac{\sqrt{\pi} \, e^{-b^2/4a^2}}{a};$$

hence, $R(\tau)$ becomes

$$R(\tau) = \frac{G_0}{2\pi} \frac{\sqrt{\pi}}{1/\sqrt{2}\omega_0} e^{-\tau^2/4(1/2\omega_0^2)} = \frac{G_0\omega_0}{\sqrt{2\pi}} e^{-\omega_0^2\tau^2/2},$$

which is shown in Fig. 10.14. Thus, a random process whose power density spectrum is Gaussian has an autocorrelation function which is also Gaussian.

PROBLEM 10.28 Determine the autocorrelation function of a random process whose spectral density is bandpass Gaussian, that is,

$$G(\omega) = G_0 \left[e^{-(\omega-\omega_c)^2/2\omega_0^2} + e^{-(\omega+\omega_c)^2/2\omega_0^2} \right],$$

as shown in Fig. 10.15.

Solution: Using the results of Prob. 10.22,

$$R(\tau) = \frac{1}{2\pi} \int_{-\infty}^{\infty} G(\omega)e^{j\omega\tau} \, d\omega = R_0(\tau)(e^{j\omega_c\tau} + e^{-j\omega_c\tau}),$$

where

$$R_0(\tau) = \frac{1}{2\pi} \int_{-\infty}^{\infty} G_0 e^{-\omega^2/2\omega_0^2} e^{j\omega\tau} \, d\omega,$$

which has been calculated in Prob. 10.27. Thus,

$$R(\tau) = 2R_0(\tau) \cos \omega_c\tau = \sqrt{\frac{2}{\pi}} \, G_0\omega_0 e^{-\omega_0^2\tau^2/2} \cos \omega_c\tau,$$

which is shown in Fig. 10.16 for the narrow-band case ($\omega_0 \ll \omega_c$).

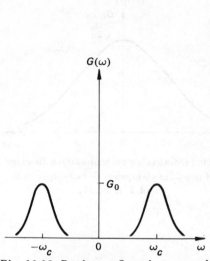

Fig. 10.15 Band-pass Gaussian spectral density of a random process.

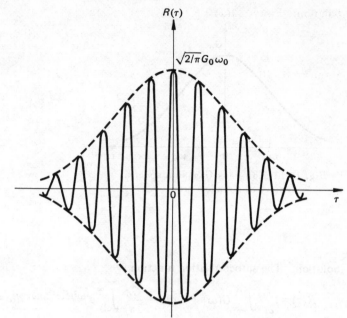

Fig. 10.16 Narrow-band case of the band-pass Gaussian autocorrelation of the band-pass Gaussian spectral density of Fig. 10.15.

10.4 Linear System Relationships

When a random process $x(t)$ is passed through a linear time-invariant system whose impulse response is $h(t)$, the power density spectrum at the output is modified. This is illustrated in Fig. 10.17. If the power density spectrum of the input $x(t)$ and the output $y(t)$ are represented by $G_x(\omega)$ and $G_y(\omega)$, then

$$G_y(\omega) = |H(\omega)|^2 \, G_x(\omega), \qquad (10.25)$$

where $H(\omega)$ is the Fourier transform of $h(t)$, i.e., the transfer function of the linear system. Thus,

$$H(\omega) = \int_{-\infty}^{\infty} h(t)e^{-j\omega t} \, dt. \qquad (10.26)$$

As seen in (10.25), $G_y(\omega)$ depends only on the magnitude of $H(\omega)$ and not the phase.

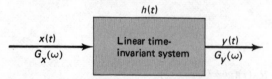

Fig. 10.17 Linear system variables. The power density spectra of $x(t)$ and $y(t)$ are $G_x(\omega)$ and $G_y(\omega)$.

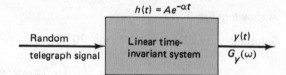

Fig. 10.18 Linear system of Prob. 10.29.

PROBLEM 10.29 The input to a linear system is a random telegraph signal with ν zero-crossings per second and amplitude a. If the impulse response of the linear system is

$$h(t) = Ae^{-\alpha t} \quad \text{for } t \geqslant 0$$

$$= 0 \qquad \text{for } t < 0,$$

determine the power density spectrum at the output. (See Fig. 10.18 and Prob. 10.18.)

Solution: From Table 10.1, the Fourier transform of $h(t)$ is

$$H(\omega) = \frac{A}{j\omega + \alpha}.$$

From Prob. (10.18), the power density spectrum at the input is

$$G_x(\omega) = \frac{a^2/v}{1 + (\omega/2v)^2}.$$

Using (10.25), the power density spectrum at the output is

$$G_y(\omega) = |H(j\omega)|^2 G_x(\omega)$$

$$= \left| \frac{A}{j\omega + \alpha} \right|^2 \left[\frac{a^2/v}{1 + (\omega/2v)^2} \right]$$

$$= \frac{A^2 a^2/v}{(\alpha^2 + \omega^2)[1 + (\omega/2v)^2]}.$$

PROBLEM 10.30 Determine the autocorrelation function of the output of the linear system of Prob. 10.29 if the input is white noise of power density $\frac{1}{2}\eta$.

Solution: Since $G_y(\omega) = |H(\omega)|^2 G_x(\omega)$, where $H(\omega) = A/(j\omega + \alpha)$ and $G_x(\omega) = \frac{1}{2}\eta$, the power density spectrum at the output is

$$G_y(\omega) = \frac{\frac{1}{2}\eta A^2}{\alpha^2 + \omega^2} = \frac{\eta A^2/(2\alpha^2)}{1 + (\omega/\alpha)^2}.$$

This is of the same form as the power density spectrum of the random telegraph signal. Therefore, the autocorrelation function $R_y(\tau)$ will also be similar in form to that of the random telegraph signal. Hence, from Prob. 10.18,

$$R_y(\tau) = \frac{\eta A^2}{4\alpha} e^{-\alpha|\tau|}.$$

PROBLEM 10.31 The input to a linear system is a random process whose autocorrelation function is

$$R_x(\tau) = \frac{G_0 \omega_0}{\pi} \frac{\sin \omega_0 \tau}{\omega_0 \tau}.$$

If the impulse response of the system is

$$h(t) = \frac{\omega_1}{\pi} \frac{\sin \omega_1 t}{\omega_1 t},$$

determine the autocorrelation function at the output for (a) $\omega_0 \geqslant \omega_1$ and (b) $\omega_0 < \omega_1$.

Solution: Using the results of Prob. 10.25,

$$G_x(\omega) = G_0 \quad \text{for } |\omega| < \omega_0$$

$$= 0 \quad \text{elsewhere.}$$

Since $h(t)$ is of the same form as $R_x(\tau)$,

$$H(\omega) = 1 \quad \text{for } |\omega| < \omega_1$$

$$= 0 \quad \text{elsewhere.}$$

The power density spectrum $G_y(\omega)$ at the output is

$$G_y(\omega) = |H(\omega)|^2 G_x(\omega).$$

Both $G_x(\omega)$ and $|H(\omega)|^2$ are shown in Fig. 10.19.

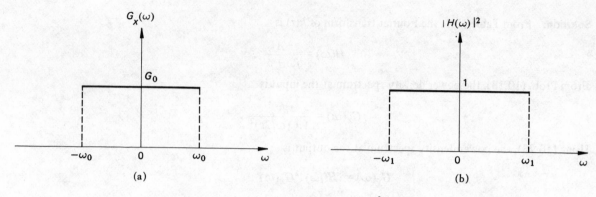

Fig. 10.19 Graphs of (a) $G_x(\omega)$ vs. ω and (b) $|H(\omega)|^2$ vs. ω of Prob. 10.31.

(a) When $\omega_0 \geqslant \omega_1$, the power density spectrum at the output is $G_y(\omega) = G_0 |H(\omega)|^2$; hence,

$$R_y(\tau) = \frac{G_0 \omega_1}{\pi} \frac{\sin \omega_1 \tau}{\omega_1 \tau}.$$

(b) When $\omega_1 > \omega_0$, $G_y(\omega) = G_x(\omega)$; hence, the autocorrelation function is

$$R_y(\tau) = R_x(\tau) = \frac{G_0 \omega_0}{\pi} \frac{\sin \omega_0 \tau}{\omega_0 \tau}.$$

PROBLEM 10.32 The input to a narrow-band linear system is a random process whose power density spectrum is

$$G_x(\omega) = \frac{G_0}{1 + (\omega/\omega_0)^2},$$

as shown in Fig. 10.20. If the transfer function of the linear system has the band-pass characteristic

$$H(\omega) = H_0 \quad \text{for} \quad \omega_1 < |\omega| < \omega_2$$

$$= 0 \qquad \text{elsewhere},$$

as shown in Fig. 10.21, to a good approximation, find the autocorrelation function of the output. Assume that $\omega_1 \gg \omega_0$, $\omega_2 \gg \omega_0$, and $(\omega_2 - \omega_1)/\omega_2 \ll 1$.

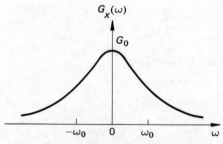

Fig. 10.20 Power density spectrum of
the input to a narrow-band system
for Prob. 10.32.

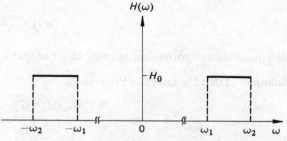

Fig. 10.21 Transfer function of the linear system
of Prob. 10.32.

Solution: The change in value of $G_x(\omega)$ over the interval $\omega_1 < |\omega| < \omega_2$ is small so that the input can be considered to be white noise. This can be seen from

$$G_x(\omega_1) = \frac{G_0}{1 + (\omega_1/\omega_0)^2} \approx \frac{G_0 \omega_0^2}{\omega_1^2}.$$

Similarly,

$$G_x(\omega_2) \approx \frac{G_0 \omega_0^2}{\omega_2^2}.$$

The fractional change of $G_x(\omega)$ over this interval is then

$$\frac{G_x(\omega_2)}{G_x(\omega_1)} \approx \left(\frac{\omega_1}{\omega_2}\right)^2.$$

Since $\frac{\Delta\omega}{\omega_2} = \frac{\omega_2 - \omega_1}{\omega_2} \ll 1$,

$$\frac{G_x(\omega_2)}{G_x(\omega_1)} \approx \left(\frac{\omega_2 - \Delta\omega}{\omega_2}\right)^2 = \left(1 - \frac{\Delta\omega}{\omega_2}\right)^2 \approx 1 - 2\frac{\Delta\omega}{\omega_2},$$

which is nearly equal to unity. Thus, the power density function of the output is

$$G_y(\omega) = |H(\omega)|^2 G_x(\omega) \approx |H(\omega)|^2 \frac{G_0 \omega_0^2}{\omega_1^2}.$$

Using the results of Prob. 10.24, the autocorrelation function of the output is

$$R_y(\tau) \approx \frac{2G_0 \omega_0^2 H_0^2}{\pi\tau\omega_1^2} \left[\cos \tfrac{1}{2}(\omega_1 + \omega_2)\tau \sin \tfrac{1}{2}(\omega_2 - \omega_1)\tau\right].$$

PROBLEM 10.33 Show that narrow-band noise, whose power density spectrum $W(\omega)$ is shown in Fig. 10.22, can be represented by

$$n(t) = x(t) \cos \omega_0 t - y(t) \sin \omega_0 t,$$

where $x(t)$ and $y(t)$ are slowly-varying normally distributed quantities. Assume that $2\omega_b \ll \omega_0$ and approximate the continuous power density spectrum by a discrete spectrum.

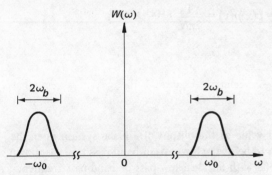

Fig. 10.22 Power density spectrum $W(\omega)$ of narrow-band noise.

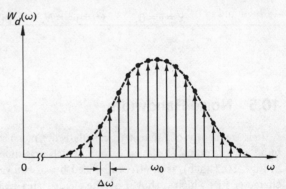

Fig. 10.23 Approximation of $W(\omega)$ of Fig. 10.22 by a discrete power density spectrum $W_d(\omega)$.

Solution: Figure 10.23 shows the approximation of $W(\omega)$ by a discrete power density spectrum $W_d(\omega)$ for positive frequencies only. The spectrum $W(\omega)$ is broken into a series of narrow intervals, which are $\Delta\omega$ wide. The contribution to $n(t)$ from the ith interval $|\omega_i| - \tfrac{1}{2}\Delta\omega < \omega < |\omega_i| + \tfrac{1}{2}\Delta\omega$ is represented by

$$\Delta n_i(t) = 2\sqrt{W(\omega_i)\left(\frac{\Delta\omega}{2\pi}\right)} \cos (\omega_i t + \varphi_i), \tag{10.27}$$

where φ_i is a random phase angle uniformly distributed between 0 and 2π. The above expression correctly gives the contribution of the ith interval to the total average power of $n(t)$. By Parseval's theorem, the average power of $n(t)$ in the ith interval is

$$P_i \approx W(\omega_i)\left(\frac{\Delta\omega}{2\pi}\right) \cdot 2,$$

where the factor of two in the numerator arises from the negative frequency interval, while from (10.27),

$$\overline{\Delta n_i^2(t)} = 4W(\omega_i)\left(\frac{\Delta\omega}{2\pi}\right)\overline{\cos^2(\omega_i t + \varphi_i)} = 2W(\omega_i)\left(\frac{\Delta\omega}{2\pi}\right) = P_i.$$

The quantity $n(t)$ is then

$$n(t) = \sum_i \Delta n_i(t) = \sum_i \sqrt{2W(\omega_i)\left(\frac{\Delta\omega}{2\pi}\right)}\cos(\omega_i t + \varphi_i).$$

Setting $\omega_i t + \varphi_i = \omega_0 t + i\Delta\omega t + \varphi_i$,

$$n(t) = 2\sum_{i=-N}^{N} \sqrt{W(\omega_0 + i\Delta\omega)\left(\frac{\Delta\omega}{2\pi}\right)}\cos(\omega_0 t + i\Delta\omega t + \varphi_i),$$

where $N\Delta\omega = \omega_b$. Since $\cos(A+B) = \cos A \cos B - \sin A \sin B$,

$$n(t) = 2\sum_{i=-N}^{N} \sqrt{W(\omega_0 + i\Delta\omega)\left(\frac{\Delta\omega}{2\pi}\right)}[\cos(i\Delta\omega t + \varphi_i)\cos\omega_0 t - \sin(i\Delta\omega t + \varphi_i)\sin\omega_0 t]$$

$$= x(t)\cos\omega_0 t - y(t)\sin\omega_0 t,$$

where

$$x(t) = 2\sum_{i=-N}^{N} \sqrt{W(\omega_0 + i\Delta\omega)\left(\frac{\Delta\omega}{2\pi}\right)}\cos(i\Delta\omega t + \varphi_i), \quad y(t) = 2\sum_{i=-N}^{N} \sqrt{W(\omega_0 + i\Delta\omega)\left(\frac{\Delta\omega}{2\pi}\right)}\sin(i\Delta\omega t + \varphi_i).$$

As $N \to \infty$ (and $\Delta\omega \to 0$), both $x(t)$ and $y(t)$ become normally distributed by the central limit theorem since each is the sum of a large number of independently distributed random variables. Other properties of $x(t)$ and $y(t)$ are

$$\overline{x} = \overline{y} = 0, \qquad \overline{x^2} = \overline{y^2} = N, \qquad p(x,y) = p(x)p(y) = \frac{1}{2\pi N}e^{-(x^2+y^2)/2N}.$$

10.5 Noise Bandwidth

It is frequently of interest to calculate the mean-squared value of the output of a linear system when the input is white noise. The linear system, which is assumed here to be of the low-pass or band-pass type, as shown in Figs. 10.24(a–b), is in effect replaced by an equivalent one with an ideal low-pass or band-pass frequency characteristic, which is shown by the shaded area in Fig. 10.24. The quantity ω_n is known as the *noise bandwidth* and is chosen such that for input white noise of power density

$$G_x(\omega) = \tfrac{1}{2}\eta, \tag{10.28}$$

the mean-squared output from the system is given by

$$\overline{y^2} = G_x(\omega)H_0^2 \cdot 2(\omega_n/2\pi) \tag{10.29}$$

$$= \frac{\eta\omega_n H_0^2}{2\pi}, \tag{10.30}$$

where ω_n is in units of rad/sec. Since $R_x(\tau) = \dfrac{1}{2\pi}\displaystyle\int_{-\infty}^{\infty} G_x(\omega)e^{j\omega\tau}\,d\omega$ and $\overline{y^2(t)} = R_x(0)$,

$$\overline{y^2(t)} = \frac{1}{2\pi}\int_{-\infty}^{\infty}\frac{\eta}{2}|H(\omega)|^2\,d\omega. \tag{10.31}$$

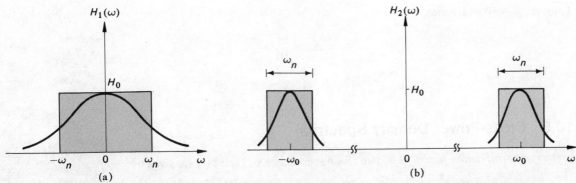

Fig. 10.24 (a) Equivalent low-pass transfer function. (b) Equivalent band-pass transfer function.

Equating (10.30) and (10.31), the noise bandwidth is

$$\omega_n = \frac{1}{2} \int_{-\infty}^{\infty} \left| \frac{H(\omega)}{H_0} \right|^2 d\omega = \int_0^{\infty} \left| \frac{H(\omega)}{H_0} \right|^2 d\omega. \qquad (10.32)$$

PROBLEM 10.34 Determine the noise bandwidth of a linear system whose impulse response is $Ae^{-\alpha t}$.

Solution: From Table 10.1,

$$H(\omega) = \frac{A}{j\omega + \alpha}, \qquad |H(\omega)|^2 = \frac{A^2}{\omega^2 + \alpha^2}.$$

Using (10.30), the noise bandwidth is

$$\omega_n = \int_0^{\infty} \frac{|H(\omega)|^2}{H_0^2} d\omega,$$

where

$$H_0 = H(\omega)\big|_{\omega=0} = \frac{A}{\alpha}, \qquad \omega_n = \alpha^2 \int_0^{\infty} \frac{d\omega}{\omega^2 + \alpha^2}.$$

Using a table of integrals, $\omega_n = \frac{1}{2}\pi\alpha$.

Note that $\omega = \alpha$ is known as the "3-db bandwidth," where db denotes decibels, since the value of $|H(\omega)|^2$ at this frequency is one-half its zero frequency value, that is,

$$|H(\alpha)|^2 = \frac{A^2}{2\alpha^2} = \frac{1}{2} |H(0)|^2.$$

PROBLEM 10.35 Determine the ratio of the noise bandwidth to the 3-db bandwidth of the transfer function $H(\omega) = \dfrac{4}{j\omega + 10}$.

Solution: Using the results of Prob. 10.34, the noise bandwidth of the transfer function $H(\omega) = A/(j\omega + \alpha)$ is $\omega_n = \frac{1}{2}\pi\alpha$. Thus, since $\alpha = 10$, $\omega_n = 5\pi$.

The 3-db bandwidth, that is, the value of ω for which $\dfrac{|H(\omega)|^2}{|H(0)|^2} = \dfrac{1}{2}$ is found by setting

$$\frac{|4/(j\omega + 10)|^2}{|4/10|^2} = \frac{1}{2}.$$

Simplifying,

$$\frac{1}{|j\omega/10 + 1|^2} = \frac{1}{2} \quad \text{or} \quad \frac{\omega^2}{100} + 1 = 2.$$

Thus, $\omega_{3\,db} = 10$ and, hence,

$$\frac{\omega_n}{\omega_{3\,db}} = \frac{5\pi}{10} = \frac{\pi}{2}.$$

10.6 Cross-Power Density Spectrum

The *cross-correlation functions* of two random processes $x(t)$ and $y(t)$ are given by

$$R_{xy}(\tau) = E[x(t)y(t+\tau)], \tag{10.33}$$

$$R_{yx}(\tau) = E[y(t)x(t+\tau)]. \tag{10.34}$$

The corresponding *cross-power density spectra* are defined by

$$W_{xy}(\omega) = \int_{-\infty}^{\infty} R_{xy}(\tau)e^{-j\omega\tau}\,d\tau, \tag{10.35}$$

$$W_{yx}(\omega) = \int_{-\infty}^{\infty} R_{yx}(\tau)e^{-j\omega\tau}\,d\tau. \tag{10.36}$$

As in the case of the autocorrelation function, the cross-correlation function and the cross-power density spectrum comprise a Fourier transform pair. The inverse relationships are

$$R_{xy}(\tau) = \frac{1}{2\pi}\int_{-\infty}^{\infty} W_{xy}(\omega)e^{j\omega\tau}\,d\omega, \tag{10.37}$$

$$R_{yx}(\tau) = \frac{1}{2\pi}\int_{-\infty}^{\infty} W_{yx}(\omega)e^{j\omega\tau}\,d\omega. \tag{10.38}$$

The cross-power spectra $W_{xy}(\omega)$ and $W_{yx}(\omega)$ can also be defined by a limiting process although (10.37-8) are more generally useful definitions. Thus,

$$W_{xy}(\omega) = \lim_{T\to\infty}\frac{F_x(-\omega)F_y(\omega)}{T}, \tag{10.39}$$

$$W_{yx}(\omega) = \lim_{T\to\infty}\frac{F_y(-\omega)F_x(\omega)}{T}, \tag{10.40}$$

where

$$F_x(\omega) = \int_0^T x(t)e^{-j\omega t}\,dt, \tag{10.41}$$

$$F_y(\omega) = \int_0^T y(t)e^{-j\omega t}\,dt. \tag{10.42}$$

Two zero-mean random processes are said to be *uncorrelated* if their cross-power density spectrum is identically zero. If the mean values of the random processes described above are not zero, the cross-power density spectrum is zero everywhere except at the origin where it consists of a delta function.

Random processes which are uncorrelated are in general, *not* statistically independent. However, if two uncorrelated random processes are jointly Gaussian, then they are also statistically independent.

If the inputs to two linear systems with transfer functions $H_1(\omega)$ and $H_2(\omega)$ are random processes, $x(t)$ and $y(t)$, then the cross-power density spectra of the outputs $u(t)$ and $v(t)$ are given by

$$W_{uv}(\omega) = H_1(-\omega)H_2(\omega)W_{xy}(\omega), \tag{10.43}$$

$$W_{vu}(\omega) = H_1(\omega)H_2(-\omega)W_{yx}(\omega). \tag{10.44}$$

(Cf., Fig. 10.25.)

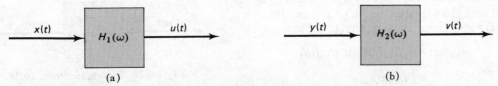

Fig. 10.25 Inputs $x(t)$ and $y(t)$ and outputs $u(t)$ and $v(t)$ for two linear systems with transfer functions $H_1(\omega)$ and $H_2(\omega)$.

PROBLEM 10.36 Determine the cross-power density spectrum $W_{xy}(\omega)$ of two independent random processes $x(t)$ and $y(t)$ with zero means.

Solution: From (9.32), the cross-correlation of two random processes with zero means is

$$R_{xy}(\tau) = \int_{-\infty}^{\infty} \int_{-\infty}^{\infty} x_1 y_2 p(x_1, y_2) dx_1 dy_2.$$

Since x and y are independent, $p(x_1, y_2) = p_1(x_1) p_2(y_2)$; hence,

$$R_{xy}(\tau) = \int_{-\infty}^{\infty} x_1 p_1(x_1) dx_1 \int_{-\infty}^{\infty} y_2 p_2(y_2) dy_2 = \overline{x_1}\,\overline{y_2} = 0.$$

Therefore, from (10.35),

$$W_{xy}(\omega) = 0.$$

PROBLEM 10.37 Express $R_{xy}(\tau)$ in terms of the real and imaginary parts of $W_{xy}(\omega)$.

Solution: Note that $W_{xy}(\omega)$ can be written as

$$W_{xy}(\omega) = r_{xy}(\omega) + jI_{xy}(\omega),$$

where

$$r_{xy}(\omega) = \text{real part of } W_{xy}(\omega),$$

$$I_{xy}(\omega) = \text{imaginary part of } W_{xy}(\omega),$$

and both r_{xy} and I_{xy} are real functions of ω. Using (10.37),

$$R_{xy}(\tau) = \frac{1}{2\pi} \int_{-\infty}^{\infty} W_{xy}(\omega) e^{j\omega\tau} d\omega.$$

Substituting for $W_{xy}(\omega)$,

$$R_{xy}(\tau) = \frac{1}{2\pi} \int_{-\infty}^{\infty} [r_{xy}(\omega) + jI_{xy}(\omega)][\cos \omega\tau + j \sin \omega\tau] d\omega$$

$$= \frac{1}{2\pi} \int_{-\infty}^{\infty} [r_{xy}(\omega) \cos \omega\tau - I_{xy}(\omega) \sin \omega\tau] d\omega + \frac{j}{2\pi} \int_{-\infty}^{\infty} [I_{xy}(\omega) \cos \omega\tau + r_{xy}(\omega) \sin \omega\tau] d\omega.$$

Since the random processes $x(t)$ and $y(t)$ are real, (10.32) shows that $R_{xy}(\tau)$ must also be real. Accordingly, the second integral in the above equation must vanish. Thus,

$$R_{xy}(\tau) = \frac{1}{2\pi} \int_{-\infty}^{\infty} [r_{xy}(\omega) \cos \omega\tau - I_{xy} \sin \omega\tau] d\omega.$$

PROBLEM 10.38 The input to a linear system is a random process $x(t)$ with power density spectrum $W_x(\omega)$, as shown in Fig. 10.26. If the linear system has a transfer function $H(\omega)$, determine the cross-power density spectrum $W_{xu}(\omega)$ of x and u.

Solution: The cross-power density spectrum $W_{xu}(\omega)$ can be found from (10.44) by setting $y(t) = x(t)$ and $H_2(\omega) = 1$. Then, $v(t) = x(t)$; hence, $W_{vu}(\omega) = W_{xu}(\omega)$. Thus,

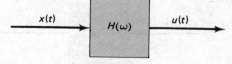

$$W_{xu}(\omega) = H_1(\omega)H_2(-\omega)W_{xy}(\omega)$$

$$= H(\omega)W_x(\omega)$$

Fig. 10.26 System for Prob. 10.38.

since $H_1(\omega) = H(\omega)$ and $W_{yx} = W_{xx} = W_x$.

PROBLEM 10.39 If the input in Prob. 10.38 is white noise, determine the cross-power spectrum $W_{xu}(\omega)$.

Solution: If the input is white noise, $W_x(\omega) = W_0$. Substituting in the result of Prob. 10.38, $W_{xu}(\omega) = W_0 H(\omega)$; that is, $W_{xu}(\omega)$ is proportional to $H(\omega)$.

PROBLEM 10.40 Determine the relationship between $W_{\dot{x}y}(\omega)$ and $W_{xy}(\omega)$, and between $W_{y\dot{x}}(\omega)$ and $W_{yx}(\omega)$. Note that $\dot{x} = dx/dt$ and $\dot{y} = dy/dt$. (See Fig. 10.25.)

Solution: Using (10.43-4) with $u = \dot{x}$ and $v = y$, and $H_2(\omega) = 1$,

$$W_{\dot{x}y}(\omega) = H_1(-\omega)W_{xy}(\omega), \qquad W_{y\dot{x}}(\omega) = H_1(\omega)W_{yx}(\omega).$$

The transfer function of the differentiator is

$$H_1(\omega) = j\omega.$$

This can be found from the Fourier transform relationship

$$f(t) = \frac{1}{2\pi} \int_{-\infty}^{\infty} F(\omega)e^{j\omega t}\, d\omega.$$

Differentiating,

$$\frac{df}{dt} = \frac{1}{2\pi} \int_{-\infty}^{\infty} j\omega F(\omega)e^{j\omega t}\, d\omega;$$

hence, if $f(t)$ and $F(\omega)$ comprise a Fourier transform pair, then df/dt and $j\omega F(\omega)$ are also a Fourier transform pair. Thus,

$$W_{\dot{x}y}(\omega) = -j\omega W_{xy}(\omega), \qquad W_{y\dot{x}}(\omega) = j\omega W_{yx}(\omega).$$

PROBLEM 10.41 Determine the relationship between $R_{\dot{x}y}(\tau)$ and $R_{xy}(\tau)$ in Fig. 10.27.

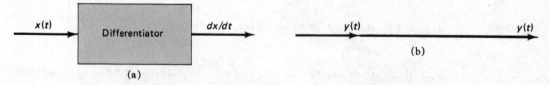

(a)

(b)

Fig. 10.27 Inputs $x(t)$ and $y(t)$ and outputs dx/dt and $y(t)$ for Prob. 10.41.

Solution: The cross-correlation function, from (10.37), is

$$R_{\dot{x}y}(\tau) = \frac{1}{2\pi} \int_{-\infty}^{\infty} W_{\dot{x}y}(\omega)e^{j\omega\tau}\, d\omega.$$

From the results of Prob. 10.41, $W_{\dot{x}y}(\omega) = -j\omega W_{xy}(\omega)$; hence,

$$R_{\dot{x}y}(\tau) = \frac{-1}{2\pi} \int_{-\infty}^{\infty} j\omega W_{xy}(\omega)e^{j\omega\tau}\, d\omega = \frac{-1}{2\pi}\frac{d}{d\tau}\int_{-\infty}^{\infty} W_{xy}(\omega)e^{j\omega\tau}\, d\omega = -\frac{d}{d\tau}R_{xy}(\tau).$$

PROBLEM 10.42 Determine the relationship between $R_{\dot{x}x}(\tau)$ and $R_x(\tau)$.

Solution: Substituting $y = x$ in the result of Prob. 10.41,

$$R_{\dot{x}x} = -\frac{d}{d\tau} R_{xx}(\tau) = -\frac{d}{d\tau} R_x(\tau).$$

PROBLEM 10.43 Determine the relationship between $R_{xu}(\tau)$ and $R_x(\tau)$ in Prob. 10.38.

Solution: From the results of Prob. 10.38,

$$W_{xu}(\omega) = H(\omega)W_x(\omega).$$

Since the inverse Fourier transforms of $W_{xu}(\omega)$, $H(\omega)$, and $W_x(\omega)$ are $R_{xu}(\tau)$, $h(\tau)$, and $R_x(\tau)$, where $h(\tau)$ is the impulse response of the linear system,

$$R_{xu}(\tau) = h(\tau) * R_x(\tau),$$

where the $*$ denotes convolution. Thus,

$$R_{xu}(\tau) = \int_{-\infty}^{\infty} h(\tau - u)R_x(u)du.$$

PROBLEM 10.44 If the input is white noise for the data of Prob. 10.43, determine the relationship between $R_{xu}(\tau)$ and $R_x(\tau)$.

Solution: For a white noise input, $R_x(\tau) = R_0 \delta(\tau)$, where $\delta(\tau)$ is the delta function. Hence,

$$R_{xu}(\tau) = R_0 \int_{-\infty}^{\infty} h(\tau - u)\delta(u)du = R_0 h(\tau).$$

Thus, $R_{xu}(\tau)$ is proportional to $h(\tau)$.

10.7 Supplementary Problems

PROBLEM 10.45 Show that an arbitrary function $f(t)$ may be decomposed into the sum of two components, one even and one odd.

PROBLEM 10.46 Determine the Fourier series expansion for the function

$$x(t) = \left| A \cos \frac{\pi}{T} t \right|.$$

Answer: $x(t) = \frac{4}{\pi} A \left[\frac{1}{2} + \frac{1}{3} \cos \frac{2\pi}{T} t - \frac{1}{15} \cos \frac{4\pi}{T} t + \cdots + (-1)^{n+1} \frac{1}{4n^2 - 1} \cos \frac{2\pi nt}{T} + \cdots \right].$

PROBLEM 10.47 Determine the Fourier series expansion for the function

$$x(t) = \left| A \sin \frac{\pi}{T} t \right|.$$

Answer: $x(t) = \frac{4}{\pi} A \left[\frac{1}{2} + \frac{1}{3} \sin \frac{2\pi}{T} t - \frac{1}{15} \sin \frac{4\pi}{T} t + \cdots + (-1)^{n+1} \frac{1}{4n^2 - 1} \sin \frac{2\pi nt}{T} + \cdots \right].$

PROBLEM 10.48 Determine the Fourier series of the function $x(t)$ which is periodic with period T and defined by

$$x(t) = A \quad \text{for} -\tfrac{1}{4}T \leqslant t \leqslant \tfrac{1}{4}T$$

$$= 0 \quad \text{for} \tfrac{1}{4}T < t < \tfrac{3}{4}T.$$

Answer: $x(t) = A \left[\dfrac{1}{2} + \dfrac{2}{\pi} \cos \dfrac{2\pi}{T} t - \dfrac{2}{3\pi} \cos \dfrac{6\pi}{T} t + \cdots \right].$

PROBLEM 10.49 Calculate the Fourier transform for the rectangular pulse

$$x(t) = A \quad \text{for } T_0 - \tfrac{1}{2}T \leqslant t \leqslant \tfrac{1}{2}T + T_0$$
$$= 0 \quad \text{elsewhere.}$$

Answer: $X(\omega) = AT \dfrac{\sin (\omega T/2)}{\omega T/2} e^{-j\omega T_0}.$

PROBLEM 10.50 Calculate the Fourier transform for the function $x(t) = Ae^{-[1/(2T^2)](t^2 - t + \frac{1}{4})}$.

Answer: $X(\omega) = \sqrt{2\pi} \, AT e^{-(1/2)/\omega^2 T^2} e^{-j\omega/2}.$

PROBLEM 10.51 Determine the power density spectrum of the periodic function

$$x(t) = A \sin (\omega t + \phi).$$

Answer: $G(\omega) = \tfrac{1}{4}A^2 [\delta(f + f_0) + \delta(f - f_0)]$, where $\omega = 2\pi f$ and $\omega_0 = 2\pi f_0$.

PROBLEM 10.52 Determine the signal corresponding to the power density

$$X(\omega) = \sum_{i=1}^{N} \delta(f - f_i).$$

Answer: $x(t) = \displaystyle\sum_{i=1}^{N} e^{[j(\omega - \omega_i)t + \phi_i]}$, where $\omega = 2\pi f$, $\omega_1 = 2\pi f_1$, and the ϕ_i are arbitrary constants.

PROBLEM 10.53 Show that the power density spectrum of a signal $x(t)$ is identical with the power density spectrum of $x(t - T)$, where T is an arbitrary constant.

PROBLEM 10.54 Calculate the energy density spectrum for

$$x(t) = e^{-\frac{1}{2}t^2}.$$

Answer: $|X(\omega)|^2 = 2\pi e^{-\frac{1}{2}\omega^2}.$

PROBLEM 10.55 A random process has an autocorrelation function given by

$$R(\tau) = 1 - \frac{\tau}{\tau_0} \quad \text{for } 0 \leqslant \tau \leqslant \tau_0$$

$$= 1 + \frac{\tau}{\tau_0} \quad \text{for } -\tau_0 \leqslant \tau \leqslant 0$$

$$= 0 \qquad \text{elsewhere.}$$

Calculate the power density spectrum of the process.

Answer: $G(\omega) = \tau_0 \dfrac{\sin^2(\omega \tau_0/2)}{(\omega \tau_0/2)^2}.$

PROBLEM 10.56 Show that the average power of the random telegraph signal of Prob. 10.18 is equal to a^2. Use the power density spectrum to obtain this result.

PROBLEM 10.57 Calculate the energy density spectrum for the signal

$$x(t) = e^{-\alpha|t|}.$$

Answer: $|X(\omega)|^2 = \dfrac{4}{\alpha^2} \dfrac{1}{[1 + (\omega/\alpha)^2]^2}$.

PROBLEM 10.58 An arbitrary real function $x(t)$ can be broken up into the sum of an even function $\frac{1}{2}[x(t) + x(-t)]$ and an odd function $\frac{1}{2}[x(t) - x(-t)]$. Show that the transform of the even part is equal to $\frac{1}{2}[X(f) + X(-f)]$. In addition, show that it is purely real and an even function of f.

PROBLEM 10.59 Show that the transform of the odd part of any arbitrary real function $x(t)$ (cf., Prob. 10.58) is equal to $\frac{1}{2}[X(f) - X(-f)]$, is imaginary, and is an odd function of f.

PROBLEM 10.60 Show that the power density spectrum of the product of two independent functions is equal to the convolution of their power spectra.

PROBLEM 10.61 The *finite time average* or *running average* of a time function $x(t)$ is defined by

$$\overline{x_f(t)} = \frac{1}{T} \int_{t-T}^{t} x(\alpha)d\alpha.$$

Determine the relationship between the power density spectra of $\overline{x_f(t)}$ and $x(t)$.

Answer: $G_f(f) = G(f) \dfrac{\sin^2 \pi fT}{(\pi fT)^2}$, where $G_f(f)$ and $G(f)$ are the spectra of x_f and x, respectively.

11

CHAPTER

DISCRETE RANDOM PROCESSES

11.1 Introduction

A *discrete random process* or a *random sequence* is a process $f(t)$ in which the independent variable t assumes only specified (i.e., discrete) values. For example, if t assumes the values of $t_0, t_{\pm 1}, t_{\pm 2}, \cdots$, with $\cdots t_{-2} < t_{-1} < t_0 < t_1 < t_2 < \cdots$, then the discrete process is defined as the corresponding set of values $\cdots, f(t_{-2}), f(t_{-1}), f(t_0), f(t_1), f(t_2) \cdots$. Note that the term discrete random process is used here as an abbreviation for discrete parameter random process and should not be confused with continuous processes in which only the dependent variable assumes discrete values.

A discrete process can be produced by sampling a continuous random process at specified values of the independent variable. Figure 11.1 shows a continuous random process $f(t)$ sampled *periodically* at a rate of $1/T$ samples/sec. The discrete process is the sequence of values $f(nt)$, $n = 0, \pm 1, \pm 2, \cdots$, where each value in the sequence is itself a random variable.

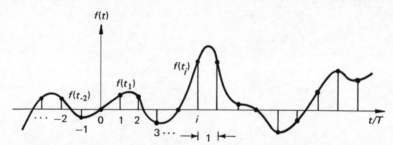

Fig. 11.1 A continuous random process $f(t)$ periodically sampled
at a rate of $1/T$ samples/sec.

The *normalized variable*

$$n = t/T \quad \text{for } n = 0, \pm 1, \pm 2, \cdots,$$

for an interval T between adjacent samples is often introduced for a periodically sampled process so that such a process has values $\cdots, f(-2), f(-1), f(0), f(1), f(2), \cdots$ corresponding to the times $\cdots, -2T, -T, 0, T, 2T \cdots$.

The *time* average of a discrete stochastic process $f(n)$ is given by

$$\overline{f(n)} = \lim_{N \to \infty} \frac{1}{2N + 1} \sum_{k=-N}^{N} f(k). \tag{11.1}$$

The *ensemble average* (or *expected value*) of a discrete stochastic process is given by

$$\overline{f_e(n)} = \lim_{N \to \infty} \frac{1}{N + 1} \sum_{i=0}^{N} f_i(n), \quad i = 1, 2, \cdots, \tag{11.2}$$

where $f_i(n)$ are sample functions of the process $f(n)$. (Cf., Chap. 9.)

A discrete random process $f(n)$ is said to be *stationary in the wide sense* if the joint distribution of $[f(j),$ $f(j + k)]$ where j and k are integers depends only on k. Note that if a *continuous* stochastic process is stationary, then any derived *discrete* process is also stationary, and if the ensemble is stationary then the ensemble average is not a function of n; i.e.,

$$\overline{f_e(n)} = f_e. \tag{11.3}$$

(Cf., Chap. 9.)

If a continuous stochastic process $f(t)$ is *ergodic*, its statistics can be found from any sample function $f(t, \zeta)$ of the process. If $f(t)$ is ergodic, its time and ensemble averages are equal; note that if an ensemble of *continuous* processes is sampled periodically, the resulting ensemble of *discrete* processes is ergodic when the original ensemble is ergodic, and if the ensemble is ergodic, then the time average is equal to the ensemble average; i.e.,

$$\overline{f(n)} = f_e. \tag{11.4}$$

PROBLEM 11.1 The air temperature in New York is measured once an hour for a year. Is the ensemble of discrete random processes defined by the variation of the temperature measurements over time in each year stationary?

Solution: Assume that all members of the ensemble have a common origin; for example, midnight of January first. Since each member of the ensemble represents the temperature variation with time in a single year, the probability density function of temperature *across* the ensemble (that is, at a specified hour and day of a month) varies with time. Thus, for example, the average temperature at noon on January first is obviously different from that at 3:00 p.m. on July second. Hence, the process is nonstationary, for if it were not, there would not be such statistical variations.

PROBLEM 11.2 The data of Prob. 11.1 are rearranged to form a new ensemble in which each member of the ensemble consists of temperature measurements taken at a specified hour and day of a month. The year in which the measurements were taken now becomes the independent variable. Determine if the processes are (a) stationary and (b) ergodic.

Solution: (a) They are stationary since the probability distribution of temperature across the ensemble is not dependent on the independent variable (assuming that there are no long-term systematic changes in climate).

(b) Since, for example, the average temperature calculated across the ensemble (that is, the average yearly temperature) is not equal to the average temperature calculated from each member of the ensemble, the processes are not ergodic.

PROBLEM 11.3 The amplitude of each member of the ensemble shown in Fig. 11.2 is constant, but varies from member-to-member according to an arbitrary probability density function. Determine if the ensemble is (a) stationary and (b) ergodic.

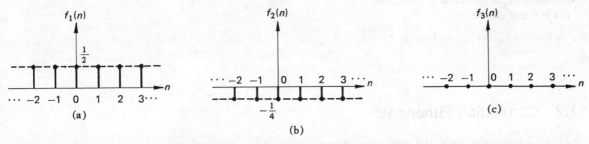

Fig. 11.2 A stationary, nonergodic, ensemble.

Solution: (a) It is stationary because the distribution of amplitudes across the ensemble (that is, at a specific value of n) is not a function of n.

(b) Since the ensemble average is not equal to the time average of each member of the ensemble, the ensemble is not ergodic.

PROBLEM 11.4 A large number of identical, but biased, coins are independently and repeatedly flipped. If the occurrence of a head is denoted by a 1 and that of tail by a 0, the ensemble of discrete stochastic processes shown in Fig. 11.3 is obtained. Determine if the ensemble is (a) stationary and (b) ergodic. (c) Are the results to parts (a–b) affected if the coins are not biased?

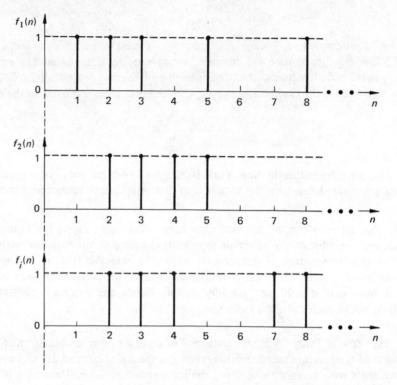

Fig. 11.3 Ensemble of discrete stochastic processes obtained on tossing
a large number of identical coins.

Solution: If p and q denote the probabilities of tossing a head and tail, respectively, on any given toss with any given coin, then $p + q = 1$. The probability density function for each member of the ensemble, corresponding to each coin, is given by

$$p(x) = p\delta(x - 1) + q\delta(x),$$

where $\delta(x)$ is Dirac's delta function. Calculation of $p(x)$ on an ensemble basis [that is, from $f_1(n), f_2(n), \cdots$, where $n = n_0$] yields the same result, independent of n_0.

   (a) The ensemble is stationary because $p(x)$ is independent of n_0.

   (b) The ensemble is ergodic because the resulting statistical description is the same regardless of whether it is calculated on an ensemble or time basis.

   (c) It is not affected.

11.2   Correlation Functions

In the following sections, the properties of stationarity and ergodicity are assumed, and the processes $f(n)$ and $g(n)$ considered are real and stationary in the wide sense. (Cf., Chap. 9.)

The *autocorrelation* $\phi(k)$, $k = 0, \pm 1, \pm 2, \cdots$, of a discrete process $f(n)$, $n = 0, \pm 1, \pm 2, \cdots$, is a statistical measure of the relationship of the value of $f(n)$ at one time to the value at another time. Mathematically,

$$\phi(k) = \overline{f(n)f(n + k)}, \tag{11.5}$$

where the bar denotes the average value. Alternately, (11.5) can be written as

$$\phi(k) = \lim_{N \to \infty} \frac{1}{2N+1} \sum_{n=-N}^{N} f(n)f(n+k). \tag{11.6}$$

The *cross-correlation* $\phi_{fg}(k)$, $k = 0, \pm 1, \pm 2, \cdots$, of two discrete stochastic processes $f(n)$ and $g(n)$ is a measure of the relationship of the value of $f(n)$ at one time to the value of $g(n)$ at another time. Mathematically, the cross-correlation ϕ_{fg} of $f(n)$ and $g(n)$ is given by

$$\phi_{fg}(k) = \overline{f(n)g(n+k)}, \tag{11.7}$$

or, alternatively,

$$\phi_{fg}(k) = \lim_{N \to \infty} \frac{1}{2N+1} \sum_{n=-N}^{N} f(n)g(n+k); \tag{11.8}$$

the cross-correlation ϕ_{gf} of $g(n)$ and $f(n)$ is given by

$$\phi_{gf} = \overline{g(n)f(n+k)} = \lim_{N \to \infty} \frac{1}{2N+1} \sum_{n=-N}^{N} g(n)f(n+k). \tag{11.9}$$

In general, neither ϕ_{fg} or ϕ_{gf} are necessarily symmetrical about $k = 0$, but are related by

$$\phi_{fg}(k) = \phi_{gf}(-k). \tag{11.10}$$

(Cf., Prob. 11.6)

PROBLEM 11.5 Show that $\phi(k)$ is symmetric about $k = 0$; that is, show that

$$\phi(k) = \phi(-k). \tag{11.11}$$

Solution: From the definition (11.5) of autocorrelation,

$$\phi(k) = \overline{f(n)\, f(n+k)} \qquad \text{and} \qquad \phi(-k) = \overline{f(n)\, f(n-k)}.$$

Making the transformation of variable $m = n - k$, $\phi(-k) = \overline{f(m+k)\, f(m)}$, or $\phi(-k) = \overline{f(n+k)\, f(n)}$ on substituting the dummy variable m for n. Hence, $\phi(k) = \phi(-k)$; that is, $\phi(k)$ is symmetric about $k = 0$.

PROBLEM 11.6 Establish (11.10).

Solution: From the definition (11.7) of the cross-correlation of $f(n)$ and $g(n)$,

$$\phi_{fg}(k) = \overline{f(n)\, g(n+k)}.$$

Making the transformation of variable $n = m - k$,

$$\phi_{fg}(k) = \overline{f(m-k)\, g(m)}.$$

Replacing m by n and rearranging,

$$\phi_{fg}(k) = \overline{g(n)f(n-k)}.$$

Comparison with (11.9) shows that $\phi_{fg}(k) = \phi_{gf}(-k)$.

PROBLEM 11.7 Show that $\phi(k)$ has a maximum point at $k = 0$; that is,

$$\phi(0) \geqslant \phi(k),$$

when $f(n)$ is real.

Solution: Equation (11.5) clearly shows that $\phi(0)$ is nonnegative; that is, $\phi(0) = \overline{[f(n)]^2} \geqslant 0$. Since $f(n)$ is real and the square of any real number is nonnegative,

$$[f(n) \pm f(n+k)]^2 \geqslant 0 \qquad \text{or} \qquad \overline{[f(n)]^2 \pm 2f(n)f(n+k) + [f(n+k)]^2} \geqslant 0.$$

Now, since $\phi(0) = \overline{[f(n)]^2} = \overline{[f(n+k)]^2}$ and $\phi(k) = \overline{f(n)f(n+k)}$ from (11.5),

$$\overline{[f(n)]^2 \pm 2f(n)f(n+k) + [f(n+k)]^2} = \overline{[f(n)]^2} \pm \overline{2f(n)f(n+k)} + \overline{[f(n+k)]^2}$$

$$= \phi(0) \pm 2\phi(k) + \phi(0).$$

Hence, $2\phi(0) \pm 2\phi(k) = 0$. Thus, $\phi(k)$ has a maximum at the origin since $\phi(0) \geqslant \phi(k)$.

PROBLEM 11.8   Show that the autocorrelation of the sum $h(n) = f(n) + g(n)$ is given by

$$\phi_h(k) = \phi_f(k) + \phi_g(k) + \phi_{fg}(k) + \phi_{gf}(k). \tag{11.12}$$

Solution: From (11.5), the autocorrelation $\phi_h(k)$ of $h(n) = f(n) + g(n)$ is

$$\phi_h(k) = \overline{h(n)h(n+k)}$$

$$= \overline{[f(n) + g(n)]\,[f(n+k) + g(n+k)]}$$

$$= \overline{f(n)f(n+k)} + \overline{g(n)g(n+k)} + \overline{f(n)g(n+k)} + \overline{g(n)f(n+k)}.$$

Using (11.5) and (11.7),

$$\phi_h(k) = \phi_f(k) + \phi_g(k) + \phi_{fg}(k) + \phi_{gf}(k).$$

The autocorrelation of the product $f(n)g(n)$ cannot, in general, be expressed in terms of the auto- and cross-correlations of f and g since

$$\overline{f(n)\,g(n)\,f(n+k)\,g(n+k)} \neq \overline{[f(n)\,f(n+k)]}\;\overline{[g(n)\,g(n+k)]}. \tag{11.13}$$

But if f and g are *independent*, the inequality in (11.13) becomes an equality. (Cf., Prob. 11.9.)

PROBLEM 11.9   If $f(n)$ and $g(n)$ are independent stationary processes, show that autocorrelation $\phi_h(k)$ of the process $h(n) = f(n)g(n)$ is given by

$$\phi_h(k) = \phi_f(k)\,\phi_g(k). \tag{11.14}$$

Solution: From (11.5), the autocorrelation of $h(n) = f(n)g(n)$ is

$$\phi_h(k) = \overline{h(n)\,h(n+k)} = \overline{f(n)\,g(n)\,f(n+k)\,g(n+k)} = \overline{[f(n)\,f(n+k)]}\;\overline{[g(n)\,g(n+k)]}.$$

Then, (11.5) establishes (11.14).

PROBLEM 11.10   If $f(n)$ and $g(n)$ are real stationary processes, show that

(a)
$$\phi_{fg}^2(k) \leqslant \phi_f(0)\,\phi_g(0), \tag{11.15}$$

(b)
$$2\,|\,\phi_{fg}(k)\,| \leqslant \phi_f(0) + \phi_g(0). \tag{11.16}$$

Solution: (a)   Since the square of any real number is nonnegative, for any real α,

$$\overline{[f(n) + \alpha g(n+k)]^2} = \overline{[f(n)]^2} + 2\alpha\overline{f(n)g(n+k)} + \alpha^2\overline{[g(n+k)]^2} \geqslant 0.$$

Now this quadratic in α is nonnegative; that is, its discriminant is nonpositive. Hence,

$$4\,\overline{[f(n)g(n+k)]}^2 - 4\left\{\overline{[f(n)]^2}\right\}\left\{\overline{[g(n+k)]^2}\right\} \leqslant 0.$$

From Prob. 11.7, $\phi_f(0) = \overline{[f(n)]^2} \geqslant 0$ and $\phi_g(0) = \overline{[g(n+k)]^2} \geqslant 0$, and from (11.7), $\phi_{fg}(k) = \overline{f(n)g(n+k)}$. Hence, $\phi_{fg}^2(k) \leqslant \phi_f(k)\phi_g(k)$.

(b) Since the geometric mean of two numbers does not exceed their arithmetic mean, (11.15) establishes (11.16).

PROBLEM 11.11 A discrete random process is generated by successive tossings of an unbiased coin. If the occurrence of a head is denoted by 1 and that of a tail by −1, determine the autocorrelation function of the process.

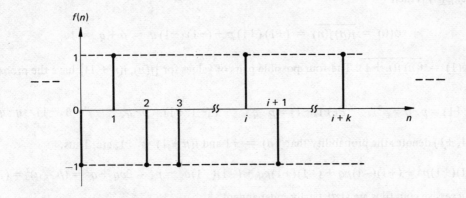

Fig. 11.4 Discrete random process generated by repeated tossings of a single coin.

Solution: The typical appearance of the process is shown in Fig. 11.4. The autocorrelation function of the process can be calculated using (11.5). Thus, $\phi(k) = \overline{f(n)f(n+k)}$; from which,

$$\phi(0) = \overline{f^2(n)}, \qquad \phi(1) = \overline{f(n)f(n+1)}, \cdots. \tag{11.17}$$

Table 11.1 shows the four possible pairs $(A-D)$ of values for $f(n)$ and $f(n+k)$, each occurring with probability $\frac{1}{4}$ for $k \neq 0$.

TABLE 11.1 Data for Prob. 11.11

Possibility	A	B	C	D
$f(n)$	+1	+1	−1	−1
$f(n+k)$	+1	−1	+1	−1

Since the coin is unbiased, $f(n)$ assumes the values of +1 and −1 with probability $\frac{1}{2}$. Hence,

$$\phi(0) = (+1)^2\, \tfrac{1}{2} + (-1)^2\, \tfrac{1}{2} = 1.$$

From Table 11.1 and (11.17), the values of $\phi(1), \phi(2), \cdots$ are

$$\phi(1) = (+1)(+1)\tfrac{1}{4} + (+1)(-1)\tfrac{1}{4} + (-1)(-1)\tfrac{1}{4} + (-1)(+1)\tfrac{1}{4} = 0, \qquad \phi(2) = \phi(3) = \cdots = 0.$$

Therefore, the autocorrelation of the process is

$$\phi(k) = 1 \quad \text{for } k = 0$$
$$= 0 \quad \text{for } k \neq 0.$$

PROBLEM 11.12 A discrete random process is generated by repeated tossings of a biased coin. If the occurrence of a head is denoted by 1 and that of a tail by -1, determine the autocorrelation function of the process. The probabilities p and q of obtaining a head and tail are unspecified. (Cf., Prob. 11.11.)

Solution: The discrete random process $f(n)$ generated by successive tossings of a coin takes on the value (for any arbitrary value of n) $+1$ with probability p, and -1 with probability $q = 1 - p$. From (11.5), the autocorrelation function of the process is given by

$$\phi(k) = \overline{f(n)\,f(n+k)}.$$

The quantity $\phi(0)$ is then

$$\phi(0) = \overline{f(n)f(n)} = (+1)(+1)p + (-1)(-1)q = p + q = 1.$$

Similarly, $\phi(1) = \overline{f(n)\,f(n+1)}$. The four possible pairs of values for $[f(n), f(n+1)]$ have the probabilities of occurrence

$$P(+1,+1) = p \cdot p = p^2, \qquad P(+1,-1) = p \cdot q, \qquad P(-1,+1) = p \cdot q, \qquad P(-1,-1) = q \cdot q = q^2,$$

where $P(+1,+1)$ denotes the probability that $f(n) = +1$ and $f(n+1) = +1$, etc. Thus,

$$\phi(1) = (+1)(+1)p^2 + (+1)(-1)pq + (-1)(+1)pq + (-1)(-1)q^2 = p^2 - 2pq + q^2 = (p-q)^2 = (2p-1)^2.$$

Since the successive coin flips are statistically independent,

$$\phi(2) = \phi(3) = \cdots = \phi(1) = (p-q)^2 = (2p-1)^2.$$

Therefore, the autocorrelation is

$$\phi(k) = 1 \qquad \text{for } k = 0$$
$$= (2p-1)^2 \quad \text{for } k \neq 0,$$

which reduces to the result obtained in Prob. 11.11 by setting $p = \frac{1}{2}$.

PROBLEM 11.13 The discrete stochastic process $f(n)$ defined in Prob. 11.11 is modified to produce a new process $g(n) = f(n-3)$. Calculate the cross-correlation function $\phi_{fg}(k)$ of the two processes.

Solution: From (11.7), the cross-correlation function of two processes $f(n)$ and $g(n)$ is given by

$$\phi_{fg}(k) = \overline{f(n)\,g(n+k)} = \overline{f(n)\,f(n+k-3)}$$

since $g(n) = f(n-3)$, and, hence, $g(n+k) = f(n+k-3)$.

From (11.5), the autocorrelation of $f(n)$ is $\phi(k) = \overline{f(n)\,f(n+k)}$, so that $\phi_{fg}(k) = \phi(k-3)$. Therefore, using the results of Prob. 11.11,

$$\phi_{fg}(k) = 1 \qquad \text{for } k = 3$$
$$= 0 \qquad \text{for } k \neq 3.$$

This result is in accordance with what is intuitively expected, viz., since $g(n)$ is an exact replica of $f(n)$ delayed by three units, the values of the two processes correlate perfectly when shifted three units in a positive direction. The two processes are completely uncorrelated for all other shifts as a consequence of the statistical independence of the successive coin flips used to generate $f(n)$.

PROBLEM 11.14 A discrete process $f(n)$ has an autocorrelation function $\phi(k)$. Show that the cross-correlation $\phi_{fg}(k)$ of $f(n)$ and $g(n) = af(n) + b$, where a and b are arbitrary constants, is given by

$$\phi_{fg}(k) = a\,\phi_f(k). \tag{11.18}$$

Assume that $f(n)$ has zero mean.

Solution: From (11.7), the cross-correlation of $f(n)$ and $g(n)$ is given by

$$\phi_{fg}(k) = \overline{f(n)g(n+k)} = \overline{f(n)\,[af(n+k)+b]} = \overline{af(n)f(n+k)+bf(n)} = \overline{af(n)f(n+k)+bf(n)}$$

since $g(n) = af(n) + b$. Now, from (11.5), $\overline{af(n)f(n+k)} = a\phi_f(k)$, and since the average value of $f(n)$ is zero, $\overline{bf(n)} = b\,\overline{f(n)} = 0$. Hence, the cross-correlation is $\phi_{fg}(k) = a\phi(k)$.

PROBLEM 11.15 A discrete process $f(n)$ has an autocorrelation function $\phi_f(k)$. Show that the autocorrelation function $\phi_g(k)$ of the process $g(n) = af(n) + b$, where a and b are arbitrary constants, is given by

$$\phi_g(k) = a^2\phi_f(k) + b^2. \tag{11.19}$$

Assume that $f(n)$ has zero mean.

Solution: From (11.5), the autocorrelation function of $g(n)$ can be written as

$$\phi_g(k) = \overline{g(n)\,g(n+k)} = \overline{[af(n)+b]\,[af(n+k)+b]}$$

$$= \overline{a^2 f(n)\,f(n+k) + abf(n+k) + abf(n) + b^2}$$

$$= a^2\overline{f(n)\,f(n+k)} + ab\,\overline{f(n+k)} + ab\,\overline{f(n)} + b^2$$

since $g(n) = af(n) + b$. The term $\overline{f(n)\,f(n+k)}$ is by definition equal to $\phi_f(k)$ while the terms $\overline{f(n+k)}$ and $\overline{f(n)}$ are both equal to zero since the process $f(n)$ has zero mean. Thus, $\phi_g(k) = a^2\phi_f(k) + b^2$.

PROBLEM 11.16 Two statistically independent discrete stochastic processes $f_1(n)$ and $f_2(n)$ are combined to form a new process $g(n) = f_1(n) + f_2(n)$. If the autocorrelation functions of $f_1(n)$ and $f_2(n)$ are given by

$$\phi_{f_1}(k) = \left(\tfrac{1}{2}\right)^{|k|} \qquad \text{and} \qquad \phi_{f_2}(k) = \left(\tfrac{1}{3}\right)^{|k|},$$

determine the autocorrelation function $\phi_g(k)$ of $g(n)$. Assume that $\overline{f_1(n)} = \overline{f_2(n)} = 0$.

Solution: From the result (11.12) of Prob. 11.8,

$$\phi_g(k) = \phi_{f_1}(k) + \phi_{f_2}(k) + \phi_{f_1 f_2}(k) + \phi_{f_2 f_1}(k).$$

However, since $f_1(n)$ and $f_2(n)$ are statistically independent and have zero mean, $\phi_{f_2 f_1}(k) = \phi_{f_1 f_2}(k) = 0$. Thus,

$$\phi_g(k) = \phi_{f_1}(k) + \phi_{f_2}(k) = \left(\tfrac{1}{2}\right)^{|k|} + \left(\tfrac{1}{3}\right)^{|k|}.$$

11.3 Linear System Relationships

A discrete system is said to be *time-invariant* if an arbitrary input $f(n)$ produces an output $g(n)$, and the shifted input $f(n + j)$ produces the output $g(n + j)$, where j is an arbitrary integer.

The *unit sample response* $h(n)$ is the output of a time-invariant discrete system when the input is

$$f_0(n) = 1 \quad \text{for } n = 0$$

$$= 0 \quad \text{for } n \neq 0.$$

It is analogous to the unit impulse response of continuous systems.

A discrete system is said to be *linear* if arbitrary inputs $f_1(n)$ and $f_2(n)$ produce outputs $g_1(n)$ and $g_2(n)$, respectively, and the input $af_1(n) + bf_2(n)$ produces the output $ag_1(n) + bg_2(n)$, where a and b are arbitrary constants.

A discrete linear system is characterized by its unit sample response $h(n)$, which is used to calculate system outputs for arbitrary inputs. (Cf., Fig. 11.5.)

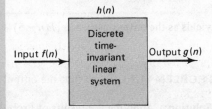

Fig. 11.5 A discrete linear system characterized by its unit sample response.

Note that a discrete linear system is not necessarily time-invariant although all systems considered in this chapter are assumed time-invariant.

In the case of continuous linear systems, the system output resulting from an arbitrary applied input is given in terms of the input and the unit impulse response by the convolution integral. In the case of discrete linear systems, this relationship becomes the *convolution summation* and can be written as

$$g(n) = \sum_{k=-\infty}^{\infty} f(k)h(n-k) \tag{11.20a}$$

$$= f(n) * h(n) \tag{11.20b}$$

$$= \sum_{k=-\infty}^{\infty} h(k)f(n-k) \tag{11.20c}$$

$$= h(n) * f(n), \tag{11.20d}$$

where $f(n)$ is the system input, $h(n)$ is the system unit sample response, $g(n)$ is the system output, and the shorthand notation $*$ denotes the convolution summations.

PROBLEM 11.17 The input to a discrete linear system whose unit sample response is $h(n)$ is given by

$$f(n) = c_1 \quad \text{for } n = 5$$

$$= c_2 \quad \text{for } n = 10$$

$$= 0 \quad \text{for } n \neq 5 \text{ and } n \neq 10.$$

Determine the output $g(n)$ of the system by using (a) (11.20a), (b) (11.20c), and (c) the properties of linearity and time-invariance.

Solution: (a) Using (11.20a) and retaining only the nonvanishing terms,

$$g(n) = f(5)h(n-5) + f(10)h(n-10) = c_1 h(n-5) + c_2 h(n-10).$$

(b) Using (11.20c), the two nonvanishing terms are those for which $f(n-k) = f(5)$ and $f(n-k) = f(10)$. Thus,

$$g(n) = h(n-5)f(5) + h(n-10)f(10) = c_1 h(n-5) + c_2 h(n-10).$$

(c) From the principle of linearity, if the response to a unit sample is $h(n)$, then the response to a sample of amplitude c_1 is $c_1 h(n)$. From the principle of time-invariance, if the response to an input is $c_1 h(n)$, then the response to the same input delayed by five units is $c_1 h(n-5)$. Similarly, the response to an input

$$f_2(n) = c_2 \quad \text{for } n = 10$$

$$= 0 \quad \text{for } n \neq 10$$

is $c_2 h(n-10)$. Application of the principle of linearity to the sum $f_1(n) + f_2(n)$, where

$$f_1(n) = c_1 \quad \text{for } n = 5$$

$$= 0 \quad \text{for } n \neq 5,$$

yields as the output $g(n) = c_1 h(n-5) + c_2 h(n-10)$.

PROBLEM 11.18 Show that the output of a discrete linear system is given by either (11.20a) or (11.20c).

Solution: Applying the results of Prob. 11.17, the output to an input

$$f(n) = f(k) \quad \text{for } n = k$$

$$= 0 \quad \text{for } n \neq k$$

is equal to $f(k)h(n - k)$. Since the actual input to the system $f(n)$ is equal to the superposition of inputs $\cdots$, $f(-1), f(0), f(1), \cdots$, from the principle of linearity, the output $g(n)$ is

$$g(n) = \sum_{k=-\infty}^{\infty} f(k)h(n-k).$$

By the change of variable $m = n - k$, $g(n)$ can be written as

$$g(n) = \sum_{k=-\infty}^{\infty} f(n-m)h(m).$$

Replacing the dummy variable m by k,

$$g(n) = \sum_{m=-\infty}^{\infty} h(k)f(n-k).$$

PROBLEM 11.19 Determine the response of a discrete linear system to an input

$$f(n) = \alpha^n \quad \text{for } n \geqslant 0$$
$$= 0 \quad \text{for } n < 0$$

if the unit sample response is

$$h(n) = \beta^n \quad \text{for } n \geqslant 0$$
$$= 0 \quad \text{for } n < 0,$$

where $|\alpha| < 1$ and $|\beta| < 1$.

Solution: From (11.20a), the system output is given by

$$g(n) = \sum_{k=-\infty}^{\infty} f(k)h(n-k).$$

Since $f(k) = 0$ for $k < 0$ and $h(n-k) = 0$ for $k > n$,

$$g(n) = \sum_{k=0}^{n} f(k)h(n-k).$$

Substituting for $f(k)$ and $h(n-k)$,

$$g(n) = \sum_{k=0}^{n} \alpha^k \beta^{(n-k)} \quad \text{for } n \geqslant 0$$
$$= 0 \quad \text{for } n < 0.$$

The sum can be written as

$$\sum_{k=0}^{\infty} \alpha^k \beta^{(n-k)} = \beta^n \sum_{k=0}^{n} \alpha^k \beta^{-k} = \beta^n \sum_{k=0}^{n} \left(\frac{\alpha}{\beta}\right)^k = \beta^n \left[\frac{1-(\alpha/\beta)^{n+1}}{1-(\alpha/\beta)}\right],$$

where the formula for the sum of a finite geometric series has been used. Thus,

$$g(n) = \frac{\beta^{n+1} - \alpha^{n+1}}{\beta - \alpha} \quad \text{for } n \geqslant 0$$
$$= 0 \quad \text{for } n < 0.$$

PROBLEM 11.20 Determine the response of a discrete linear system to an input

$$f(n) = \beta^n \quad \text{for } n \geq 0$$
$$= 0 \quad \text{for } n < 0,$$

and unit sample response

$$h(n) = \alpha^n \quad \text{for } n \geq 0$$
$$= 0 \quad \text{for } n < 0,$$

where $|\alpha| < 1$ and $|\beta| < 1$. (Cf., Prob. 11.19.)

Solution: Comparison of (11.20a) and (11.20c) shows that the output $g(n)$ is unaffected by an interchange of $f(k)$ and $h(k)$. Thus,

$$g(n) = \frac{\beta^{n+1} - \alpha^{n+1}}{\beta - \alpha} \quad \text{for } n \geq 0$$
$$= 0 \quad \text{for } n < 0.$$

PROBLEM 11.21 Two discrete linear systems with unit sample responses $h_1(n)$ and $h_2(n)$ are cascaded as shown in Fig. 11.6. The output of the first system $g_1(n)$ provides the input to the second. Express the output $g_2(n)$ in terms of the input $f_1(n)$ and the unit sample responses.

Solution: Using (11.20b), the outputs $g_1(n)$ and $g_2(n)$ are given by

$$g_1(n) = f_1(n) * h_1(n),$$
$$g_2(n) = g_1(n) * h_2(n).$$

Substituting for $g_1(n)$,

$$g_2(n) = f_1(n) * h_1(n) * h_2(n).$$

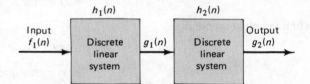

Fig. 11.6 Cascade of two discrete linear systems with unit sample responses $h_1(n)$ and $h_2(n)$.

Thus, the cascade of the two systems has an equivalent unit sample response $h_e(n)$ given by the convolution of $h_1(n)$ and $h_2(n)$; that is, $h_e(n) = h_1(n) * h_2(n)$ and $g_2(n) = f_1(n) * h_e(n)$.

11.4 Linear Systems with Stochastic Inputs

If a discrete stochastic process $f(n)$ is applied as the input to a discrete linear system, the output $g(n)$ is also a discrete stochastic process.

The *autocorrelation functions* $\phi_f(k)$ and $\phi_g(k)$ of the input $f(n)$ and the output $g(n)$ are given by

$$\phi_f(k) = \overline{f(n)f(n+k)}, \tag{11.21}$$
$$\phi_g(k) = \overline{g(n)g(n+k)}. \tag{11.22}$$

Since $g(n)$ is related to $f(n)$ by the convolution summation, $\phi_g(k)$ can be expressed in terms of $\phi_f(k)$ and the unit sample response of the system $h(n)$. Thus,

$$\phi_g(k) = \sum_{i=\infty}^{\infty} \sum_{j=-\infty}^{\infty} h(i)h(i+j)\phi_f(k-j). \tag{11.23}$$

(Cf., Prob. 11.22.)

The *cross-correlation function* $\phi_{fg}(k)$ of $f(n)$ and $g(n)$ is given by

$$\phi_{fg}(k) = \overline{f(n)g(n+k)}. \tag{11.24}$$

Using the convolution summation, $\phi_{fg}(k)$ can be expressed in terms of $\phi_f(k)$ by

$$\phi_{fg}(k) = \sum_{j=-\infty}^{\infty} h(j)\phi_f(k-j). \qquad (11.25)$$

(Cf., Prob. 11.23.)

It is assumed throughout that the input process is stationary and that $\overline{f(n)}$ and $\overline{f^2(n)}$ exist and are finite.

PROBLEM 11.22 Verify (11.23).

Solution: From (11.20c), the output $g(n)$ of a discrete linear system is given in terms of the input $f(n)$ and the unit sample response $h(n)$ by

$$g(n) = \sum_{i=-\infty}^{\infty} h(i)f(n-i).$$

Substituting for $g(n)$ in (11.11),

$$\phi_g(k) = \overline{g(n)g(n+k)} = \overline{\sum_{i=-\infty}^{\infty} h(i)f(n-i) \sum_{j=-\infty}^{\infty} h(j)f(n+k-j)}.$$

Changing the variable in the second summation from j to $i+j$,

$$\phi_g(k) = \overline{\sum_{i=-\infty}^{\infty} h(i)f(n-i) \sum_{j=-\infty}^{\infty} h(i+j)f(n-i+k-j)}$$

$$= \sum_{i=-\infty}^{\infty} \sum_{j=-\infty}^{\infty} h(i)h(i+j)\overline{f(n-i)f(n-i+k-j)}$$

$$= \sum_{i=-\infty}^{\infty} \sum_{j=-\infty}^{\infty} h(i)h(i+j)\phi_f(k-j).$$

PROBLEM 11.23 Verify (11.25).

Solution: From (11.24), the cross-correlation of the input $f(n)$ and output $g(n)$ of a discrete linear system is $\phi_{fg}(k) = \overline{f(n)g(n+k)}$. Using the convolution summation,

$$\phi_{fg}(k) = \overline{f(n) \sum_{j=-\infty}^{\infty} h(j)f(n+k-j)} = \sum_{j=-\infty}^{\infty} h(j)\overline{f(n)f(n+k-j)} = \sum_{j=-\infty}^{\infty} h(j)\phi_f(k-j).$$

PROBLEM 11.24 A discrete random process $f(n)$ applied to a discrete linear system produces an output $g(n)$. A process $p(n)$ is defined by

$$p(n) = f(n+i) - g(n).$$

Show that the mean-squared value $\overline{p^2(n)}$ of $p(n)$ in terms of the correlation functions $\phi_f(k)$, $\phi_g(k)$, and $\phi_{fg}(k)$ of $f(n)$ and $g(n)$ is given by

$$\overline{p^2(n)} = \phi_f(0) - 2\phi_{gf}(i) + \phi_g(0) \qquad \text{or} \qquad \overline{p^2(n)} = \phi_f(0) - 2\phi_{fg}(-i) + \phi_g(0).$$

Solution: The mean-squared value of $p(n)$ is given by

$$\overline{p^2(n)} = \overline{[f(n+i) - g(n)]^2} = \overline{f(n+i)\,f(n+i) - 2g(n)\,f(n+i) + g(n)\,g(n)}$$

$$= \overline{f(n+i)\,f(n+i)} - \overline{2g(n)\,f(n+i)} + \overline{g(n)\,g(n)}.$$

From (11.21-2), $\phi_f(0) = \overline{f(n+i)\,f(n+i)}$ and $\phi_g(0) = \overline{g(n)\,g(n)}$, and from (11.24) and Prob. 11.5, $\phi_{gf}(i) = \overline{g(n)\,f(n+i)} = \overline{f(m)\,g(m-i)} = \phi_{fg}(-i)$. Substituting these values immediately yields the required results.

PROBLEM 11.25 Determine the autocorrelation function of the output of a discrete linear system whose unit sample response is $h(n)$ if the input autocorrelation function is given by

$$\phi_f(k) = 1 \quad \text{for } k = 0$$
$$= 0 \quad \text{for } k \neq 0.$$

Solution: The autocorrelation of the system output is,

$$\phi(k) = \sum_{i=-\infty}^{\infty} \sum_{j=-\infty}^{\infty} h(i)\,h(i+j)\,\phi_f(k-j). \qquad [11.23]$$

The autocorrelation function $\phi_f(k)$ corresponds to a discrete random process which is analogous to white noise in the case of continuous random processes. Since $\phi_f(k-j)$ vanishes except when $j = k$, $\phi_g(k)$ becomes

$$\phi_g(k) = \sum_{i=-\infty}^{\infty} h(i)\,h(i+j)\,\phi_f(k-j)\big|_{j=k} = \sum_{i=-\infty}^{\infty} h(i)\,h(i+k).$$

PROBLEM 11.26 Determine the autocorrelation function of the output of a discrete linear system if

$$h(n) = \alpha^n \quad \text{for } n \geqslant 0 \text{ and } |\alpha| < 1 \qquad \text{and} \qquad \phi_f(k) = 1 \quad \text{for } k = 0$$
$$= 0 \quad \text{for } n < 0, \qquad\qquad\qquad\qquad = 0 \quad \text{for } k \neq 0.$$

Solution: Using the results of Prob. 11.25, the autocorrelation of the output is given by

$$\phi_g(k) = \sum_{i=-\infty}^{\infty} h(i)\,h(i+k).$$

Substituting for $h(n)$, $k \geqslant 0$,

$$\phi_g(k) = \sum_{i=0}^{\infty} \alpha^i\,\alpha^{i+k} = \alpha^k \sum_{i=0}^{\infty} \alpha^{2i} = \frac{\alpha^k}{1-\alpha^2}.$$

From Prob. 11.5, an autocorrelation function is symmetric about $k = 0$; that is, $\phi_g(k) = \phi_g(-k)$. Therefore,

$$\phi_g(k) = \frac{\alpha^{-k}}{1-\alpha^2} \quad \text{for } k < 0, \qquad \text{or} \qquad \phi_g(k) = \frac{\alpha^{|k|}}{1-\alpha^2} \quad \text{for } k = 0, \pm 1, \pm 2, \cdots.$$

PROBLEM 11.27 For the conditions of Prob. 11.26, determine the cross-correlation function between the input and the output.

Solution: From (11.25), the cross-correlation function of the input $f(n)$ and the output $g(n)$ is

$$\phi_{fg}(k) = \sum_{j=-\infty}^{\infty} h(j)\,\phi_f(k-j).$$

Since $\phi_f(k-j) = 1$ for $k = j$ and $\phi_f(k-j) = 0$ for $k \neq j$, $\phi_{fg}(k) = h(k)$. Thus,

$$\phi_{fg}(k) = \alpha^k \quad \text{for } k \geqslant 0$$

$$= 0 \quad \text{for } k < 0.$$

PROBLEM 11.28 The input to a discrete linear system has an autocorrelation function $\phi_f(k)$ given by

$$\phi_f(k) = a \quad \text{for } k = 0$$

$$= 0 \quad \text{for } k \neq 0.$$

Determine the mean-squared value of the output $g(n)$ if the system unit sample response is given by

$$h(n) = b\alpha^n \quad \text{for } n \geqslant 0 \text{ and } |\alpha| < 1$$

$$= 0 \quad \text{for } n < 0.$$

Solution: Using the results of Prob. 11.25, the autocorrelation function of the output is

$$\phi_g(k) = \sum_{i=-\infty}^{\infty} h(i)\,h(i+k).$$

Since $\phi_g(k) = \overline{g(n)\,g(n+k)}$, the mean-squared value of the output $\overline{g^2(n)}$ is equal to $\phi_g(0)$. Thus, on substituting for $h(i)$,

$$\overline{g^2(n)} = \phi_g(0) = \sum_{i=-\infty}^{\infty} h^2(i) = \sum_{i=0}^{\infty} b^2\alpha^{2i} = \frac{b^2}{1-\alpha^2}.$$

11.5 Transforms, Power and Cross-Power Spectra

The *z-transform* $F(z)$ of a discrete signal $f(n)$ is given by

$$F(z) = \sum_{n=-\infty}^{\infty} f(n)z^{-n}. \tag{11.26}$$

The *transfer function* $H(z)$ of a discrete system with a unit sample response $h(n)$ is the z-transform given by

$$H(z) = \sum_{n=-\infty}^{\infty} h(n)z^{-n}. \tag{11.27}$$

The *z-transform $G(z)$ of the output of a discrete linear system in the transform domain* is the product of the z-transform $F(z)$ of the system input and the system transfer function $H(z)$; that is,

$$G(z) = F(z)\,H(z). \tag{11.28}$$

An equivalent transform formulation of the discrete system can be obtained directly from the Laplace transform of continuous systems. If the sequence of samples $f(n)$ are assumed to modulate (that is, multiply) a periodic train of unit impulses (that is, impulses of unit area), the z-transform of the modulated impulse train is equal to the Laplace transform of the impulse train with $z = e^{j\omega T}$, where ω is the angular frequency in radians, T is the period, and $j = \sqrt{-1}$.

Thus, the *spectrum* of a discrete signal $f(n)$ is the z-transform $F(z)$ of $f(n)$ with $z = e^{j\omega T}$. Since $e^{j\omega T} = e^{j(\omega T + 2\pi n)}$, $n = 0, \pm 1, \pm 2, \cdots$, the spectrum of a discrete signal is *periodic* in the frequency domain with period $\omega_\rho = 2\pi/T$.

The spectrum of a process is used by the time series analyst to determine the mechanism generating an observed time series, and by the communication theorist to study the behavior of stochastic processes — signals or noise — passing through linear devices.

The z-transforms $\Phi(z)$ and $\Phi_{fg}(z)$ of an autocorrelation function $\phi(k)$ and a cross-correlation function $\phi_{fg}(k)$ are given by

$$\Phi(z) = \sum_{k=-\infty}^{\infty} \phi(k)z^{-k}, \tag{11.29}$$

$$\Phi_{fg}(z) = \sum_{k=-\infty}^{\infty} \phi_{fg}(k)z^{-k}. \tag{11.30}$$

If $\Phi_f(z)$, $\Phi_g(z)$, and $H(z)$ are the transforms of the input $f(n)$, the output $g(n)$, and the transfer function of the system,

$$\Phi_g(z) = H(z^{-1})H(z)\Phi_f(z), \tag{11.31}$$

$$\Phi_{fg}(z) = H(z)\Phi_f(z). \tag{11.32}$$

The *power density spectrum* (or *spectral density*) of a discrete stochastic process is the z-transform of its autocorrelation $\phi_f(k)$ with $z = e^{j\omega T}$.

The *cross-power density spectrum* of two discrete processes $f(n)$ and $g(n)$ is the z-transform of their cross-correlation $\phi_{fg}(k)$ with $z = e^{j\omega T}$.

The power density spectrum of a real discrete stochastic process is always real and nonnegative. (Cf., Probs. 11.39-40.)

PROBLEM 11.29 Find the transform of a delayed unit sample $f(n)$; that is, $f(n) = 1$ for $n = j$ and $f(n) = 0$ for $n \neq j$.

Solution: From (11.26) and on substituting the given values, the transform of $f(n)$ *is*

$$F(z) = \sum_{n=-\infty}^{\infty} f(n)z^{-n} = f(j)z^{-j} = z^{-j}.$$

For a unit sample with zero delay, that is, at the origin, $F(z) = 1$. In this case, (11.28) shows that the transform of the output of a discrete linear system is equal to the transform $H(z)$ of the unit sample response, in accordance with the basic definition of $h(n)$.

PROBLEM 11.30 Determine the transform of $f(n)$ if

$$f(n) = \alpha^n \quad \text{for } n \geqslant 0 \text{ and } |\alpha| < 1$$

$$= 0 \quad \text{for } n < 0.$$

Solution: Substituting for $f(n)$ in the definition (11.26), the transform of $f(n)$ is

$$F(z) = \sum_{n=-\infty}^{\infty} = f(n)z^{-n} = \sum_{n=0}^{\infty} \alpha^n z^{-n} = \sum_{n=0}^{\infty} (\alpha z^{-1})^n = \frac{1}{1-\alpha z^{-1}}.$$

PROBLEM 11.31 Calculate the transform of the output of a discrete linear system whose unit sample response is

$$h(n) = \beta^n \quad \text{for } n \geqslant 0 \text{ and } |\beta| < 1$$

$$= 0 \quad \text{for } n > 0,$$

and whose input is

$$f(n) = \gamma^n \quad \text{for } n \geqslant 0 \text{ and } |\gamma| < 1$$
$$= 0 \quad \text{for } n < 0.$$

Solution: Using the results of Prob. 11.30, the transforms of $f(n)$ and $h(n)$ are given by

$$F(z) = \frac{1}{1 - \gamma z^{-1}}, \qquad H(z) = \frac{1}{1 - \beta z^{-1}}.$$

The transform of the output $g(n)$ is given by

$$G(z) = F(z)\, H(z) = \frac{1}{(1 - \gamma z^{-1})(1 - \beta z^{-1})}.$$

PROBLEM 11.32 Calculate the transfer function of a linear system whose unit sample response is $h(n) = \alpha^{|n|}$ for $|\alpha| < 1$.

Solution: Substituting the value of $h(n)$ in the definition (11.27), the transfer function is

$$H(z) = \sum_{n=-\infty}^{\infty} h(n)z^{-n} = \sum_{n=-\infty}^{\infty} \alpha^{|n|} z^{-n} = \sum_{n=-\infty}^{0} \alpha^{-n} z^{-n} + \sum_{n=0}^{\infty} \alpha^n z^{-n} - 1.$$

Replacing n by $-n$ in the first summation,

$$H(z) = \sum_{n=0}^{\infty} \alpha^n z^n + \sum_{n=0}^{\infty} \alpha^n z^{-n} - 1 = \frac{1}{1 - \alpha z} + \frac{1}{1 - \alpha z^{-1}} - 1 = \frac{1}{1 - \alpha z} + \frac{\alpha z^{-1}}{1 - \alpha z^{-1}}.$$

PROBLEM 11.33 The transform of a discrete signal $f(n)$ is given by

$$F(z) = \frac{z^{-1}(1 + z^{-1})}{(1 - z^{-1})^3}.$$

Evaluate $f(3)$.

Solution: From (11.26),

$$F(z) = \sum_{n=-\infty}^{\infty} f(n)z^{-n} = \cdots + f(2)z^{-2} + f(3)z^{-3} + f(4)z^{-4} + \cdots \,;$$

from which it is seen that $f(3)$ is the coefficient of z^{-3} in the series expansion of $F(z)$. Thus, by the process of long division,

$$F(z) = \frac{z^{-1}(1 + z^{-1})}{(1 - z^{-1})^3} = \frac{z^{-1} + z^{-2}}{1 - 3z^{-1} + 3z^{-2} - z^{-3}} = \cdots + 4z^{-2} + 9z^{-3} + \cdots \,;$$

that is, $f(3) = 9$.

PROBLEM 11.34 Verify (11.31).

Solution: The autocorrelation of the output of a discrete linear system is

$$\phi_g(k) = \sum_{i=-\infty}^{\infty} \sum_{j=-\infty}^{\infty} h(i)h(i+j)\phi_f(k-j). \qquad [11.23]$$

Multiplying both sides by z^{-k} and summing with respect to k results in

$$\sum_{k=-\infty}^{\infty} \phi_g(k)z^{-k} = \sum_{k=-\infty}^{\infty} \sum_{i=-\infty}^{\infty} \sum_{j=-\infty}^{\infty} z^{-k}h(i)h(i+j)\phi_f(k-j),$$

where the left-hand side of the equation is $\Phi_g(z)$. Since $z^{-k} = z^i z^{-i-j} z^{-k+j}$, $\Phi_g(z)$ can be written as

$$\Phi(z) = \sum_{k=-\infty}^{\infty} \sum_{i=-\infty}^{\infty} \sum_{j=-\infty}^{\infty} h(i)z^i h(i+j)z^{-i-j}\phi_f(k-j)z^{-k+j}.$$

Defining the new variables $m = i + j$ and $n = k - j$,

$$\Phi_g(k) = \sum_{i=-\infty}^{\infty} h(i)z^i \sum_{m=-\infty}^{\infty} h(m)z^{-m} \sum_{n=-\infty}^{\infty} \phi_f(n)z^{-n} = H(z^{-1})H(z)\Phi_f(z).$$

PROBLEM 11.35 Verify (11.32).

Solution: From (11.25), the cross-correlation of the input and output of a discrete linear system is given by

$$\phi_{fg}(k) = \sum_{j=-\infty}^{\infty} h(j)\phi_f(k-j).$$

Multiplying both sides of the equation by z^{-k} and summing with respect to k,

$$\sum_{k=-\infty}^{\infty} \phi_{fg}(k)z^{-k} = \sum_{k=-\infty}^{\infty} \sum_{j=-\infty}^{\infty} z^{-k}h(j)\phi_f(k-j) = \sum_{k=-\infty}^{\infty} \sum_{j=-\infty}^{\infty} h(j)z^{-j}\phi_f(k-j)z^{-k+j}.$$

Defining a new variable $n = k - j$, and noting that $\displaystyle\sum_{k=-\infty}^{\infty} \phi_{fg}(k)z^{-k} = \Phi_{fg}(z)$,

$$\Phi_{fg}(z) = \sum_{j=-\infty}^{\infty} h(j)z^{-j} \sum_{n=-\infty}^{\infty} \phi_f(n)z^{-n} = H(z)\phi_f(z).$$

PROBLEM 11.36 Determine the power density spectrum of a discrete random process whose autocorrelation function is given by

$$\phi_f(k) = A\beta^{|k|} \quad \text{for } |\beta| < 1.$$

Assume the spacing between adjacent samples in the process is $T = 1$.

Solution: The power density spectrum of the process can be found by first calculating the z-transform of $\phi_f(k)$. Thus, using the results of Prob. 11.32,

$$\Phi_f(z) = \sum_{k=-\infty}^{\infty} \phi_f(k)z^{-k} = \frac{A}{1-\beta z} + \frac{A\beta z^{-1}}{1-\beta z^{-1}}.$$

The power density spectrum is obtained in terms of the frequency variable ω by the substitution $z = e^{j\omega T}$ or since $T = 1$,

$$\Phi_f(e^{j\omega}) = A\left[\frac{1}{1-\beta e^{j\omega}} + \frac{\beta e^{-j\omega}}{1-\beta e^{-j\omega}}\right],$$

which is periodic in the frequency domain with period 2π rad/sec.

PROBLEM 11.37 The unit sample response of a discrete linear system is given by

$$h(n) = \alpha^n \quad \text{for } n \geqslant 0 \text{ and } |\alpha| < 1$$

$$= 0 \quad \text{for } n < 0.$$

The input to the system is a random process whose autocorrelation function is given by

$$\phi_f(k) = 1 \quad \text{for } k = 0$$

$$= 0 \quad \text{for } k \neq 0.$$

Determine the transform of the autocorrelation function of the output.

Solution: From (11.30), the transform of the autocorrelation of the output is $\Phi_g(z) = H(z^{-1})H(z)\Phi_f(z)$, where

$$\Phi_f(z) = \sum_{k=-\infty}^{\infty} \phi_f(k)z^{-k} \quad \text{and} \quad H(z) = \sum_{n=-\infty}^{\infty} h(n)z^{-n}.$$

Substituting for $\phi_f(k)$, $\Phi_f(z) = 1 \cdot z^0 = 1$. Using the results of Prob. 11.30, $H(z) = 1/(1-\alpha z^{-1})$. Thus, the required transform is

$$\Phi_g(z) = \frac{1}{1-\alpha z} \cdot \frac{1}{1-\alpha z^{-1}}.$$

PROBLEM 11.38 For the conditions of Prob. 11.37, determine the cross-power density spectrum of the input and output.

Solution: The z-transform of the cross-correlation of the input and the output is $\Phi_{fg}(z) = H(z)\Phi_f(z)$. Since $\Phi_f(z) = 1$ and $H(z) = 1/(1-\alpha z^{-1})$,

$$\Phi_{fg}(z) = \frac{1}{1-\alpha z^{-1}}.$$

The cross-power density spectrum is obtained by substituting $z = e^{j\omega T}$, where T is the sampling period and ω is the angular frequency in the expression for $\Phi_{fg}(z)$. Thus, the cross-power density spectrum is

$$\Phi_{fg}(e^{j\omega T}) = \frac{1}{1-\alpha e^{-j\omega T}}.$$

PROBLEM 11.39 A discrete stochastic process is generated by passing uncorrelated samples through a linear system whose unit sample response is $h(n)$. Show that the power density spectrum of the output is real and nonnegative.

Solution: The z-transform of the autocorrelation function of the output is given by $\Phi_g(z) = H(z^{-1})H(z)\Phi_f(z)$. Since the input $f(n)$ consists of uncorrelated samples, $\phi_f(k) = 1$ for $k = 0$, and $\phi_f(k) = 0$ for $k \neq 0$. Therefore, $\Phi_f(z) = 1$. Thus,

$$\Phi_g(z) = H(z^{-1})H(z).$$

Setting $z = e^{j\omega T}$, the power density spectrum is

$$\Phi_g(e^{j\omega T}) = H(e^{-j\omega T})H(e^{j\omega T}).$$

Since the functions $H(e^{-j\omega T})$ and $H(e^{j\omega T})$ are complex conjugates,

$$\Phi_g(e^{j\omega T}) = |H(e^{-j\omega T})|^2,$$

which is real and nonnegative.

PROBLEM 11.40 Determine if the function

$$\phi_f(k) = 1 \quad \text{for } k = 0$$

$$= \tfrac{3}{4} \quad \text{for } k = \pm 3$$

$$= 0 \quad \text{for } k \neq 0, k \neq \pm 3$$

can be an autocorrelation function.

Solution: Taking the z-transform of $\phi_f(k)$,

$$\Phi_f(z) = \sum_{k=-\infty}^{\infty} \phi_f(k) z^{-k} = 1 + \tfrac{3}{4} z^{-3} + \tfrac{3}{4} z^3.$$

Substituting $z = e^{j\omega T}$,

$$\Phi_f(e^{j\omega T}) = 1 + \tfrac{3}{4}[e^{-3j\omega T} + e^{3j\omega T}].$$

Since $e^{j\theta} = \cos\theta + j\sin\theta$, $e^{j\theta} + e^{-j\theta} = 2\cos\theta$. Hence,

$$\Phi_f(e^{j\omega T}) = 1 + \tfrac{3}{2}\cos 3\omega T.$$

Since $\cos 3\omega T$ varies in value between -1 and $+1$, $\Phi_f(e^{j\omega T})$ is not a nonnegative function of frequency. Therefore, $\phi_f(k)$ is not a possible autocorrelation function of a real discrete stochastic process.

11.6 Supplementary Problems

PROBLEM 11.41 A discrete random process is generated by repeated tosses of a fair die in which the value of the random variable is equal to the result of the tosses. Determine the average and mean-squared values of the process.
Answer: Average value = 3.5; mean-squared value = $15\tfrac{1}{6}$.

PROBLEM 11.42 Determine the autocorrelation function of the random process of Prob. 11.41.
Answer: $\phi(k) = 15\tfrac{1}{6}$ for $k = 0$
$\qquad\quad = 12\tfrac{1}{4}$ for $k = \pm 1, \pm 2, \cdots$.

PROBLEM 11.43 A pair of dice is used to generate two independent discrete random processes in the manner of Prob. 11.41. Determine the cross-correlation function of the two processes.
Answer: $\phi_{fg}(k) = 12\tfrac{1}{4}$, $k = 0, \pm 1, \pm 2, \cdots$.

PROBLEM 11.44 A discrete random process $f(n)$ is generated by repeated tosses of a coin in which the occurrence of a head is denoted by 1 and that of a tail by -1. A new process $g(n)$ is generated by

$$g(2n) = f(n) \quad \text{for } n = 0, \pm 1, \pm 2, \cdots, \quad \text{and} \quad g(n) = g(n+1) \quad \text{for } n \text{ even}.$$

Determine the autocorrelation function of the process $g(n)$.
Answer: $\phi_g(k) = 1$ for $k = 0$
$\qquad\quad = \tfrac{1}{2}$ for $k = \pm 1$
$\qquad\quad = 0$ for $k \neq 0$ and $k \neq \pm 1$.

PROBLEM 11.45 A discrete process $f(n)$ is defined by

$$f(n) = (-1)^{n+m},$$

where m is an arbitrary integer. Determine the correlation function $\phi_f(k)$.
Answer: $\phi_f(k) = (-1)^{|k|}$.

PROBLEM 11.46 Show that the autocorrelation function of the sum of two independent discrete random processes with zero means is equal to the sum of the autocorrelation functions of the individual processes.

PROBLEM 11.47 If the autocorrelation function of a process $f(n)$ is $\phi_f(k)$, determine the autocorrelation function of $g(n) = f(n) + C$.
Answer: $\phi_g(k) = \phi_f(k) + C^2 + 2C\bar{f}$.

PROBLEM 11.48   A random process $f(n)$ has an autocorrelation function $\phi_f(k)$. Evaluate the expected value of

$$[f(n+m) - f(n-m)]^2.$$

Answer: $2\phi_f(0) - 2\phi_f(2m)$.

PROBLEM 11.49   Show that if $f(n)$ is a discrete stationary random process, then $\lim\limits_{|k| \to \infty} \phi_f(k) = \{E[f(n)]\}^2$, where E denotes the expected value.

PROBLEM 11.50   A discrete random process $f(n)$ is applied to a linear system whose unit sample response is $h(n)$, producing an output $g(n)$. Express the mean-squared value of the quantity $p(n) = f(n+i) - g(n)$ in terms of $\phi_f(k)$ and $h(n)$.

Answer: $\overline{p^2(n)} = \phi_f(0) - 2 \sum\limits_{k=-\infty}^{\infty} h(k)\phi_f(i+k) + \sum\limits_{m=-\infty}^{\infty} \sum\limits_{k=-\infty}^{\infty} h(m)h(m+k)\phi_f(k).$

PROBLEM 11.51   Using the results of Prob. 11.50, show that when the input consists of uncorrelated samples of zero mean, that is, $\phi_f(k) = 1$ for $k = 0$ and $\phi_f(k) = 0$ for $k \neq 0$, then the minimum mean-squared error with which future values of $f(n)$ can be linearly predicted is equal to or greater than $\overline{f^2(n)}$.
[*Hint:* Cf., Prob. 11.50].

PROBLEM 11.52   A discrete linear system has a unit sample response $h(n)$. If the cross-correlation function between the input and output is given by

$$\phi_{fg}(k) = 2h(k) + h(k+1) + h(k-1),$$

determine the autocorrelation function of the input.
Answer: $\phi_f(k) = 2 \quad$ for $k = 0$
$\qquad\qquad = 1 \quad$ for $k = \pm 1$
$\qquad\qquad = 0 \quad$ for $k = \pm 2, \pm 3, \cdots$.

PROBLEM 11.53   Show that the power density spectrum of the sum of n independent random processes of zero mean is equal to the sum of the power density spectra of the individual processes.

PROBLEM 11.54   Determine the power density spectrum of uncorrelated samples of zero mean and unit variance.
Answer: $\Phi_f(z) = 1$.

PROBLEM 11.55   A discrete random process has a power density spectrum given by

$$\Phi_f(z) = \frac{1}{1 - \alpha z} \frac{1}{1 - \alpha z^{-1}}.$$

Determine both the transform of the unit sample response of the linear system which will convert the process into uncorrelated samples of mean zero and variance one, and the corresponding unit sample response.
Answer: $H(z) = 1 - \alpha z$, $h(0) = 1$, $h(1) = -\alpha$, $h(n) = 0$ for $n \neq 0, 1$.

PROBLEM 11.56   The power density spectrum of a discrete random process is given by

$$\Phi_f(z) = \frac{1}{\frac{7}{6} - \frac{1}{2}z - \frac{1}{3}z^{-1}}.$$

Does this spectrum correspond to a real process?
Answer: No.

STATISTICAL TABLES

Table I. Table of Integrals

Rational algebraic integrals

1. $\int x^m \, dx = \dfrac{x^{m+1}}{m+1}, \quad m \neq -1$

2. $\int \dfrac{dx}{x} = \log_e x$

3. $\int (ax+b)^m \, dx = \dfrac{(ax+b)^{m+1}}{a(m+1)}, \quad m \neq -1$

4. $\int \dfrac{dx}{ax+b} = \dfrac{1}{a} \log_e (ax+b)$

5. $\int \dfrac{x \, dx}{ax+b} = \dfrac{1}{a^2} [ax + b - b \log_e (ax+b)]$

6. $\int \dfrac{x \, dx}{(ax+b)^2} = \dfrac{1}{a^2} \left[\dfrac{b}{ax+b} + \log_e (ax+b) \right]$

7. $\int \dfrac{dx}{x(ax+b)} = \dfrac{1}{b} \log_e \dfrac{x}{ax+b}$

8. $\int \dfrac{dx}{x(ax+b)^2} = \dfrac{1}{b(ax+b)} + \dfrac{1}{b^2} \log_e \dfrac{x}{ax+b}$

9. $\int \dfrac{dx}{x^2(ax+b)} = -\dfrac{1}{bx} + \dfrac{a}{b^2} \log_e \dfrac{ax+b}{x}$

10. $\int \dfrac{dx}{x^2(ax+b)^2} = -\dfrac{2ax+b}{b^2 x(ax+b)} + \dfrac{2a}{b^2} \log_e \dfrac{ax+b}{x}$

11. $\int \dfrac{dx}{x^2 + a^2} = \dfrac{1}{a} \tan^{-1} \dfrac{x}{a}$

12. $\int \dfrac{dx}{x^2 - a^2} = \dfrac{1}{2a} \log \dfrac{x-a}{x+a} = -\dfrac{1}{a} \tanh^{-1} \dfrac{a}{x}$

13. $\int \dfrac{dx}{(ax^2+b)^m} = \dfrac{x}{2(m-1)b(ax^2+b)^{m-1}} + \dfrac{2m-3}{2(m-1)b} \int \dfrac{dx}{(ax^2+b)^{m-1}}, \quad m \neq 1$

14. $\int \dfrac{x \, dx}{(ax^2+b)^m} = -\dfrac{1}{2(m-1)a(ax^2+b)^{m-1}}, \quad m \neq 1$

15. $\int \dfrac{x\,dx}{ax^2 + b} = \dfrac{1}{2a}\log_e(ax^2 + b)$

16. $\int \dfrac{x^2\,dx}{ax^2 + b} = \dfrac{x}{a} - \dfrac{b}{a}\int \dfrac{dx}{ax^2 + b}$

17. $\int \dfrac{x^2\,dx}{(ax^2 + b)^m} = -\dfrac{x}{2(m-1)a(ax^2 + b)^{m-1}} + \dfrac{1}{2(m-1)a}\int \dfrac{dx}{(ax^2 + b)^{m-1}},\quad m \neq 1$

18. $\int \dfrac{dx}{ax^3 + b} = \dfrac{k}{3b}\left(\sqrt{3}\,\tan^{-1}\dfrac{2x - k}{k\sqrt{3}} + \log_e\dfrac{k + x}{\sqrt{k^2 - kx + x^2}}\right),\quad$ where $k = \sqrt[3]{b/a}$

19. $\int \dfrac{x\,dx}{ax^3 + b} = \dfrac{1}{3ak}\left(\sqrt{3}\,\tan^{-1}\dfrac{2x - k}{k\sqrt{3}} - \log_e\dfrac{k + x}{\sqrt{k^2 - kx + x^2}}\right),\quad$ where $k = \sqrt[3]{b/a}$

20. $\int \dfrac{dx}{x(ax^n + b)} = \dfrac{1}{bn}\log_e\dfrac{x^n}{ax^n + b}$

Let $X = ax^2 + bx + c$ and $q = b^2 - 4ac$.

21. $\int \dfrac{dx}{X} = \dfrac{1}{\sqrt{q}}\log_e\dfrac{2ax + b - \sqrt{q}}{2ax + b + \sqrt{q}},\quad$ when $q > 0$

For the case $q = 0$, use equation 3 with $m = -2$.

22. $\int \dfrac{dx}{X} = \dfrac{2}{\sqrt{-q}}\,\tan^{-1}\dfrac{2ax + b}{\sqrt{-q}},\quad$ when $q < 0$

23. $\int \dfrac{dx}{X^n} = -\dfrac{2ax + b}{(n-1)qX^{n-1}} - \dfrac{2(2n-3)a}{q(n-1)}\int \dfrac{dx}{X^{n-1}},\quad n \neq 1$

24. $\int \dfrac{x\,dx}{X} = \dfrac{1}{2a}\log_e X - \dfrac{b}{2a}\int \dfrac{dx}{X}$

25. $\int \dfrac{x^2\,dx}{X} = \dfrac{x}{a} - \dfrac{b}{2a^2}\log_e X + \dfrac{b^2 - 2ac}{2a^2}\int \dfrac{dx}{X}$

Integrals involving $\sqrt{ax + b}$:

26. $\int x\sqrt{ax + b}\,dx = \dfrac{2(3ax - 2b)\sqrt{(ax + b)^3}}{15a^2}$

27. $\int x^2\sqrt{ax + b}\,dx = \dfrac{2(15a^2x^2 - 12abx + 8b^2)\sqrt{(ax + b)^3}}{105a^3}$

28. $\int x^m\sqrt{ax + b}\,dx = \dfrac{2}{a(2m + 3)}\left[x^m\sqrt{(ax + b)^3} - mb\int x^{m-1}\sqrt{ax + b}\,dx\right]$

29. $\int \dfrac{\sqrt{ax + b}\,dx}{x} = 2\sqrt{ax + b} + \sqrt{b}\log_e\dfrac{\sqrt{ax + b} - \sqrt{b}}{\sqrt{ax + b} + \sqrt{b}},\quad b > 0$

$\qquad\qquad = 2\sqrt{ax + b} - 2\sqrt{-b}\,\tan^{-1}\sqrt{\dfrac{ax + b}{-b}},\quad b < 0$

30. $\int \dfrac{\sqrt{ax + b}\,dx}{x^m} = -\dfrac{1}{(m-1)b}\left[\dfrac{\sqrt{(ax + b)^3}}{x^{m-1}} + \dfrac{(2m - 5)a}{2}\int \dfrac{\sqrt{ax + b}\,dx}{x^{m-1}}\right],\quad m \neq 1$

31. $\int \dfrac{x\,dx}{\sqrt{ax + b}} = \dfrac{2(ax - 2b)}{3a^2}\sqrt{ax + b}$

32. $\int \dfrac{x^2\,dx}{\sqrt{ax + b}} = \dfrac{2(3a^2x^2 - 4abx + 8b^2)}{15a^3}\sqrt{ax + b}$

33. $\int \dfrac{x^m\, dx}{\sqrt{ax+b}} = \dfrac{2}{a(2m+1)}\left(x^m\sqrt{ax+b} - mb\int \dfrac{x^{m-1}\, dx}{\sqrt{ax+b}}\right), \quad m \neq 1$

34. $\int \dfrac{dx}{x\sqrt{ax+b}} = \dfrac{1}{\sqrt{b}}\, \log_e \dfrac{\sqrt{ax+b}-\sqrt{b}}{\sqrt{ax+b}+\sqrt{b}}, \quad b > 0$

$$= \dfrac{2}{\sqrt{-b}}\, \tan^{-1}\sqrt{\dfrac{ax+b}{-b}}, \quad b < 0$$

35. $\int \dfrac{dx}{x^m\sqrt{ax+b}} = -\dfrac{\sqrt{ax+b}}{(m-1)bx^{m-1}} - \dfrac{(2m-3)a}{(2m-2)b}\int \dfrac{dx}{x^{m-1}\sqrt{ax+b}}, \quad m \neq 1$

Integrals involving $\sqrt{x^2 \pm a^2}$ and $\sqrt{a^2 - x^2}$:

36. $\int \sqrt{x^2 \pm a^2}\, dx = \frac{1}{2}\left[x\sqrt{x^2 \pm a^2} \pm a^2 \log_e\left(x + \sqrt{x^2 \pm a^2}\right)\right]$

37. $\int \sqrt{a^2 - x^2}\, dx = \frac{1}{2}\left(x\sqrt{a^2 - x^2} + a^2 \sin^{-1}\dfrac{x}{a}\right)$

38. $\int \dfrac{dx}{\sqrt{x^2 \pm a^2}} = \log_e\left(x + \sqrt{x^2 \pm a^2}\right)$

39. $\int \dfrac{dx}{\sqrt{a^2 - x^2}} = \sin^{-1}\left(\dfrac{x}{a}\right)$

40. $\int x\sqrt{x^2 \pm a^2}\, dx = \frac{1}{3}\sqrt{(x^2 \pm a^2)^3}$

41. $\int x^2\sqrt{x^2 \pm a^2}\, dx = \dfrac{x}{4}\sqrt{(x^2 \pm a^2)^3} \mp \dfrac{a^2}{8}\left[x\sqrt{x^2 \pm a^2} \pm a^2 \log_e\left(x + \sqrt{x^2 \pm a^2}\right)\right]$

42. $\int x\sqrt{a^2 - x^2}\, dx = -\frac{1}{3}\sqrt{(a^2 - x^2)^3}$

43. $\int x^2\sqrt{a^2 - x^2}\, dx = -\dfrac{x}{4}\sqrt{(a^2 - x^2)^3} + \dfrac{a^2}{8}\left[x\sqrt{a^2 - x^2} + a^2 \sin^{-1}\left(\dfrac{x}{a}\right)\right]$

44. $\int \dfrac{\sqrt{a^2 \pm x^2}}{x}\, dx = \sqrt{a^2 \pm x^2} - a \log_e\left(\dfrac{a + \sqrt{a^2 \pm x^2}}{x}\right)$

45. $\int \dfrac{\sqrt{x^2 - a^2}}{x}\, dx = \sqrt{x^2 - a^2} - a \cos^{-1}\left(\dfrac{a}{x}\right)$

46. $\int \dfrac{\sqrt{x^2 \pm a^2}}{x^2}\, dx = -\dfrac{\sqrt{x^2 \pm a^2}}{x} + \log_e\left(x + \sqrt{x^2 \pm a^2}\right)$

47. $\int \dfrac{\sqrt{a^2 - x^2}}{x^2}\, dx = -\dfrac{\sqrt{a^2 - x^2}}{x} - \sin^{-1}\left(\dfrac{x}{a}\right)$

48. $\int \dfrac{x\, dx}{\sqrt{a^2 - x^2}} = -\sqrt{a^2 - x^2}$

49. $\int \dfrac{x\, dx}{\sqrt{x^2 \pm a^2}} = \sqrt{x^2 \pm a^2}$

50. $\int \dfrac{x^2\, dx}{\sqrt{x^2 \pm a^2}} = \dfrac{x}{2}\sqrt{x^2 \pm a^2} \mp \dfrac{a^2}{2}\log_e\left(x + \sqrt{x^2 \pm a^2}\right)$

51. $\int \dfrac{x^2\, dx}{\sqrt{a^2 - x^2}} = -\dfrac{x}{2}\sqrt{a^2 - x^2} + \dfrac{a^2}{2}\sin^{-1}\left(\dfrac{x}{a}\right)$

52. $\int \dfrac{dx}{x\sqrt{x^2 - a^2}} = \dfrac{1}{a}\,\cos^{-1}\!\left(\dfrac{a}{x}\right)$

53. $\int \dfrac{dx}{x\sqrt{a^2 \pm x^2}} = -\dfrac{1}{a}\,\log_e\!\left(\dfrac{a + \sqrt{a^2 \pm x^2}}{x}\right)$

54. $\int \dfrac{dx}{x^2\sqrt{x^2 \pm a^2}} = \pm\,\dfrac{\sqrt{x^2 \pm a^2}}{a^2 x}$

55. $\int \dfrac{dx}{x^2\sqrt{a^2 - x^2}} = -\,\dfrac{\sqrt{a^2 - x^2}}{a^2 x}$

56. $\int \sqrt{(x^2 \pm a^2)^3}\,dx = \tfrac{1}{4}\left[x\sqrt{(x^2 \pm a^2)^3} \pm \dfrac{3a^2 x}{2}\,\sqrt{x^2 \pm a^2} + \dfrac{3a^4}{2}\,\log_e(x + \sqrt{x^2 \pm a^2}) \right]$

57. $\int \sqrt{(a^2 - x^2)^3}\,dx = \tfrac{1}{4}\left[x\sqrt{(a^2 - x^2)^3} + \dfrac{3a^2 x}{2}\,\sqrt{a^2 - x^2} + \dfrac{3a^4}{2}\,\sin^{-1}\!\left(\dfrac{x}{a}\right) \right]$

58. $\int \dfrac{dx}{\sqrt{(x^2 \pm a^2)^3}} = \dfrac{\pm x}{a^2\sqrt{x^2 \pm a^2}}$

59. $\int \dfrac{dx}{\sqrt{(a^2 - x^2)^3}} = \dfrac{x}{a^2\sqrt{a^2 - x^2}}$

Integrals involving $\sqrt{ax^2 + bx + c}$:

Let $X = ax^2 + bx + c$ and $q = b^2 - 4ac$

60. $\int \dfrac{dx}{\sqrt{X}} = \dfrac{1}{\sqrt{a}}\,\log_e\!\left(\sqrt{X} + \dfrac{2ax + b}{2\sqrt{a}}\right), \quad a > 0$

$\qquad = \dfrac{1}{\sqrt{-a}}\,\sin^{-1}\!\left(\dfrac{-2ax - b}{\sqrt{q}}\right), \quad a < 0$

61. $\int \dfrac{x\,dx}{\sqrt{X}} = \dfrac{\sqrt{X}}{a} - \dfrac{b}{2a}\!\int \dfrac{dx}{\sqrt{X}}$

62. $\int \dfrac{x^2\,dx}{\sqrt{X}} = \dfrac{(2ax - 3b)\sqrt{X}}{4a^2} + \dfrac{3b^2 - 4ac}{8a^2}\!\int \dfrac{dx}{\sqrt{X}}$

63. $\int \dfrac{dx}{x\sqrt{X}} = -\dfrac{1}{\sqrt{c}}\,\log_e\!\left(\dfrac{\sqrt{X} + \sqrt{c}}{x} + \dfrac{b}{2\sqrt{c}}\right), \quad c > 0$

64. $\int \dfrac{dx}{x\sqrt{X}} = \dfrac{1}{\sqrt{-c}}\,\sin^{-1}\!\left(\dfrac{bx + 2c}{x\sqrt{q}}\right), \quad c < 0$

65. $\int \dfrac{dx}{x\sqrt{X}} = -\dfrac{2\sqrt{X}}{bx}, \quad c = 0$

66. $\int \dfrac{dx}{(mx + n)\sqrt{X}} = \dfrac{1}{\sqrt{k}}\,\log_e\!\left(\dfrac{\sqrt{k} - m\sqrt{X}}{mx + n} + \dfrac{bm - 2an}{2\sqrt{k}}\right), \quad k > 0$

$\qquad = \dfrac{1}{\sqrt{-k}}\,\sin^{-1}\!\left[\dfrac{(bm - 2an)(mx + n) + 2k}{m(mx + n)\sqrt{q}}\right], \quad k < 0$

67. $\int \dfrac{dx}{(mx + n)\sqrt{X}} = -\dfrac{2m\sqrt{X}}{(bm - 2an)(mx + n)}, \qquad k = 0$

where $k = an^2 - bmn + cm^2$.

68. $\int \dfrac{dx}{x^2\sqrt{X}} = -\dfrac{\sqrt{X}}{cx} - \dfrac{b}{2c}\int \dfrac{dx}{x\sqrt{X}}$

69. $\int \sqrt{X}\, dx = \dfrac{(2ax+b)\sqrt{X}}{4a} - \dfrac{q}{8a}\int \dfrac{dx}{\sqrt{X}}$

70. $\int x\sqrt{X}\, dx = \dfrac{X\sqrt{X}}{3a} - \dfrac{b(2ax+b)\sqrt{X}}{8a^2} + \dfrac{bq}{16a^2}\int \dfrac{dx}{\sqrt{X}}$

71. $\int x^2\sqrt{X}\, dx = \dfrac{(6ax-5b)X\sqrt{X}}{24a^2} + \dfrac{(5b^2-4ac)(2ax+b)\sqrt{X}}{64a^3} - \dfrac{(5b^2-4ac)q}{128a^3}\int \dfrac{dx}{\sqrt{X}}$

72. $\int \dfrac{\sqrt{X}\, dx}{x} = \sqrt{X} + \dfrac{x}{2}\int \dfrac{dx}{\sqrt{X}} + c\int \dfrac{dx}{x\sqrt{X}}$

73. $\int \dfrac{\sqrt{X}\, dx}{mx+n} = \dfrac{\sqrt{X}}{m} + \dfrac{bm-2an}{2m^2}\int \dfrac{dx}{\sqrt{X}} + \dfrac{an^2-bmn+cm^2}{m^2}\int \dfrac{dx}{(mx+n)\sqrt{X}}$

74. $\int \dfrac{\sqrt{X}\, dx}{x^2} = -\dfrac{\sqrt{X}}{x} + \dfrac{b}{2}\int \dfrac{dx}{x\sqrt{X}} + a\int \dfrac{dx}{\sqrt{X}}$

75. $\int \dfrac{dx}{X\sqrt{X}} = -\dfrac{2(2ax+b)}{q\sqrt{X}}$

76. $\int X\sqrt{X}\, dx = \dfrac{2(2ax+b)X\sqrt{X}}{8a} - \dfrac{3q(2ax+b)\sqrt{X}}{64a^2} + \dfrac{3q^2}{128a^2}\int \dfrac{dx}{\sqrt{X}}$

Miscellaneous irrational integrals

77. $\int \sqrt{2ax-x^2}\, dx = \dfrac{x-a}{2}\sqrt{2ax-x^2} + \dfrac{a^2}{2}\sin^{-1}\!\left(\dfrac{x-a}{a}\right)$

78. $\int \dfrac{dx}{\sqrt{2ax-x^2}} = \cos^{-1}\!\left(\dfrac{a-x}{a}\right)$

79. $\int \sqrt{\dfrac{mx+n}{ax+b}}\, dx = \int \dfrac{(mx+n)dx}{\sqrt{amx^2+(bm+an)x+bn}}$

Logarithmic integrals

80. $\int \log_a x\, dx = x\log_a\!\left(\dfrac{x}{a}\right)$

81. $\int \log_e x\, dx = x(\log_e x - 1)$

82. $\int x^m \log_a x\, dx = x^{m+1}\left(\dfrac{\log_a x}{m+1} - \dfrac{\log_a e}{(m+1)^2}\right)$

83. $\int x^m \log_e x\, dx = x^{m+1}\left(\dfrac{\log_e x}{m+1} - \dfrac{1}{(m+1)^2}\right)$

Exponential integrals

84. $\int a^x\, dx = \dfrac{a^x}{\log_e a}$

85. $\int e^x\, dx = e^x$

86. $\int xe^x\,dx = e^x(x-1)$

87. $\int x^m e^x\,dx = x^m e^x - m\int x^{m-1}e^x\,dx$

Trigonometric integrals

In these equations m and n are *positive integers* unless otherwise indicated, and r and s are any integers.

88. $\int \sin x\,dx = -\cos x$

89. $\int \sin^2 x\,dx = \frac{1}{2}(x - \sin x \cos x)$

90. $\int \sin^n x\,dx = -\frac{\sin^{n-1}x\cos x}{n} + \frac{n-1}{n}\int \sin^{n-2}x\,dx$

91. $\int \dfrac{dx}{\sin^n x} = -\dfrac{\cos x}{(n-1)\sin^{n-1}x} + \dfrac{n-2}{n-1}\int \dfrac{dx}{\sin^{n-2}x}, \quad n \neq 1$

92. $\int \cos x\,dx = \sin x$

93. $\int \cos^2 x\,dx = \frac{1}{2}(x + \sin x \cos x)$

94. $\int \cos^n x\,dx = \frac{\cos^{n-1}x\sin x}{n} + \frac{n-1}{n}\int \cos^{n-2}x\,dx$

95. $\int \dfrac{dx}{\cos^n x} = \dfrac{\sin x}{(n-1)\cos^{n-1}x} + \dfrac{n-2}{n-1}\int \dfrac{dx}{\cos^{n-2}x}, \quad n \neq 1$

96. $\int \sin^n x \cos x\,dx = \dfrac{\sin^{n+1}x}{n+1}$

97. $\int \cos^n x \sin x\,dx = -\dfrac{\cos^{n+1}x}{n+1}$

98. $\int \sin^2 x \cos^2 x\,dx = \dfrac{4x - \sin 4x}{32}$

99. $\int \dfrac{dx}{\sin x \cos x} = \log_e \tan x$

100. $\int \sin^r x \cos^s x\,dx = \dfrac{\cos^{s-1}x \sin^{r+1}x}{r+s} + \dfrac{s-1}{r+s}\int \sin^r x \cos^{s-2}x\,dx, \quad r+s \neq 0$

$\qquad = -\dfrac{\sin^{r-1}x \cos^{s+1}x}{r+s} + \dfrac{r-1}{r+s}\int \sin^{r-2}x \cos^s x\,dx, \quad r+s \neq 0$

$\qquad = \dfrac{\sin^{r+1}x \cos^{s+1}x}{r+1} + \dfrac{s+r+2}{r+1}\int \sin^{r+2}x \cos^s x\,dx, \quad r \neq -1$

$\qquad = -\dfrac{\sin^{r+1}x \cos^{s+1}x}{s+1} + \dfrac{s+r+2}{s+1}\int \sin^r x \cos^{s+2}x\,dx, \quad s \neq -1$

101. $\int \tan x\,dx = -\log_e \cos x$

102. $\int \tan^n x \, dx = \dfrac{\tan^{n-1} x}{n-1} - \int \tan^{n-2} x \, dx$

103. $\int \cot x \, dx = \log_e \sin x$

104. $\int \cot^n x \, dx = - \dfrac{\cot^{n-1} x}{n-1} \int \cot^{n-2} x \, dx$

105. $\int \sec x \, dx = \log_e (\sec x + \tan x)$

106. $\int \sec^2 x \, dx = \tan x$

107. $\int \sec^n x \, dx = \dfrac{\sin x}{(n-1) \cos^{n-1} x} + \dfrac{n-2}{n-1} \int \sec^{n-2} x \, dx, \quad n \neq 1$

108. $\int \csc^2 x \, dx = -\cot x$

109. $\int \csc x \, dx = \log_e (\csc x - \cot x)$

110. $\int \csc^n x \, dx = \dfrac{\cos x}{(n-1) \sin^{n-1} x} + \dfrac{n-2}{n-1} \int \csc^{n-2} x \, dx, \quad n \neq 1$

111. $\int \sec^n x \tan x \, dx = \dfrac{\sec^n x}{n}$

112. $\int \csc^n x \cot x \, dx = - \dfrac{\csc^n x}{n}$

$\left. \right\}$ n is *any constant* $\neq 0$

113. $\int \tan^n x \sec^2 x \, dx = \dfrac{\tan^{n+1} x}{n+1}$

114. $\int \cot^n x \csc^2 x \, dx = - \dfrac{\cot^{n+1} x}{n+1}$

$\left. \right\}$ n is *any constant* $\neq -1$

115. $\int \dfrac{dx}{a + b \sin x} = \dfrac{-1}{\sqrt{a^2 - b^2}} \sin^{-1} \left(\dfrac{b + a \sin x}{a + b \sin x} \right),$ $\qquad a^2 > b^2$

$\qquad = \dfrac{+1}{\sqrt{b^2 - a^2}} \log_e \left[\dfrac{b + a \sin x - \sqrt{b^2 - a^2}\,(\cos x)}{a + b \sin x} \right],$ $\qquad b^2 > a^2$

116. $\int \dfrac{dx}{a + b \cos x} = - \dfrac{1}{\sqrt{a^2 - b^2}} \sin^{-1} \left(\dfrac{b + a \cos x}{a + b \cos x} \right),$ $\qquad a > b > 0$

$\qquad = \dfrac{1}{\sqrt{a^2 - b^2}} \cdot \sin^{-1} \left(\dfrac{\sqrt{a^2 - b^2} \cdot \sin x}{a + b \cos x} \right),$ $\qquad a > b > 0$

$\qquad = \dfrac{1}{\sqrt{a^2 - b^2}} \cdot \tan^{-1} \left(\dfrac{\sqrt{a^2 - b^2} \cdot \sin x}{b + a \cos x} \right),$ $\qquad a > b > 0$

$\qquad = \dfrac{1}{\sqrt{b^2 - a^2}} \log_e \left(\dfrac{b + a \cos x + \sqrt{b^2 - a^2} \sin x}{a + b \cos x} \right)$ $\qquad$ when $b^2 > a^2, \quad a < 0$

117. $\int \sqrt{1 - \cos x} \, dx = -2\sqrt{2} \cos \dfrac{x}{2}$

118. $\int \sqrt{(1 - \cos x)^3} \, dx = \frac{4\sqrt{2}}{3} \left(\cos^3 \frac{x}{2} - 3 \cos \frac{x}{2} \right)$

119. $\int x \sin x \, dx = \sin x - x \cos x$

120. $\int x^2 \sin x \, dx = 2x \sin x + (2 - x^2) \cos x$

121. $\int x \cos x \, dx = \cos x + x \sin x$

122. $\int x^2 \cos x \, dx = 2x \cos x + (x^2 - 2) \sin x$

123. $\int x \sin nx \, dx = \frac{\sin nx}{n^2} - \frac{x \cos nx}{n}$

124. $\int x \cos nx \, dx = \frac{\cos nx}{n^2} + \frac{x \sin nx}{n}$

125. $\int x^2 \sin nx \, dx = \frac{2x \sin nx}{n^2} - \left(\frac{x^2}{n} - \frac{2}{n^3} \right) \cos nx$

126. $\int x^2 \cos nx \, dx = \frac{2x \cos nx}{n^2} + \left(\frac{x^2}{n} - \frac{2}{n^3} \right) \sin nx$

Inverse trigonometric integrals

127. $\int \sin^{-1} x \, dx = x \sin^{-1} x + \sqrt{1 - x^2}$

128. $\int \cos^{-1} x \, dx = x \cos^{-1} x - \sqrt{1 - x^2}$

129. $\int \tan^{-1} x \, dx = x \tan^{-1} x - \log_e \sqrt{1 + x^2}$

130. $\int \cot^{-1} x \, dx = x \cot^{-1} x + \log_e \sqrt{1 + x^2}$

131. $\int \sec^{-1} x \, dx = x \sec^{-1} x - \log_e (x + \sqrt{x^2 - 1}) = x \sec^{-1} x - \cosh^{-1} x$

132. $\int \csc^{-1} x \, dx = x \csc^{-1} x + \log_e (x + \sqrt{x^2 - 1}) = x \csc^{-1} x + \cosh^{-1} x$

Definite integrals

133. $\int_0^\infty \frac{a \, dx}{a^2 + x^2} = \frac{\pi}{2}$, if $a > 0$; $= 0$, if $a = 0$; $= -\frac{\pi}{2}$, if $a < 0$

134. (*) $\int_0^\infty x^{n-1} e^{-x} \, dx = \int_0^1 \left[\log\left(\frac{1}{x}\right) \right]^{n-1} dx \equiv \Gamma(n)$

135. (*) $\int_0^1 x^{m-1}(1 - x)^{n-1} \, dx = \int_0^\infty \frac{x^{m-1} \, dx}{(1 + x)^{m+n}} = \frac{\Gamma(m)\Gamma(n)}{\Gamma(m + n)}$

136. $\int_0^{\pi/2} \sin^n x \, dx = \int_0^{\pi/2} \cos^n x \, dx = \frac{1}{2} \sqrt{\pi} \; \frac{\Gamma\left(\dfrac{n + 1}{2}\right)}{\Gamma\left(\dfrac{n}{2} + 1\right)}, \quad n > -1$

*$\Gamma(n)$ = gamma function.

137. $\int_0^\infty \dfrac{\sin mx\, dx}{x} = \dfrac{\pi}{2}$, if $m > 0$; $= 0$, if $m = 0$; $= -\dfrac{\pi}{2}$, if $m < 0$

138. $\int_0^\infty \dfrac{\sin x \cdot \cos mx\, dx}{x} = 0$, if $m < -1$ or $m > 1$; $= \dfrac{\pi}{4}$, if $m = -1$ or $m = 1$; $= \dfrac{\pi}{2}$, if $-1 < m < 1$

139. $\int_0^\infty \dfrac{\sin^2 x\, dx}{x^2} = \dfrac{\pi}{2}$

140. $\int_0^\infty \cos(x^2)\, dx = \int_0^\infty \sin(x^2)\, dx = \dfrac{1}{2}\sqrt{\dfrac{\pi}{2}}$

141. $\int_0^\infty \dfrac{\cos mx\, dx}{1 + x^2} = \dfrac{\pi}{2} \cdot e^{-m}, \quad m > 0$

142. $\int_0^\infty \dfrac{\cos x\, dx}{\sqrt{x}} = \int_0^\infty \dfrac{\sin x\, dx}{\sqrt{x}} = \sqrt{\dfrac{\pi}{2}}$

143. $\int_0^\infty e^{-a^2 x^2}\, dx = \dfrac{1}{2a}\sqrt{\pi} = \dfrac{1}{2a}\Gamma(\tfrac{1}{2}), \quad a > 0 \quad (*)$

144. $\int_0^\infty x^{2n} e^{-ax^2}\, dx = \dfrac{1 \cdot 3 \cdot 5 \cdots (2n-1)}{2^{n+1} a^n}\sqrt{\dfrac{\pi}{a}}$

145. $\int_0^\infty e^{-x^2 - a^2/x^2}\, dx = \dfrac{e^{-2a}\sqrt{\pi}}{2}, \quad a > 0$

146. $\int_0^\infty e^{-nx}\sqrt{x}\, dx = \dfrac{1}{2n}\sqrt{\dfrac{\pi}{n}}$

147. $\int_0^\infty \dfrac{e^{-nx}}{\sqrt{x}}\, dx = \sqrt{\dfrac{\pi}{n}}$

148. $\int_0^\infty e^{-a^2 x^2} \cos bx\, dx = \dfrac{\sqrt{\pi} \cdot e^{-b^2/4a^2}}{2a}, \quad a > 0$

149. $\int_0^1 \dfrac{\log_e x}{1 - x}\, dx = -\dfrac{\pi^2}{6}$

150. $\int_0^1 \dfrac{\log_e x}{1 + x}\, dx = -\dfrac{\pi^2}{12}$

151. $\int_0^1 \dfrac{\log_e x}{1 - x^2}\, dx = -\dfrac{\pi^2}{8}$

152. $\int_0^1 \log_e\left(\dfrac{1 + x}{1 - x}\right) \cdot \dfrac{dx}{x} = \dfrac{\pi^2}{4}$

153. $\int_0^1 \dfrac{\log_e x\, dx}{\sqrt{1 - x^2}} = -\dfrac{\pi}{2}\log_e 2$

154. $\displaystyle\int_0^1 \frac{(x^p - x^q)\,dx}{\log_e x} = \log_e\left(\frac{p+1}{q+1}\right), \quad p+1 > 0,\ q+1 > 0$

155. $\displaystyle\int_0^1 (\log_e x)^n\,dx = (-1)^n \cdot n!$

156. $\displaystyle\int_0^1 \frac{dx}{\sqrt{\log_e\left(\dfrac{1}{x}\right)}} = \sqrt{\pi}$

157. $\displaystyle\int_0^1 x^m \left[\log_e\left(\frac{1}{x}\right)\right]^n dx = \frac{\Gamma(n+1)}{(m+1)^{n+1}}, \quad m+1 > 0,\ n+1 > 0 \quad (*)$

158. $\displaystyle\int_0^\infty \log_e\left(\frac{e^x + 1}{e^x - 1}\right) dx = \frac{\pi^2}{4}$

159. $\displaystyle\int_0^{\pi/2} \log_e(\sin x)\,dx = \int_0^{\pi/2} \log_e(\cos x)\,dx = -\frac{\pi}{2}\log_e 2$

160. $\displaystyle\int_0^\pi x \cdot \log_e(\sin x)\,dx = -\frac{\pi^2}{2}\log_e 2$

161. $\displaystyle\int_0^\pi \log_e(a \pm b\cos x)\,dx = \pi\log_e\left(\frac{a + \sqrt{a^2 - b^2}}{2}\right), \quad a \geqslant b$

162. $\displaystyle\int_{-\pi/2}^{\pi/2} \frac{\cos^2\left(\dfrac{\pi}{2}\sin x\right)dx}{\cos x} = 1.22$

Table II.   Common Logarithms

	0	1	2	3	4	5	6	7	8	9
10	0000	0043	0086	0128	0170	0212	0253	0294	0334	0374
11	0414	0453	0492	0531	0569	0607	0645	0682	0719	0755
12	0792	0828	0864	0899	0934	0969	1004	1038	1072	1106
13	1139	1173	1206	1239	1271	1303	1335	1367	1399	1430
14	1461	1492	1523	1553	1584	1614	1644	1673	1703	1732
15	1761	1790	1818	1847	1875	1903	1931	1959	1987	2014
16	2041	2068	2095	2122	2148	2175	2201	2227	2253	2279
17	2304	2330	2355	2380	2405	2430	2455	2480	2504	2529
18	2553	2577	2601	2625	2648	2672	2695	2718	2742	2765
19	2788	2810	2833	2856	2878	2900	2923	2945	2967	2989
20	3010	3032	3054	3075	3096	3118	3139	3160	3181	3201
21	3222	3243	3263	3284	3304	3324	3345	3365	3385	3404
22	3424	3444	3464	3483	3502	3522	3541	3560	3579	3598
23	3617	3636	3655	3674	3692	3711	3729	3747	3766	3784
24	3802	3820	3838	3856	3874	3892	3909	3927	3945	3962
25	3979	3997	4014	4031	4048	4065	4082	4099	4116	4133
26	4150	4166	4183	4200	4216	4232	4249	4265	4281	4298
27	4314	4330	4346	4362	4378	4393	4409	4425	4440	4456
28	4472	4487	4502	4518	4533	4548	4564	4579	4594	4609
29	4624	4639	4654	4669	4683	4698	4713	4728	4742	4757
30	4771	4786	4800	4814	4829	4843	4857	4871	4886	4900
31	4914	4928	4942	4955	4969	4983	4997	5011	5024	5038
32	5051	5065	5079	5092	5105	5119	5132	5145	5159	5172
33	5185	5198	5211	5224	5237	5250	5263	5276	5289	5302
34	5315	5328	5340	5353	5366	5378	5391	5403	5416	5428
35	5441	5453	5465	5478	5490	5502	5514	5527	5539	5551
36	5563	5575	5587	5599	5611	5623	5635	5647	5658	5670
37	5682	5694	5705	5717	5729	5740	5752	5763	5775	5786
38	5798	5809	5821	5832	5843	5855	5866	5877	5888	5899
39	5911	5922	5933	5944	5955	5966	5977	5988	5999	6010
40	6021	6031	6042	6053	6064	6075	6085	6096	6107	6117
41	6128	6138	6149	6160	6170	6180	6191	6201	6212	6222
42	6232	6243	6253	6263	6274	6284	6294	6304	6314	6325
43	6335	6345	6355	6365	6375	6385	6395	6405	6415	6425
44	6435	6444	6454	6464	6474	6484	6493	6503	6513	6522
45	6532	6542	6551	6561	6571	6580	6590	6599	6609	6618
46	6628	6637	6646	6656	6665	6675	6684	6693	6702	6712
47	6721	6730	6739	6749	6758	6767	6776	6785	6794	6803
48	6812	6821	6830	6839	6848	6857	6866	6875	6884	6893
49	6902	6911	6920	6928	6937	6946	6955	6964	6972	6981
50	6990	6998	7007	7016	7024	7033	7042	7050	7059	7067
51	7076	7084	7093	7101	7110	7118	7126	7135	7143	7152
52	7160	7168	7177	7185	7193	7202	7210	7218	7226	7235
53	7243	7251	7259	7267	7275	7284	7292	7300	7308	7316
54	7324	7332	7340	7348	7356	7364	7372	7380	7388	7396

	0	1	2	3	4	5	6	7	8	9
55	7404	7412	7419	7427	7435	7443	7451	7459	7466	7474
56	7482	7490	7497	7505	7513	7520	7528	7536	7543	7551
57	7559	7566	7574	7582	7589	7597	7604	7612	7619	7627
58	7634	7642	7649	7657	7664	7672	7679	7686	7694	7701
59	7709	7716	7723	7731	7738	7745	7752	7760	7767	7774
60	7782	7789	7796	7803	7810	7818	7825	7832	7839	7846
61	7853	7860	7868	7875	7882	7889	7896	7903	7910	7917
62	7924	7931	7938	7945	7952	7959	7966	7973	7980	7987
63	7993	8000	8007	8014	8021	8028	8035	8041	8048	8055
64	8062	8069	8075	8082	8089	8096	8102	8109	8116	8122
65	8129	8136	8142	8149	8156	8162	8169	8176	8182	8189
66	8195	8202	8209	8215	8222	8228	8235	8241	8248	8254
67	8261	8267	8274	8280	8287	8293	8299	8306	8312	8319
68	8325	8331	8338	8344	8351	8357	8363	8370	8376	8382
69	8388	8395	8401	8407	8414	8420	8426	8432	8439	8445
70	8451	8457	8463	8470	8476	8482	8488	8494	8500	8506
71	8513	8519	8525	8531	8537	8543	8549	8555	8561	8567
72	8573	8579	8585	8591	8597	8603	8609	8615	8621	8627
73	8633	8639	8645	8651	8657	8663	8669	8675	8681	8686
74	8692	8698	8704	8710	8716	8722	8727	8733	8739	8735
75	8751	8756	8762	8768	8774	8779	8785	8791	8797	8802
76	8808	8814	8820	8825	8831	8837	8842	8848	8854	8859
77	8865	8871	8876	8882	8887	8893	8899	8904	8910	8915
78	8921	8927	8932	8938	8943	8949	8954	8960	8965	8971
79	8976	8982	8987	8993	8998	9004	9009	9015	9020	9025
80	9031	9036	9042	9047	9053	9058	9063	9069	9074	9079
81	9085	9090	9096	9101	9106	9112	9117	9122	9128	9133
82	9138	9143	9149	9154	9159	9165	9170	9175	9180	9186
83	9191	9196	9201	9206	9212	9217	9222	9227	9232	9238
84	9243	9248	9253	9258	9263	9269	9274	9279	9284	9289
85	9294	9299	9304	9309	9315	9320	9325	9330	9335	9340
86	9345	9350	9355	9360	9365	9370	9375	9380	9385	9390
87	9395	9400	9405	9410	9415	9420	9425	9430	9435	9440
88	9445	9450	9455	9460	9465	9469	9474	9479	9484	9489
89	9494	9499	9504	9509	9513	9518	9523	9528	9533	9538
90	9542	9547	9552	9557	9562	9566	9571	9576	9581	9586
91	9590	9595	9600	9605	9609	9614	9619	9624	9628	9633
92	9638	9643	9647	9652	9657	9661	9666	9671	9675	9680
93	9685	9689	9694	9699	9703	9708	9713	9717	9722	9727
94	9731	9636	9741	9745	9750	9754	9759	9763	9768	9773
95	9777	9782	9786	9791	9795	9800	9805	9809	9814	9818
96	9823	9827	9832	9836	9841	9845	9850	9854	9859	9863
97	9868	9872	9877	9881	9886	9890	9894	9899	9903	9908
98	9912	9917	9921	9926	9930	9934	9939	9943	9948	9952
99	9956	9961	9965	9969	9974	9978	9983	9987	9991	9996

Table III.   Infinite Series

1. $(1 \pm x)^n = 1 \pm nx + \dfrac{n(n-1)}{2!} x^2 \pm \dfrac{n(n-1)(n-2)}{3!} x^3 + \cdots.$

2. $\log_e (1 + x) = x - \dfrac{x^2}{2} + \dfrac{x^3}{3} - \dfrac{x^4}{4} + \cdots, \ |x| < 1$

3. $e^x = 1 + x + \dfrac{x^2}{2!} + \dfrac{x^3}{3!} + \cdots, |x| < \infty$

4. $\sin x = x - \dfrac{x^3}{3!} + \dfrac{x^5}{5!} - \dfrac{x^7}{7!} + \cdots$

$\left. \vphantom{\begin{array}{c} 1 \\ 1 \\ 1 \end{array}} \right\} \ |x| < \infty; \ x \text{ in radians}$

5. $\cos x = 1 - \dfrac{x^2}{2!} + \dfrac{x^4}{4!} - \dfrac{x^6}{6!} + \cdots$

6. $\sinh x = x + \dfrac{x^3}{3!} + \dfrac{x^5}{5!} + \dfrac{x^7}{7!} + \cdots$

$\left. \vphantom{\begin{array}{c} 1 \\ 1 \\ 1 \end{array}} \right\} \ |x| < \infty$

7. $\cosh x = 1 + \dfrac{x^2}{2!} + \dfrac{x^4}{4!} + \dfrac{x^6}{6!} + \cdots$

8. $\tan x = x + \dfrac{x^3}{3} + \dfrac{2x^5}{15} + \dfrac{17x^7}{315} + \dfrac{62x^9}{2835} + \cdots, \ |x| < \dfrac{\pi}{2}$

9. $\cot x = \dfrac{1}{x} - \dfrac{x}{3} - \dfrac{x^3}{45} - \dfrac{2x^5}{945} - \dfrac{x^7}{4725} - \cdots, \ |x| < \pi$

10. $\arcsin x = x + \dfrac{1}{2} \dfrac{x^3}{3} + \dfrac{1 \cdot 3}{2 \cdot 4} \dfrac{x^5}{5} + \dfrac{1 \cdot 3 \cdot 5}{2 \cdot 4 \cdot 6} \dfrac{x^7}{7} + \cdots, \ |x| < 1$

Statistical Tables

Table IV. Cumulative Normal Distribution Function

$$P(x) = \frac{1}{\sigma(2\pi)^{1/2}} \int_{-\infty}^{z} \exp -\frac{1}{2}\left(\frac{x-z}{\sigma}\right)^2 dx$$

x	$P(x)$	x	$P(x)$	x	$P(x)$
$z - 4.0\sigma$	$3 \cdot 10^{-5}$	$z - 1.3\sigma$	0.0968	$z + 1.4\sigma$	0.9192
$z - 3.9\sigma$	$5 \cdot 10^{-5}$	$z - 1.2\sigma$	0.1151	$z + 1.5\sigma$	0.9332
$z - 3.8\sigma$	$7 \cdot 10^{-5}$	$z - 1.1\sigma$	0.1357	$z + 1.6\sigma$	0.9452
$z - 3.7\sigma$	0.0001	$z - 1.0\sigma$	0.1587	$z + 1.7\sigma$	0.9554
$z - 3.6\sigma$	0.0002	$z - 0.9\sigma$	0.1841	$z + 1.8\sigma$	0.9641
$z - 3.5\sigma$	0.0002	$z - 0.8\sigma$	0.2119	$z + 1.9\sigma$	0.9713
$z - 3.4\sigma$	0.0003	$z - 0.7\sigma$	0.2420	$z + 2.0\sigma$	0.9772
$z - 3.3\sigma$	0.0005	$z - 0.6\sigma$	0.2743	$z + 2.1\sigma$	0.9821
$z - 3.2\sigma$	0.0007	$z - 0.5\sigma$	0.3085	$z + 2.2\sigma$	0.9861
$z - 3.1\sigma$	0.0010	$z - 0.4\sigma$	0.3446	$z + 2.3\sigma$	0.9893
$z - 3.0\sigma$	0.0013	$z - 0.3\sigma$	0.3821	$z + 2.4\sigma$	0.9918
$z - 2.9\sigma$	0.0019	$z - 0.2\sigma$	0.4207	$z + 2.5\sigma$	0.9938
$z - 2.8\sigma$	0.0026	$z - 0.1\sigma$	0.4602	$z + 2.6\sigma$	0.9953
$z - 2.7\sigma$	0.0035	z	0.5000	$z + 2.7\sigma$	0.9965
$z - 2.6\sigma$	0.0047	$z + 0.1\sigma$	0.5398	$z + 2.8\sigma$	0.9974
$z - 2.5\sigma$	0.0062	$z + 0.2\sigma$	0.5793	$z + 2.9\sigma$	0.9981
$z - 2.4\sigma$	0.0082	$z + 0.3\sigma$	0.6179	$z + 3.0\sigma$	0.9987
$z - 2.3\sigma$	0.0107	$z + 0.4\sigma$	0.6554	$z + 3.1\sigma$	0.9990
$z - 2.2\sigma$	0.0139	$z + 0.5\sigma$	0.6915	$z + 3.2\sigma$	0.9993
$z - 2.1\sigma$	0.0179	$z + 0.6\sigma$	0.7257	$z + 3.3\sigma$	0.9995
$z - 2.0\sigma$	0.0228	$z + 0.7\sigma$	0.7580	$z + 3.4\sigma$	0.9997
$z - 1.9\sigma$	0.0287	$z + 0.8\sigma$	0.7881	$z + 3.5\sigma$	0.9998
$z - 1.8\sigma$	0.0359	$z + 0.9\sigma$	0.8159	$z + 3.6\sigma$	0.9998
$z - 1.7\sigma$	0.0446	$z + 1.0\sigma$	0.8413	$z + 3.7\sigma$	0.9999
$z - 1.6\sigma$	0.0548	$z + 1.1\sigma$	0.8643	$z + 3.8\sigma$	$1 - (7 \cdot 10^{-5})$
$z - 1.5\sigma$	0.0668	$z + 1.2\sigma$	0.8849	$z + 3.9\sigma$	$1 - (5 \cdot 10^{-5})$
$z - 1.4\sigma$	0.0808	$z + 1.3\sigma$	0.9032	$z + 4.0\sigma$	$1 - (3 \cdot 10^{-5})$

Table V.   Student's *t*-Distribution

Degrees of freedom ν	Probability a			
	0.10	0.05	0.01	0.001
1	6.314	12.706	63.657	636.619
2	2.920	4.303	9.925	31.598
3	2.353	3.182	5.841	12.941
4	2.132	2.776	4.604	8.610
5	2.015	2.571	4.032	6.859
6	1.943	2.447	3.707	5.959
7	1.895	2.365	3.499	5.405
8	1.860	2.306	3.355	5.041
9	1.833	2.262	3.250	4.781
10	1.812	2.228	3.169	4.587
11	1.796	2.201	3.106	4.437
12	1.782	2.179	3.055	4.318
13	1.771	2.160	3.012	4.221
14	1.761	2.145	2.977	4.140
15	1.753	2.131	2.947	4.073
16	1.746	2.120	2.921	4.015
17	1.740	2.110	2.898	3.965
18	1.734	2.101	2.878	3.922
19	1.729	2.093	2.861	3.883
20	1.725	2.086	2.845	3.850
21	1.721	2.080	2.831	3.819
22	1.717	2.074	2.819	3.792
23	1.714	2.069	2.807	3.767
24	1.711	2.064	2.797	3.745
25	1.708	2.060	2.787	3.725
26	1.706	2.056	2.779	3.707
27	1.703	2.052	2.771	3.690
28	1.701	2.048	2.763	3.674
29	1.699	2.045	2.756	3.659
30	1.697	2.042	2.750	3.646
40	1.684	2.021	2.704	3.551
60	1.671	2.000	2.660	3.460
120	1.658	1.980	2.617	3.373
∞	1.645	1.960	2.576	3.291

Table VI. *F*-Distribution for the 1% Level of Significance

ν_2 \ ν_1	1	2	3	4	5	6	7	8	9	10	12	15	20	24	30	40	60	120	∞
1	4,052.4	4,999.5	5,403.3	5,624.6	5,763.7	5,859.0	5,928.3	5,981.6	6,022.5	6,055.8	6,106.3	6,157.3	6,208.7	6,234.6	6,260.7	6,286.8	6,313.0	6,339.4	6,366.0
2	98.50	99.00	99.17	99.25	99.30	99.33	99.36	99.37	99.39	99.40	99.42	99.43	99.45	99.46	99.47	99.47	99.48	99.49	99.50
3	34.12	30.82	29.46	28.71	28.24	27.91	27.67	27.49	27.34	27.23	27.05	26.87	26.69	26.60	26.50	26.41	26.32	26.22	26.12
4	21.20	18.00	16.69	15.98	15.52	15.21	14.98	14.80	14.66	14.55	14.37	14.20	14.02	13.93	13.84	13.74	13.65	13.56	13.46
5	16.26	13.27	12.06	11.39	10.97	10.67	10.46	10.29	10.16	10.05	9.89	9.72	9.55	9.47	9.38	9.29	9.20	9.11	9.02
6	13.74	10.92	9.78	9.15	8.75	8.47	8.26	8.10	7.98	7.87	7.72	7.56	7.40	7.31	7.23	7.14	7.06	6.97	6.88
7	12.25	9.55	8.45	7.85	7.46	7.19	6.99	6.84	6.72	6.62	6.47	6.31	6.16	6.07	5.99	5.91	5.82	5.74	5.65
8	11.26	8.65	7.59	7.01	6.63	6.37	6.18	6.03	5.91	5.81	5.67	5.52	5.36	5.28	5.20	5.12	5.03	4.95	4.86
9	10.56	8.05	6.99	6.42	6.06	5.80	5.61	5.47	5.35	5.26	5.11	4.96	4.81	4.73	4.65	4.57	4.48	4.40	4.31
10	10.04	7.56	6.55	5.99	5.64	5.39	5.20	5.06	4.94	4.85	4.71	4.56	4.41	4.33	4.25	4.17	4.08	4.00	3.91
11	9.65	7.21	6.22	5.67	5.32	5.07	4.89	4.74	4.63	4.54	4.40	4.25	4.10	4.02	3.94	3.86	3.78	3.69	3.60
12	9.33	6.93	5.95	5.41	5.06	4.82	4.64	4.50	4.39	4.30	4.16	4.01	3.86	3.78	3.70	3.62	3.54	3.45	3.36
13	9.07	6.70	5.74	5.21	4.86	4.62	4.44	4.30	4.19	4.10	3.96	3.82	3.66	3.59	3.51	3.43	3.34	3.25	3.17
14	8.86	6.51	5.56	5.04	4.70	4.46	4.28	4.14	4.03	3.94	3.80	3.66	3.51	3.43	3.35	3.27	3.18	3.09	3.00
15	8.68	6.36	5.42	4.89	4.56	4.32	4.14	4.00	3.89	3.80	3.67	3.52	3.37	3.29	3.21	3.13	3.05	2.96	2.87
16	8.53	6.23	5.29	4.77	4.44	4.20	4.03	3.89	3.78	3.69	3.55	3.41	3.26	3.18	3.10	3.02	2.93	2.84	2.75
17	8.40	6.11	5.18	4.67	4.34	4.10	3.93	3.79	3.68	3.59	3.46	3.31	3.16	3.08	3.00	2.92	2.83	2.75	2.65
18	8.29	6.01	5.09	4.58	4.25	4.01	3.84	3.71	3.60	3.51	3.37	3.23	3.08	3.00	2.92	2.84	2.75	2.66	2.57
19	8.18	5.93	5.01	4.50	4.17	3.94	3.77	3.63	3.52	3.43	3.30	3.15	3.00	2.92	2.84	2.76	2.67	2.58	2.49
20	8.10	5.85	4.94	4.43	4.10	3.87	3.70	3.56	3.46	3.37	3.23	3.09	2.94	2.86	2.78	2.69	2.61	2.52	2.42
21	8.02	5.78	4.87	4.37	4.04	3.81	3.64	3.51	3.40	3.31	3.17	3.03	2.88	2.80	2.72	2.64	2.55	2.46	2.36
22	7.95	5.72	4.82	4.31	3.99	3.76	3.59	3.45	3.35	3.26	3.12	2.98	2.83	2.75	2.67	2.58	2.50	2.40	2.31
23	7.88	5.66	4.76	4.26	3.94	3.71	3.54	3.41	3.30	3.21	3.07	2.93	2.78	2.70	2.62	2.54	2.45	2.35	2.26
24	7.82	5.61	4.72	4.22	3.90	3.67	3.50	3.36	3.26	3.17	3.03	2.89	2.74	2.66	2.58	2.49	2.40	2.31	2.21
25	7.77	5.57	4.68	4.18	3.86	3.63	3.46	3.32	3.22	3.13	2.99	2.85	2.70	2.62	2.54	2.45	2.36	2.27	2.17
26	7.72	5.53	4.64	4.14	3.82	3.59	3.42	3.29	3.18	3.09	2.96	2.82	2.66	2.58	2.50	2.42	2.33	2.23	2.13
27	7.68	5.49	4.60	4.11	3.78	3.56	3.39	3.26	3.15	3.06	2.93	2.78	2.63	2.55	2.47	2.38	2.29	2.20	2.10
28	7.64	5.45	4.57	4.07	3.75	3.53	3.36	3.23	3.12	3.03	2.90	2.75	2.60	2.52	2.44	2.35	2.26	2.17	2.06
29	7.60	5.42	4.54	4.04	3.73	3.50	3.33	3.20	3.09	3.00	2.87	2.73	2.57	2.49	2.41	2.33	2.23	2.14	2.03
30	7.56	5.39	4.51	4.02	3.70	3.47	3.30	3.17	3.07	2.98	2.84	2.70	2.55	2.47	2.39	2.30	2.21	2.11	2.01
40	7.31	5.18	4.31	3.83	3.51	3.29	3.12	2.99	2.89	2.80	2.66	2.52	2.37	2.29	2.20	2.11	2.02	1.92	1.80
60	7.08	4.98	4.13	3.65	3.34	3.12	2.95	2.82	2.72	2.63	2.50	2.35	2.20	2.12	2.03	1.94	1.84	1.73	1.60
120	6.85	4.79	3.95	3.48	3.17	2.96	2.79	2.66	2.56	2.47	2.34	2.19	2.03	1.95	1.86	1.76	1.66	1.53	1.38
∞	6.63	4.61	3.78	3.32	3.02	2.80	2.64	2.51	2.41	2.32	2.18	2.04	1.88	1.79	1.70	1.59	1.47	1.32	1.00

Table VII. F-Distribution for the 5% Level of Significance

ν_2 \ ν_1	1	2	3	4	5	6	7	8	9	10	12	15	20	24	30	40	60	120	∞
1	161.45	199.50	215.71	224.58	230.16	233.99	236.77	238.88	240.54	241.88	243.91	245.95	248.01	249.05	250.09	251.14	252.20	253.25	254.32
2	18.51	19.00	19.16	19.25	19.30	19.33	19.35	19.37	19.38	19.40	19.41	19.43	19.45	19.45	19.46	19.47	19.48	19.49	19.50
3	10.13	9.55	9.28	9.12	9.01	8.94	8.89	8.85	8.81	8.79	8.74	8.70	8.66	8.64	8.62	8.59	8.57	8.55	8.53
4	7.71	6.94	6.59	6.39	6.26	6.16	6.09	6.04	6.00	5.96	5.91	5.86	5.80	5.77	5.75	5.72	5.69	5.66	5.63
5	6.61	5.70	5.41	5.19	5.05	4.95	4.88	4.82	4.77	4.74	4.68	4.62	4.56	4.53	4.50	4.46	4.43	4.40	4.36
6	5.99	5.14	4.76	4.53	4.39	4.28	4.21	4.15	4.10	4.06	4.00	3.94	3.87	3.84	3.81	3.77	3.74	3.70	3.67
7	5.59	4.74	4.35	4.12	3.97	3.87	3.79	3.73	3.68	3.64	3.57	3.51	3.44	3.41	3.38	3.34	3.30	3.27	3.23
8	5.32	4.46	4.07	3.84	3.69	3.58	3.50	3.44	3.39	3.35	3.28	3.22	3.15	3.12	3.08	3.04	3.01	2.97	2.93
9	5.12	4.26	3.86	3.63	3.48	3.37	3.29	3.23	3.18	3.14	3.07	3.01	2.94	2.90	2.86	2.83	2.79	2.75	2.71
10	4.96	4.10	3.71	3.48	3.33	3.22	3.14	3.07	3.02	2.98	2.91	2.84	2.77	2.74	2.70	2.66	2.62	2.58	2.54
11	4.84	3.98	3.59	3.36	3.20	3.09	3.01	2.95	2.90	2.85	2.79	2.72	2.65	2.61	2.57	2.53	2.49	2.45	2.40
12	4.75	3.89	3.49	3.26	3.11	3.00	2.91	2.85	2.80	2.75	2.69	2.62	2.54	2.51	2.47	2.43	2.38	2.34	2.30
13	4.67	3.81	3.41	3.18	3.03	2.92	2.83	2.77	2.71	2.67	2.60	2.53	2.46	2.42	2.38	2.34	2.30	2.25	2.21
14	4.60	3.74	3.34	3.11	2.96	2.85	2.76	2.70	2.65	2.60	2.53	2.46	2.39	2.35	2.31	2.27	2.22	2.18	2.13
15	4.54	3.68	3.29	3.06	2.90	2.79	2.71	2.64	2.59	2.54	2.48	2.40	2.33	2.29	2.25	2.20	2.16	2.11	2.07
16	4.49	3.63	3.24	3.01	2.85	2.74	2.66	2.59	2.54	2.49	2.42	2.35	2.28	2.24	2.19	2.15	2.11	2.06	2.01
17	4.45	3.59	3.20	2.96	2.81	2.70	2.61	2.55	2.49	2.45	2.38	2.31	2.23	2.19	2.15	2.10	2.06	2.01	1.96
18	4.41	3.55	3.16	2.93	2.77	2.66	2.58	2.51	2.46	2.41	2.34	2.27	2.19	2.15	2.11	2.06	2.02	1.97	1.92
19	4.38	3.52	3.13	2.90	2.74	2.63	2.54	2.48	2.42	2.38	2.31	2.23	2.16	2.11	2.07	2.03	1.98	1.93	1.88
20	4.35	3.49	3.10	2.87	2.71	2.60	2.51	2.45	2.39	2.35	2.28	2.20	2.12	2.08	2.04	1.99	1.95	1.90	1.84
21	4.32	3.47	3.07	2.84	2.68	2.57	2.49	2.42	2.37	2.32	2.25	2.18	2.10	2.05	2.01	1.96	1.92	1.87	1.81
22	4.30	3.44	3.05	2.82	2.66	2.55	2.46	2.40	2.34	2.30	2.23	2.15	2.07	2.03	1.98	1.94	1.89	1.84	1.78
23	4.28	3.42	3.03	2.80	2.64	2.53	2.44	2.37	2.32	2.27	2.20	2.13	2.05	2.00	1.96	1.91	1.86	1.81	1.76
24	4.26	3.40	3.01	2.78	2.62	2.51	2.42	2.36	2.30	2.25	2.18	2.11	2.03	1.98	1.94	1.89	1.84	1.79	1.73
25	4.24	3.39	2.99	2.76	2.60	2.49	2.40	2.34	2.28	2.24	2.16	2.09	2.01	1.96	1.92	1.87	1.82	1.77	1.71
26	4.23	3.37	2.98	2.74	2.59	2.47	2.39	2.32	2.27	2.22	2.15	2.07	1.99	1.95	1.90	1.85	1.80	1.75	1.69
27	4.21	3.35	2.96	2.73	2.57	2.46	2.37	2.31	2.25	2.20	2.13	2.06	1.97	1.93	1.88	1.84	1.79	1.73	1.67
28	4.20	3.34	2.95	2.71	2.56	2.45	2.36	2.29	2.24	2.19	2.12	2.04	1.96	1.91	1.87	1.82	1.77	1.71	1.65
29	4.18	3.33	2.93	2.70	2.55	2.43	2.35	2.28	2.22	2.18	2.10	2.03	1.94	1.90	1.85	1.81	1.75	1.70	1.64
30	4.17	3.32	2.92	2.69	2.53	2.42	2.33	2.27	2.21	2.16	2.09	2.01	1.93	1.89	1.84	1.79	1.74	1.68	1.62
40	4.08	3.23	2.84	2.61	2.45	2.34	2.25	2.18	2.12	2.08	2.00	1.92	1.84	1.79	1.74	1.69	1.64	1.58	1.51
60	4.00	3.15	2.76	2.53	2.37	2.25	2.17	2.10	2.04	1.99	1.92	1.84	1.75	1.70	1.65	1.59	1.53	1.47	1.39
120	3.92	3.07	2.68	2.45	2.29	2.18	2.09	2.02	1.96	1.91	1.83	1.75	1.66	1.61	1.55	1.50	1.43	1.35	1.25
∞	3.84	3.00	2.60	2.37	2.21	2.10	2.01	1.94	1.88	1.83	1.75	1.67	1.57	1.52	1.46	1.39	1.32	1.22	1.00

$p(F)$

0 F

Table VIII. χ^2 Distribution

Degrees of freedom ν	0.99	0.95	0.90	0.80	0.70	0.50	0.30	0.20	0.10	0.05	0.01	0.001
1	0.000157	0.00393	0.0158	0.0642	0.148	0.455	1.074	1.642	2.706	3.841	6.635	10.827
2	0.0201	0.103	0.211	0.446	0.713	1.386	2.408	3.219	4.605	5.991	9.210	13.815
3	0.115	0.352	0.584	1.005	1.424	2.366	3.665	4.642	6.251	7.815	11.345	16.268
4	0.297	0.711	1.064	1.649	2.195	3.357	4.878	5.989	7.779	9.488	13.277	18.465
5	0.554	1.145	1.610	2.343	3.000	4.351	6.064	7.289	9.236	11.070	15.086	20.517
6	0.872	1.635	2.204	3.070	3.828	5.348	7.231	8.558	10.645	12.592	16.812	22.457
7	1.239	2.167	2.833	3.822	4.671	6.346	8.383	9.803	12.017	14.067	18.475	24.322
8	1.646	2.733	3.490	4.594	5.527	7.344	9.524	11.030	13.362	15.507	20.090	26.125
9	2.088	3.325	4.168	5.380	6.393	8.343	10.657	12.242	14.684	16.919	21.666	27.877
10	2.558	3.940	4.865	6.179	7.267	9.342	11.781	13.442	15.987	18.307	23.209	29.588
11	3.053	4.575	5.578	6.989	8.148	10.341	12.899	14.631	17.275	19.675	24.275	31.264
12	3.571	5.226	6.304	7.807	9.034	11.340	14.011	15.812	18.549	21.026	26.217	32.909
13	4.107	5.892	7.042	8.634	9.926	12.340	15.119	16.985	19.812	22.362	27.688	34.528
14	4.660	6.571	7.790	9.467	10.821	13.339	16.222	18.151	21.064	23.685	29.141	36.123
15	5.229	7.261	8.547	10.307	11.721	14.339	17.322	19.311	22.307	24.996	30.578	37.697
16	5.812	7.962	9.312	11.152	12.624	15.338	18.418	20.465	23.542	26.296	32.000	39.252
17	6.408	8.672	10.085	12.002	13.531	16.338	19.511	21.615	24.769	27.587	33.409	40.790
18	7.015	9.390	10.865	12.857	14.440	17.338	20.601	22.760	25.989	28.869	34.805	42.312
19	7.633	10.117	11.651	13.716	15.352	18.338	21.689	23.900	27.204	30.144	36.191	43.820
20	8.260	10.851	12.443	14.578	16.266	19.377	22.775	25.038	28.412	31.410	37.566	
21	8.897	11.501	13.240	15.445	17.182	20.377	23.858	26.171	29.615	32.671	38.932	46.797
22	9.542	12.338	14.041	16.314	18.101	21.337	24.939	27.301	30.813	33.924	40.289	48.268
23	10.196	13.091	14.848	17.187	19.021	22.337	26.018	28.429	32.007	35.172	41.638	49.728
24	10.856	13.848	15.659	18.062	19.943	23.337	27.096	29.553	33.196	36.415	42.980	51.179
25	11.524	14.611	16.473	18.940	20.867	24.337	28.172	30.675	34.382	37.652	44.314	52.620
26	12.198	15.379	17.292	19.820	21.792	25.336	29.246	31.795	35.563	38.885	45.642	54.052
27	12.879	16.151	18.114	20.703	22.719	26.336	30.319	32.912	36.741	40.113	46.963	55.476
28	13.565	16.928	18.939	21.588	21.647	27.336	31.391	34.027	37.916	41.337	48.278	56.893
29	14.256	17.708	19.768	22.475	24.577	28.336	32.461	35.139	39.087	42.557	49.588	58.302
30	14.953	18.493	20.599	23.364	25.508	29.336	33.530	36.250	40.256	43.773	50.892	59.703

Table IX. Correlation Coefficient Test

5 Percent Level of Significance

ν	1	2	3	4	5	6	7	8	9	10
r	0.997	0.950	0.878	0.811	0.754	0.707	0.666	0.632	0.602	0.576

ν	11	12	13	14	15	16	17	18	19	20
r	0.553	0.532	0.514	0.497	0.482	0.468	0.456	0.444	0.433	0.423

ν	21	22	23	24	25	26	27	28	29	30
r	0.413	0.404	0.396	0.388	0.381	0.374	0.367	0.361	0.355	0.349

ν	35	40	45	50	60	70	80	90	100	125
r	0.325	0.304	0.288	0.273	0.250	0.232	0.217	0.205	0.195	0.174

ν	150	200	300	400	500	1000				
r	0.159	0.138	0.113	0.098	0.088	0.062				

1 Percent Level of Significance

ν	1	2	3	4	5	6	7	8	9	10
r	1.000	0.990	0.959	0.917	0.874	0.834	0.798	0.765	0.735	0.708

ν	11	12	13	14	15	16	17	18	19	20
r	0.684	0.661	0.641	0.623	0.606	0.590	0.575	0.561	0.549	0.537

ν	21	22	23	24	25	26	27	28	29	30
r	0.526	0.515	0.505	0.496	0.487	0.478	0.470	0.463	0.456	0.449

ν	35	40	45	50	60	70	80	90	100	125
r	0.418	0.393	0.372	0.354	0.325	0.302	0.283	0.267	0.254	0.228

ν	150	200	300	400	500	1.000				
r	0.208	0.181	0.148	0.128	0.115	0.081				

INDEX

277

Monotonically increasing and decreasing
    functions, 32
Multiplicative law of probability, 11
Mutually exclusive, 1

N

n-dimensional process, 183
Negative correlation, 174
Noise bandwidth, 230
    3 db, 231
Nonlinear scatter diagram, 162
Nonlinear transformation, 197
Normal
    asymptotically, 81
Normal distribution, 37, 56
    cumulative distribution
        function of, 57
    standard, 56
    two-dimensional, 88
Normal equations, 164
Normal population, 113
Normal process, 184, 196
Normalized autocovariance, 190
Normalized correlation coefficient, 85
Normalized variable, 238
Normally distributed random
    variables, 88
nth-order distribution of a process, 183
number of combinations, 4
number of degrees of freedom, 113
number of permutations, 4

O

Odd function, 37
Order of moments, 85

P

Parseval's identity, 218
Parseval's theorem
    for aperiodic functions, 213
    for periodic functions, 211
Perfect correlation, 174
Periodic functions, 204, 210
    cross-correlation functions of, 204
    Parseval's theorem for, 211
Periodically stationary process, 184
Permutations
    number of, 4
Phase
    angle, 211
    spectrum, 211
Physically realizable response, 200
Point
    estimate, 115
    sample, 19
Poisson distribution, 48
    mean of, 48, 50
    standard deviation of, 50
Poisson impulses, 187
Poisson increments, 187
Poisson index of dispersion, 147
Poisson process, 48, 186
Population, 110
    covariance of, 174
    mean
        q-percent confidence interval for,
            115
        normal, 113
Population correlation coefficient, 175
Positive correlation, 174

Power
    average, 194, 211
    total, 219
Power content, 211
Power density spectrum, 219, 252
    relationships, 222
Power function, 168
Price's theorem, 197
Probability, 1
    additive law, 7
    a posteriori, 14
    a priori, 14
    axiomatic definition, 1
    classical definition, 7
    conditional, 11, 14
    joint, 8
    multiplicative law, 11
    of failure, 45
    of simultaneous occurrence, 11
    of success, 45
    theorem of total, 13
Probability density function, 20, 72
    joint, 83, 129
    marginal, 83
    of a random variable, 20
        asymmetry of, 43
        skewness of, 43
    of binomial distribution, 45
    of discrete random variables, 26
    of the range, 129
    of the sum of random variables, 75, 103
    uniformly distributed, 28
Probability distribution function, 32
    (see also cumulative distribution
        function)
Processes
    complex, 184
    discrete, 238
        parameter random, 183
    distributions of, 183
    ergodic, 185, 239
    first-order distribution of, 183
    Gaussian, 196
    n-dimensional, 183
    normal, 184, 196
    nth-order distribution of, 183
    random, 183
    second-order distribution of, 183
    stationary, 184
        asymptotically, 185
        differentiable, 209
        finite-order, 184
        in an interval, 184
        increments, 184
        jointly, 184
        periodically, 184
        strict-sense, 184
        wide-sense, 184
    stochastic, 183
    uncorrelated, 194, 232

Q

q-percent confidence interval, 115

R

Random binary transmission, 189
Random sample, 110
    correlation coefficient of, 175
    covariance of, 174
Random sequence, 238
Random telegraph signal, 187, 192, 220
Random walk, 188
Random processes, 183

    continuous, 208, 238
    cross-correlation function of, 232
    differentiable, 209
    discrete, 238
        parameter, 183
    equal, 183
    ergodic, 239
    Gaussian, 196
    joint probability density
        function of, 196
    mean-squared value, 194
    normal, 196
    sampled periodically, 238
    series, 183
    stationary, 239
    uncorrelated, 194, 232
Random variables, 19
    exponentially distributed, 71
    Gaussian distributed, 88
    linear combination of, 75
    median of, 42
    mode of, 42
    normally distributed, 88
    standardized, 56
Range, 129
    expected value of, 129
    probability density function of, 129
        joint, 129
Rayleigh distribution, 60
    cumulative distribution function of, 61
Reciprocal function, 168
Regression line, 162, 171, 175
    exponential, 168
    slope of, 162
    slope test, 171
Relative frequency of occurrence, 1
Running average, 237

S

Sample
    random, 110
Sample mean, 110
Sample point, 19
Sample response
    unit, 245
Sample space
    continuous, 19
    countably infinite, 19
    discrete, 19
    finite, 19
Sample variance, 110
Sampling distribution
    of the mean, 113
    of the variance, 119
Scatter diagram, 162
    linear, 162
    nonlinear, 162
Schwartz's inequality, 195
Second-order
    density, 184
    distribution of a process, 183
Semirandom binary transmissions, 188
Shot noise, 187
Sifting properties of the Dirac delta
    function, 22
Significance
    level of, 115
    test
        correlation, 178
Simultaneous occurrence
    probability of, 11
Sinusoidal distribution, 54
    cumulative distribution function of, 56